Life Histories of North American Cuckoos, Goatsuckers, Hummingbirds, and Their Allies

by

Arthur Cleveland Bent

in two parts

PART II

DOVER PUBLICATIONS, INC.

NEW YORK

This Dover edition, first published in 1964, is an unabridged and unaltered republication of the work first published in 1940 by the United States Government Printing Office, as Smithsonian Institution United States National Museum *Bulletin 176*.

This work, which was originally published in one volume, is now published in two separate volumes.

Library of Congress Catalog Card Number: 64-14301

Manufactured in the United States of America

Dover Publications, Inc.
180 Varick Street
New York 14, N. Y.

CONTENTS

*Life Histories of North American
Cuckoos, Goatsuckers, Hummingbirds,
and Their Allies*

LIFE HISTORIES OF NORTH AMERICAN CUCKOOS, GOATSUCKERS, HUMMINGBIRDS, AND THEIR ALLIES.

ORDERS PSITTACIFORMES, CUCULIFORMES, TROGONIFORMES, CORACIIFORMES, CAPRIMULGIFORMES, AND MICROPODIIFORMES

By Arthur Cleveland Bent

Taunton, Mass.

CHORDEILES ACUTIPENNIS TEXENSIS Lawrence

TEXAS NIGHTHAWK

PLATES 37–39

HABITS

The Texas nighthawk is a large, pale race of the species *Chordeiles acutipennis*, which is divided into additional races in Central and South America. Our 1931 Check-list states that it "breeds in the Lower Austral Zone from north-central California, southern Nevada, southern Utah, and central Texas south to about lat. 30° in Lower California, and to south-central Mexico."

The Texas nighthawk is a common summer resident in the warmer portions of the Southwestern United States; we found it generally distributed throughout the arid desert regions of Arizona, along the river bottoms and dry washes, and, in the more fertile regions, about the sloughs and coursing over the alfalfa fields. H. S. Swarth (1920) writes: "In all the valley towns of southern Arizona the Texas nighthawk is a familiar sight. It has not, as yet, acquired the habit of its eastern relative of nesting upon the flat roofs of buildings, but throughout the summer the birds may be seen in numbers at dusk, hawking about, low over the houses. In walking about on the desert one is sure to flush Texas nighthawks from their resting places under the bushes, where they usually remain during the daytime."

In Texas Dr. J. C. Merrill (1878) found it most plentiful just outside of Brownsville, and he discovered several sets of eggs within the fort. In the San Bernardino Mountains, Calif., according to Dr. Grinnell (1908), "the Texas nighthawk is a characteristic breeding bird of the Lower Sonoran zone, but like several other species of the same zone wanders up even into Transition during the late summer." And farther north, "in the Yosemite section it was observed only at our lowest stations, west of the foothills" (Grinnell and Storer, 1924).

Courtship.—Mr. Swarth (1920) says: "The male Texas nighthawk performs no such spectacular evolutions as the eastern nighthawk does in the breeding season, but he has a comparable, though lesser performance, usually given when in pursuit of the female. Both birds flying low over the bushes, the male repeatedly utters a low, chuckling sound, 'tuc-tuc-tuc-a-tuc-tuc—c-r-rooo,' a rolling note, the finale very dove-like in effect. While uttering this call the wings are held stiffly extended downward. Then, in ordinary flight, there is repeatedly given a long drawn, nasal 'w-a-ng.' "

Grinnell and Storer (1924) give the following account of it:

It was the height of the nesting season [May 5] and the birds were courting actively. A male, distinguished by the larger and whiter bands on his wings and the more conspicuously white chin patch, was pursuing a female. The male always followed, but at close range, rarely more than two lengths behind the female. Occasionally a second male joined in the pursuit, but evidently with only partial interest, for he frequently circled off by himself. Less often the two male birds pursued one another, weaving an irregular course up and down, in and out, but never rising much if any over 50 feet above the ground. The progress through the air was easy yet swift, a few strokes of the long wings sufficing to carry the birds through a long glide. Often as they passed close over the observer the barred pattern of the under surface was clearly visible, as was also the broad subterminal band of white on the lower side of the tail. While the males were on the wing their low crooning trills were heard almost continually, swelling and diminishing as the birds approached or departed. When they rested on the ground between flights they gave the same notes, prolonged but also with longer intervals of quiet. One trill lasted 25 seconds and another fully a minute. These notes remind one of the quavering call of the Screech Owl save that they are longer continued, on one key, and uttered in almost the same cadence throughout.

Alden H. Miller (1937) adds the following observation: "The contrast in degree of whiteness in wing and throat patches of males and females was at once evident. That this sexual difference apparently was recognized by the birds and that it was specifically accentuated by the actions of the male were facts new to me. As a male swung into line behind a female, his white throat was displayed so that, as the pair flew toward me, the brownish white throat of the female was scarcely noticeable, whereas that of the male was a conspicuous white beard. The impression was gained that the feathers of the throat of the male were lifted and that the whole throat area was expanded. Usually, perhaps always, this 'flashing' of the throat patch was accompanied by vocal notes."

Nesting.—The nesting habits of the Texas nighthawk are no more elaborate than are those of its relatives in the *minor* group; the eggs are laid on the bare ground, without any attempt at nest building or even scooping out a hollow, in some open sandy or gravelly spot, and usually with little or no cover to shade them from the full glare of the sun. We were too early for eggs while I was in Arizona, but, after I left, my companion, Frank Willard, found two nests in Pima County on June 10, 1922; each was on the ground at the foot of a greasewood bush; he says that after the female had been flushed from one of the nests the male attempted to drive her back onto the eggs.

Bendire (1895) says that he has "found its eggs on the parched gravelly mesas of southern Arizona, miles from the nearest water. Their favorite breeding resorts here are dry, barren table-lands, the sides of canyons, and the crests of rocky hills." Dr. Merrill (1878) says that in Texas the eggs "are usually deposited in exposed situations, among sparse chaparral, on ground baked almost as hard as brick by the intense heat of the sun. One set of eggs was placed on a small piece of tin, within a foot or two of a frequented path. The female sits close, and when flushed flies a few feet and speedily returns to its eggs. They make no attempt to decoy an intruder away. I have ridden up to within five feet of a female on her eggs, dismounted, tied my horse, and put my hand on the bird before she would move."

Robert S. Woods has sent me some photographs (pls. 38, 39) of a nest that he found on April 27, 1923, in the San Gabriel Wash, in Los Angeles County, Calif., where he says this nighthawk is a common summer resident; the eggs, he says (Woods, 1924b)—

were deposited in a gravelly area covered with low second growth, mostly deer-weed or wild broom (*Syrmatium glabrum*). It may be observed in the photograph that the gravel, which was here loose because of previous leveling of the ground, had been smoothed by the removal of the larger pebbles over a space such as would be covered by the body of the nighthawk. The few stones scattered over it were probably rolled there by the movements of the bird in rising or alighting after the eggs had been laid. * * * On one hot day the eggs were moved back several inches into the partial shade of the nearest shrub, being restored to the original position after the warm weather had passed. The mother would remain on her eggs until approached within perhaps ten feet, but after being once disturbed she would not return as long as any person or suspicious object remained anywhere in the vicinity. The other parent, if present in the neighborhood, showed no interest in the family affairs.

In the Fresno district, according to John G. Tyler (1913), the great majority of the Texas nighthawks nest in the vineyards; four of the five nests observed by him were in vineyards, either at the base of a vine or on bare ground between the vines; the fifth was "on soft ground at base of a sunflower growing in a field of melons."

Mrs. Bailey (1928) says that "at Brownsville, Texas, hundreds of Texas Nighthawks are said to be found in the city nearly throughout the year nesting on the flat roofs of the adobe houses."

Eggs.—I cannot do better than to quote Bendire's (1895) description of the eggs, as follows:

They are exceedingly difficult to detect on account of their similarity in color to their general surroundings, which usually harmonize very closely. The shell is strong, close grained, and rather glossy, while in shape the eggs are more variable than those of other Nighthawks, ranging from oval to elliptical oval, and again to elliptical ovate. The ground color varies from pale gray (a sort of clay color) to pale creamy white, with a faint pinkish tint. This latter phase of coloration is rather unusual however. The whole surface is minutely marbled, speckled, or rather peppered, with fine dots of different shades of grays, lilac, and a few darker and coarser markings of fawn color, slate, and drab. Occasionally a specimen is found which, to the naked eye, appears entirely unmarked; but on more careful examination a few dark spots, mere pin points, can readily be noticed. They are much lighter colored than the average eggs of our other Nighthawks, and readily distinguished from these on this account, as well as from their smaller size.

The measurements of 52 eggs in the United States National Museum average 27.05 by 19.53 millimeters; the eggs showing the four extremes measure 29.72 by 21.08, 27.18 by 21.59, 24.89 by 19.05, and 25.65 by 18.29 millimeters.

Young.—Carroll D. Scott writes to me that one of the favorite pastimes of his childhood was playing hide and seek with young Texas nighthawks: "The sport on our part was to find the baby birds squatting on the ground, almost invisible, and to see the mother trail away, endeavoring to decoy us by the broken-wing ruse. The next day we were faced with the same puzzle—Where were the nestlings? For they were always somewhere else. We always found them again, 20, 50, or 100 feet away. We wondered if the parents carried them in their wide mouths, or shoved them over the ground, inch by inch, or flew with them on their backs."

Several other observers have noticed this same behavior; young nighthawks have moved, or been moved, for greater or lesser distances, either because they had been disturbed or to take advantage of some slight shade from the hot sun. Mr. Woods (1924b) found that young birds less than three days old "could open their eyes and crawl over the ground at a very fair rate of speed." Dr. Gayle Pickwell and Miss Emily Smith (1938), who made extensive studies of several nests of this nighthawk, found that the young could move by crawling haltingly, to the call of the female, as much as 6 or 8 inches when not over 48 hours old; these young birds were hatched between May 25 and 27; on May 29 they had moved 8 feet more, and on June 2, when about 8 days old, they were found 56 yards from the nesting site.

The same observers learned that the period of incubation was 18 days in one case and 19 days in another. Incubation was performed, during the daytime at least, by the female alone, but both sexes did their share in feeding the young.

All feedings were by means of regurgitation, wherein the bill of the parent was thrust into the open mouth of the young, the food brought forth by peristalsis in the regurgitation. Each feeding was terminated by a violent agitation of the heads of both the bird supplying the food and the one being fed. * * * Feedings noted were all crepuscular, at 9 p. m. or earlier, or again at 4:30 a. m. or later. * * *

The protective behavior of the young had the following elements: (1) as long as the young were brooded, concealment by the parent bird sufficed as protection for them: (2) flushing the parent would leave the young in crouch-concealment wherein they supplied their own self-concealment through coloration, which became strikingly protective as their feathers advanced; (3) almost from the beginning these precocial young were able to run to cover, however haltingly, though this cover consisted of the female bird who caused them to run to her by her calling; (4) not until they were about three weeks old were they able to substitute flying for running; (5) the astonishing method of protective behavior presented by the nighthawks was their intimidation display which was first presented when they were approximately 12 days old.

Plumages.—Dr. Oberholser (1914) has given us full descriptions of the various plumages of this species; of the downy young nestling, he says: "Upper surface fawn color, clouded or obscurely mottled with mars brown; lower parts fawn color, unmarked, but paling on the median portion of breast and abdomen. Very young birds, both male and female, before they are full grown, are above very pale buff, finely and sparingly spotted with black, and vermiculated with silvery gray; and below, pale buff, with narrow widely spaced bars of dusky or blackish."

In the juvenal plumage, the sexes are unlike; he describes them as follows:

In this plumage both sexes are decidedly lighter and more closely and evenly mottled than in the adult, particularly above. In the male the upper parts are also more uniform, with more ochraceous or gray and less black; the tail and wing-quills are broadly tipped with buff; the light bars of the tail are more deeply buff; the white throat-patch is more buffy; the lower surface duller, more ochraceous, more uniform, less distinctly and less broadly barred. The subterminal bar on the tail is white, about as in the adult.

The juvenal female differs from the adult female much as above detailed for the male, but somewhat less so. She is similar to the juvenal male, but has the light spot on the primaries smaller and more deeply buff or ochraceous buff, instead of white or slightly buffy; the light throat-patch more deeply buff, never whitish: and she lacks the subterminal white bar on the tail.

What he calls a first autumn plumage, which is also the plumage of the first winter, "is practically the same in both male and female as that of the adults so far as the contour feathers are concerned, and otherwise differs only in having whitish or buffy tips on the primaries, secondaries, and rectrices. These light tips mostly wear off before the next molt, but usually persist sufficiently, at least on the shortest secondaries, to serve for the discrimination of year-old birds." He says of the molts:

From the fugitive natal plumage the young bird molts directly into the juvenal plumage, growing the while, so that at least by the time, often before, it has attained full size of body and wings, the juvenal plumage is complete. Then by a practically continuous molt, usually in September, it again changes its contour feathers, but retains the remiges and rectrices. The combination plumage of the first autumn is worn apparently until the following summer, when the regular sequence of adult molt is begun. The adult of this species molts but once a year, usually between the last of July and the middle of September, most individuals chiefly in August, during which period all of the feathers, including remiges and rectrices, undergo a renewal.

Food.—The food of the Texas nighthawk consists of a variety of flying insects, which it scoops up in its capacious mouth while on the wing; almost anything in this line seems to be acceptable. Mrs. Bailey (1928) writes: "Their food consists of almost any insects that may be out when they are. The stomach of one had a mass of mosquitoes and a small bug. Another contained one or more ground beetles, injurious click beetles, large leaf chafers, leaf hoppers, and green plant bugs, together with 150 winged ants (Merrill MS)." Dr. Grinnell (1908) says that one collected in the San Bernardino Mountains "contained in its stomach four of the immense seven-lined June beetles." A. J. van Rossem (1927) made the following observations on the feeding habits of this species in Salvador:

The Texas Nighthawks were more varied in feeding habits than any of the others. During the winter they were very common in favorable lowland localities, and shortly after sundown would appear in hundreds, flying high and toward the sunset. A little later in the short interval of dusk, they flew much lower and the general direction was opposite to that taken at first. We supposed them to be working back to the localities from which they first started, feeding as they went. It was some time before we found out anything of their nocturnal activities, for their eyes gave only a pale green reflection, which was easily overlooked and not visible beyond a few feet. Many spiders gave a much brighter glow than these nighthawks, and only by careful search in suitable places, could we find them. All the individuals which we found after dark were on the ground in the open. *Chordeiles acutipennis* therefore hunts through three air levels, high in the air at sundown, closer to the ground at dusk, and on the ground after dark. Because of this versatility, its food must necessarily be more varied, and, because obtained from three strata of insect life instead of one or two, must be more regularly plentiful.

A. W. Anthony (1892) says that "a large part of his bill of fare is obtained by jumping up from the ground and catching passing insects, without taking wing—a habit also noticed in *Phalaenoptilus*."

Behavior.—Robert S. Woods (1924b) writes:

The flight of the Texas Nighthawk gives the impression of ease to a greater degree than that of any other of our smaller birds. While not slow, it appears leisurely and is frequently varied by periods of gliding. The large expanse of wing gives great buoyancy and the bird seems to float through the air almost without effort, while a turn of the wing serves to change its course at an abrupt angle. The Texas Nighthawk flies at a much lower altitude than is the usual habit of swallows and swifts. While hunting it never ascends to any great height, and often skims close to the ground, passing among the vegetation. In the evening its activities begin about sunset or earlier, usually ceasing before dark, and in the morning it is apt to remain in the air for some time after sunrise. It may sometimes be seen hunting at mid-day, especially in cloudy weather. The nighthawk displays some curiosity and often swoops down within a few feet of one's head. Even at that distance the flight is entirely inaudible.

Major Bendire (1895) says: "Its flight is equally as graceful as that of the other Nighthawks, but it rarely soars as high as the former, and generally skims just over the tops of the bushes or close to the surface of the water. In fact, I have repeatedly seen them touch the surface, as if drinking or catching insects, probably the latter." Mr. Dawson (1923) has seen them drinking "hen-fashion" from a waterhole or dipping on the wing to drink from a larger body of water.

Texas nighthawks have favorite roosting places, to which they return regularly for their daytime rest. Near our camp in the valley of the San Pedro River, Ariz., one roosted regularly, apparently sound asleep all day, sitting lengthwise on a horizontal limb of a large willow. Ned Hollister (1908) says that about Needles, Calif., "the nighthawks here spend the day in the thickets of arrow-weed from which I frequently flushed them." Grinnell and Storer (1924), referring to the Yosemite region, write: "Each individual nighthawk seemed to have a favorite resting place to which it returned regularly. This was on the gravel, at the side of, and partially shaded by, a lupine or other bush. The male bird of the pair mentioned was seen to return to the neighborhood of such a spot time and time again, and upon flushing him directly and thus ascertaining its exact location, the site was found to be marked by an accumulation of droppings of characteristic form—each a small spiralled mass composed chiefly of finely triturated insect remains."

Voice.—Mr. Woods (1924b) writes:

In general the vocal utterances of the Texas Nighthawk are of three kinds: first a low soft cluck, repeated slowly; second, a louder, querulous, nasal cry, repeated more rapidly and used when two or more of the birds are together; third, a series of throaty staccato notes delivered in monotone so rapidly as to be almost continuous, sustained for several seconds at a time and resumed after a short pause as if for breath. This trill is usually given from the ground, but sometimes also while flying. [The foregoing sentence was incorrectly printed and was revised in a letter to the author.] It is used only when the birds are undisturbed and is not ordinarily heard at close range. While the tone is soft, the carrying power is great, and sometimes on summer evenings when several of the nighthawks are about, the air seems filled with an indefinable vibration.

Alden H. Miller (1937) recognizes four main types of vocal notes:

(1) Long-continued guttural trills, well characterized by Dawson as amphibian-like, but also remindful of the sound of a motor at a distance; (2) a twing like the picking of a banjo (Dawson) or, more prosaically, like the twang of a jew's-harp; (3) staccato clucks; and (4) melodious trills of varying intensity, similar to those of western screech owls (Grinnell and Storer), except for cadence. The twang and melodious trill may follow one another in rapid succession. The guttural trill seemed not to enter into the courtship on the wing. I could not be certain that this note was given on the wing at all; its source always seemed stationary. The melodious trill was occasionally given by birds perched in mesquite trees in the heat of midday.

M. W. deLaubenfels (1925) heard an unusual note, both in Arizona and again in Texas, which he described as "a loud ringing whistle—whee-*eep*-poor-will. The notes were not at all like those of the Whip-poor-will, which are repressed and muffled by comparison."

Dr. Merrill (1878) says: "The notes are a mewing call, and a very curious call that is with difficulty described. It is somewhat like the distant and very rapid tapping of a large woodpecker, accompanied by a humming sound, and it is almost impossible to tell in what direction or at what distance the bird is that makes the noise. Both these notes are uttered on the wing or on the ground, and by both sexes."

Field marks.—The most conspicuous character by which the Texas nighthawk can be distinguished from the nighthawks of the *minor* group is the position of the white band (buffy in the female) in the wing; in *minor* this is about midway between the bend of the wing and the tip; in *acutipennis* it is nearer the tip than the bend. The Texas nighthawk is also somewhat smaller, rather browner, and has a somewhat shorter and broader wing. But perhaps the most satisfactory means of identifying the two species in the field is the decided difference in the notes, as described under each; from the Texas nighthawk one never hears the harsh, rasping *peënt* note or sees the plunging "booming" flight.

Winter.—Dickey and van Rossem (1938) record this nighthawk as an—

abundant winter visitant and migrant in the Arid Lower Tropical and locally in
the Arid Upper Tropical Zones [in El Salvador]. Although observed as high
as 3,600 feet, its metropolis is along the seacoast. * * *

At Puerto del Triunfo hundreds of these nighthawks appeared shortly after
sundown over the tide flats in front of the town, on first appearance flying at
some height toward the sunset and later, in the dusk, flying in the opposite
direction and close to the water and mud. After real darkness had set in they
were found on the ground, most frequently in open, sandy places such as corn-
fields. The visibility on sandy ground is, of course, much better than on leaf
mold or similar dark surfaces, and it may well be that this species has not so
good a nocturnal vision as have some of the other Caprimulgidae. The eyes of
texensis reflect pale, dull green and not the bright red of most members of the
family.

DISTRIBUTION

Range.—Southwestern United States, Mexico, and Central and
South America; casual in Colorado.

Breeding range.—The breeding range of the Texas nighthawk
extends **north** to central California (Red Bluff, Dales, and Grass
Valley); southern Nevada (Fish Lake and Oasis Valley); southern
Utah (St. George); east-central Arizona (Fort Verde and the Salt
River Reservation); southern New Mexico (Cuchillo, Socorro, and
Lakewood); and southern Texas (Pecos, probably Kerrville, and
Somerset). **East** to Texas (Somerset, probably Corpus Christi, and
Brownsville); Tamaulipas (Jaumave); Campeche (Campeche);
northeastern Colombia (Turbaco and Rio Hacha); Venezuela (Alta-
gracia and Guarico); French Guiana (Cayenne); and eastern Brazil
(Banaos, Barra, and Rio de Janerio). **South** to southeastern Brazil
(Rio de Janeiro); and southern Peru (Santa Lucia). **West** to
Peru (Santa Lucia and Tumbez); western Colombia (Rio San
Juan); Guerrero (Chilpancingo and Coyoca); Nayarit (Acaponeta);
southern Sinaloa (Rosario); Baja California (Triunfo, Espirito
Santo Island, and Santo Tomas); and California (Santa Barbara
Island, Winslow, Paicines, Gilroy, Coyote, and Red Bluff).

The range as above outlined is for the entire species, which has been
separated into several subspecies, all but one of which are found south
of the Mexican border. This race, the Texas nighthawk (*C. a.
texensis*), breeds south to south-central Mexico and winters from that
point south to Panama and Colombia. The San Lucas nighthawk
(*C. a. inferior*) is found in the southern part of the peninsula of Baja
California.

Winter range.—It appears that at least some of the Central and
South American races are nonmigratory, which, without extensive
collections, makes it difficult to outline the winter range of the form
occurring in the United States. Nevertheless, the winter range of
texensis may be said to extend north to southern Sinaloa (Escuinapa); Michoacan (Lake Patzcuaro); and southern Veracruz (Ori-

zaba). South at least to Panama (Colon and Veragua); and Colombia (Noanama).

Spring migration.—Early dates of spring arrival in the United States are: Texas—Brownsville, March 8; northwestern Atascosa County, March 29; Refugio County, April 11. New Mexico—State College, April 20; Apache, May 6; Deming, May 17. Arizona—Gadsden, March 6; Tucson, April 7; Fort Mojave, April 17. California—Mecca, March 20; Buena Park, March 22; Pasadena, March 31; Azusa, April 2.

Fall migration.—Late dates of fall departure are: California—Clovis, September 18; Buena Park, November 1. Nevada—Charleston Mountains, September 14. Arizona—Paradise, September 25; Yuma, October 5; Boundary, October 5. New Mexico—Apache, August 11; State College, September 21. Texas—Atascosa County, October 4; Corpus Christi, October 22.

Casual records.—A specimen was collected at Hoehne, near Trinidad, Colorado, on June 11, 1908. A winter record for Arizona is a specimen collected at Phoenix on December 27, 1897, and a similar case for California is the observation of one near Calexico on January 23, 1922.

Egg dates.—California: 60 records, April 21 to July 11; 30 records, May 11 to June 12, indicating the height of the season.

Baja California: 3 records, May 12 and July 22.

Mexico: 7 records, May 20 to July 6.

Texas: 60 records, April 16 to June 29; 30 records, May 8 to June 3.

CHORDEILES ACUTIPENNIS INFERIOR Oberholser

SAN LUCAS NIGHTHAWK

HABITS

The San Lucas nighthawk is apparently a permanent resident on the peninsula of Baja California, breeding north to about latitude 30° and wintering in the extreme southern part. It is a smaller edition of the Texas nighthawk, which it closely resembles in general appearance except in size. It is larger and and somewhat lighter in coloration than the other Central American races of the species. William Brewster (1902) observed that his specimens from Lower California "average a trifle smaller and, as a rule, are somewhat lighter colored than a number of Texas specimens," but evidently did not think that the difference was worth recognizing in nomenclature. He writes:

At Triunfo the birds were abundant during the last three weeks of June, appearing regularly every evening near the ranch, and skimming back and forth close over a large wood pile, which evidently harbored insects on which

they were feeding. After a succession of heavy showers which occurred at
this place early in July they suddenly and wholly disappeared. At San José
del Cabo a few were seen at intervals through the autumn up to November
11, and several were observed near Santiago on December 3. * * * It seems
fair to assume that the December instance * * * was not exceptional, and
that at least a few birds regularly winter in the Cape Region. Mr. Frazar
obtained a set of two eggs, slightly incubated, at Pierce's Ranch, on July 20.

We have no reason to think that the habits of the San Lucas nighthawk differ materially from those of the closely related form found
farther north.

The measurements of 9 eggs average 25.6 by 18.8 millimeters; the
eggs showing the four extremes measure **27.4** by 18.8, 26.0 by **19.8,
23.1** by 18.1, and 25.6 by **18.0** millimeters.

Order MICROPODIIFORMES

Family MICROPODIDAE: Swifts

NEPHOECETES NIGER BOREALIS (Kennerly)

NORTHERN BLACK SWIFT

PLATES 40–43

HABITS

I prefer to follow Ridgway (1911) in the use of the above common name. The name black swift properly belongs to the type race,
Nephoecetes niger niger (Gmelin), which is found in the West Indies. Moreover, Baird (1858) and some other early writers called
it the northern swift. The range of the northern black swift, as
now understood, extends from southeastern Alaska to southern Mexico,
including much of the Rocky Mountain region, Colorado, New
Mexico, Nevada, and California. It breeds wherever it can find suitable rocky cliffs in which to nest, but as these are widely scattered
its distribution is naturally spotty; however, its marvelous powers
of flight carry it over a large expanse of country, far from its nesting area.

The northern black swift is somewhat larger than the type race,
but it is apparently similar to it in coloration.

Baird (1858) states: "This remarkable swift was first indicated
as North American by Dr. Kennerly (1857), in the proceedings of
the Philadelphia Academy, where it is described as *Cypselus borealis*.
It was obtained in the northern part of Puget's Sound, at Simiahmoo
bay, the locality of the main camp of the Northwest Boundary Survey. A large flock was seen one day sailing about the camp, but,
owing to the height at which the birds flew, only one specimen
could be procured.

"It seems very remarkable that so large a swift could have remained unnoticed in North America until the present day."

J. K. Lord (1866) next reported it from British Columbia, saying: "Amongst the earliest of these visitors I noticed the Northern Swift (*Nephocaetes Niger*, Baird). It was a foggy day early in June, and, the insects being low, the birds were hovering close to the ground. I shot four. The next day I searched in vain, but never saw the birds again until the fall of the year, when they a second time made their appearance in large numbers—birds of the year as well as old ones."

On June 23, 1868, Ridgway (1877) "found it abundant" in the valley of the Carson River, Nev.; "they were observed early in the morning, hovering over the cotton-wood groves in a large swarm, after the manner of Night-Hawks. * * * They were evidently breeding in the locality, but whether their nests were in the hollow cotton-wood trees of the extensive groves along the river, or in crevices on the face of a high cliff which fronted the river nearby, we were unable to determine on account of the shortness of our stay."

Frank M. Drew (1882) discovered this swift at Howardsville, Colo., and collected a series of ten birds in 1880 and 1881; he says that "they always hunt in flocks, range far above 13,000 feet and breed up to at least 11,000 feet." During the next two decades it was noted as a migrant in New Mexico and in California; but the mystery of its nesting habits was not solved until 1901, nearly 45 years after its discovery as a North American bird.

Spring.—It is as a spring and fall migrant that the northern black swift is usually observed, as it covers a wide expanse of territory in its movements to and from its more restricted breeding grounds, often occurring in large scattered blocks, feeding more or less on the way, and giving an interesting exhibition of its great powers of flight. Samuel F. Rathbun (1925) has published in detail his numerous observations on the migrations of this swift in the vicinity of Seattle, Wash., to which excellent paper the reader is referred. He writes:

During the vernal migration in the region about the Sound the first Black Swifts will be seen sometime between the fifteenth and the twenty-fifth of May. Quite frequently during the latter half of this month there will occur a spell of foul weather, and the arrival of the birds seems to be coincident. When this fact was first noticed it was regarded as incidental, but as it occurred with a degree of regularity our attention became attracted to it and we then gave the matter especial attention. Soon after the first of May we began to closely follow the weather conditions of this region and also those existing far southward, and after a time a good idea was obtained as to when to expect the arrival of the Swifts. In fact, on several occasions our expectations were confirmed almost to a day. * * * From what we have seen of this spring movement it appears to be soon completed, not lasting much more than ten days.

Courtship.—The courtship of the black swift and apparently copulation also are accomplished on the wing. Mr. Rathbun (1925) says:

Black Swifts appear to mate in June. There is no sign that this has taken place when they arrive in May, as then the birds are always seen in companies and not in pairs as is subsequently often the case. But soon after they have become distributed in colonies about the region and begin to make the daily flight to and from the lower country, indications of mating are seen. All may be gliding about when suddenly—perhaps from a far height, a Swift will dash at one beneath, this followed by erratic flight actions on the part of both and their disappearance in the distance. This dive I have seen made with such speed that the eye could scarcely follow it, and during the time that the birds are darting and twisting about it is a common thing for them to descend almost to the ground.

He says, in some notes sent to me: "On one occasion the latter part of June, I saw a pursuit by one black swift after another that lasted a full 15 minutes. This was the longest of any we ever observed, and we have seen many of them."

Nesting.—The honor of discovering the first nest of the northern black swift belongs to A. G. Vrooman (1901), who relates the historic incident as follows:

On the morning of June 16, 1901, I, with a companion, started out with the intention of taking a few sets of Cormorants' eggs on the cliffs a few miles west of Santa Cruz, California. On reaching the locality, I noticed a pair of Black Swifts flying about over the cliffs, much lower than they usually fly. One bird rose high in the air and struck off in a bee line, at the rate of a mile a minute. I then resumed my search for the Cormorants, which I found on the face of the cliff, where shore line turns sharply inland and about where the Swifts had been seen. * * *

After moving my ladder a little, I proceeded to reach out and down for a more distant set of Baird's Cormorant eggs when suddenly, right from under the pole and not more than three or four feet from my hand, a Black Swift flew out and down toward the water and passed around the angle toward the ocean. It did not rise above the cliff, in the immediate vicinity, as my companion above the cliffs did not see it at all, though I called to him to watch if it came above.

I then moved my ladder a little closer and went down farther so that my face was about a foot and a half from the egg which the Swift had just left. It was placed on a shelf or crevice in the lower edge of a projection standing out perhaps four or five feet from the main wall and about ninety feet from the breakers below. This crevice was four or five inches high, five or six inches deep, and about twenty inches long, very narrow at one end, and about thirty feet from the top of the cliff, twenty feet of which is earth sloping back to the level land above. This portion of the cliff was wet and dripping constantly, causing tufts of grass to grow here and there, where there was earth enough to support the roots. It was just behind one of these tufts of grass, in a slight depression in the mud, formed no doubt by the bird, that the egg was laid. I did not disturb the egg or nest, not going nearer than a foot and a half, intending to return a week later to get possibly a full set, which I did, but found things just as I had left them a week before and no Swifts were in sight. I took the egg, and pealed off the nest, grass and all, and have it in my collection.

Mr. Vrooman's report of finding the black swift nesting in crevices in sea cliffs and laying only one large egg was received with incredulity by many ornithologists. The generally accepted theory was that the bird would be found nesting in cliffs in the mountains, as indicated by Major Bendire's observations on the upper Columbia River in 1879; here, he reported (1895) "quite a colony nested in a high perpendicular cliff," which "was utterly inaccessible, being fully 300 feet high." Others had seen the swifts in similar localities elsewhere, where they were doubtless breeding, but no one had ever actually seen a nest. The incredulous ones thought that Mr. Vrooman must have found an egg of some small petrel, rather than that of the swift. Mr. Vrooman remained silent over the skepticism but kept steadily at work every season, sometimes without success, and eventually collected enough eggs to convince his critics. There are six eggs and one nest of this swift in the Thayer collection in Cambridge, all from Mr. Vrooman, including the type egg and nest; the latter is a clod of mud, rather deeply hollowed, and now dry and hard, with the tuft of dried grass in front of and partly surrounding it.

Many years passed before we learned anything about the inland nesting habits of the northern black swift, and, strangely enough, the first report came from a locality that is not included in the Check-list range of the species. This report came to me in a letter from Clarence E. Chapman, who discovered a nest in Johnson Canyon, near Banff, Alberta, on September 2, 1919. He describes the incident so clearly and convincingly that there can be no doubt about it. His letter states: "A walk of a mile brought us up through a lovely, small canyon to the falls; the upper canyon, just below the falls, was crossed by a high footbridge. While I was standing on this bridge, my attention was attracted by a bird flapping its wings under and against the overhanging rock wall. Mrs. Chapman and I each had high-power glasses (8 diameters). We saw a young black swift, not quite ready to fly, and close watching showed that it was exercising and strengthening its very long wings; it could not fly, as its feathers near the base were still covered with the scaly sheaths. The nest was built in a niche in the overhanging wall; the niche was about 18 inches long, 18 inches high, and 8 inches deep at the lower part; it was evidently made by a bit of rock being broken out by frost; the bottom of the niche sloped downward. The nest was a semicircle, not much more than a dam to prevent the egg from rolling out; we could not determine what the nest was made of, but considerable mud was used."

The nest was within 20 feet of Mr. Chapman's face, and within 30 feet of the fall, close enough to have the spray blow over it in certain winds. The single black young, clinging to the rock wall and to the edge of the nest, and flapping its long wings, which projected well beyond the end of its tail, could hardly be anything but a black swift.

The next account comes from Charles W. Michael (1927), who, on July 6, 1926, discovered a colony of northern black swifts, containing at least six pairs, nesting in a canyon in the Yosemite Valley, Calif. He writes:

In the inner chasm of the Tenaya Gorge a hundred paces beyond the "wedged boulder", where vertical walls rise two hundred feet or more, the swifts had chosen a nesting site. The nest was placed on a bit of projecting rock which presented a level space of perhaps four by six inches. The projection was located within the shelter of an overhung wall, thirty feet directly above a deep pool in the creek. Towering above the nest the cliff rose sheer for a distance close to two hundred feet. The inner chasm is here very narrow; the vertical walls stand not fifty feet apart. The channel is dark and cool; in the long summer days the sun lights its depth for but a brief hour. And at no time or season does the sun ever play on the nest of the swift—cramped quarters, I should say, for birds of the wide skies.

It was the wild, erratic wingings of a lone Black Swift, as he whizzed back and forth through this narrow flight lane, that first attracted my attention. * * * While I watched, the bird suddenly swooped and fairly seemed to plaster himself to the wall not fifty feet from where I stood. Then, with fluttering wings the bird moved upward—not straight upward, however, but in an angling course across the face of the cliff. As I followed the movements of the swift the nest was suddenly descried. The swift paused, clinging to the projection that held the nest, and I thought at first that he was feeding young. After a moment he scurried on upward a few feet, fell backward, and then twinkling wings carried him away down the channel. * * *

As for the nest itself, as best I could see it, it resembled in form and construction that of the Western Wood Pewee; but in size it appeared larger. Also it reminded me of certain cormorant nests I have seen plastered to the ledges above the sea. The general appearance of the structure, its apparent adhesion to the shelf, and the droppings plastered to the granite immediately below, led me to suspect that the nest may have been occupied through several nesting seasons. The rock wall roundabout was absolutely bare and dry. There was not a growing plant within ten feet of it.

Of a later visit, July 11, he says:

Beyond the "wedged boulder" I moved cautiously, but before I had come within sight of the nest a swift was seen to leave the wall and dash down the canyon. I was afraid that I was not to find the swift at home, but as I came opposite the site, there was the bird in plain sight. She sat on the nest with her tail appressed against the wall and with one long wing drooping over the side. Her body rested in a horizontal position and she appeared much too large for the nest.

While I was watching the bird a second nest was discovered. The second one was tucked away in a niche and, but for the droppings below, it would hardly have been noticed. The nest was a little round cup, shallow, and composed, apparently, of some soft, brown material like dry leaves; the rim was tinted slightly green. On a later visit, with assistance and encouragement from "Big" Con Burns, I managed to climb to a point within eight feet of the nest. And then it was learned that the nest was composed of the delicate pinnae of the five-fingered fern. Great banks of these ferns hung from neighboring walls, and it would be quite possible for the swifts to procure material while on the wing. Perhaps, though, the swifts may gather nesting material while clinging to a wall, as I have often seen swifts alight on a ferny ledge above Vernal Fall. In any event, this nest was rimmed with fresh green leaves.

Another nest was later discovered near these two, all three within a radius of three feet. Three other nests were discovered later in the same canyon. Summing up his experiences, he says:

I now feel that I have the system for locating Black Swifts' nests. Knowing the precise requirements demanded by a nesting swift, the thing to do is to find the locality that approximates these requirements. * * * What really simplifies the problem is the scarcity of suitable nesting localities for Black Swifts. There must be cozy niches in which to place the nests, and these niches must be so situated as to afford complete protection against rain, wind, and sunshine. Perhaps, too, there should be many of these niches, that nesting swifts may have nesting neighbors.

Then comes Emily Smith (1928) with her report of finding three nests of black swifts close to and behind Berry Creek Falls in a not very remote canyon in Redwood Park, Santa Cruz Mountains, Calif. The first nest seen "was not behind the falls, but a little to one side in a niche twenty feet above the pool which lies at the base of the sheer seventy-foot cliff. * * * I could not get closer than the edge of the pool, but from there the nest thirty feet away was in plain view, a thick, round mat of moss and possibly some mud, set in an almost square little niche in the rock wall. The wall roundabout, covered with mosses, five-finger ferns, and other moisture-loving plants, was dripping wet."

The other two nests were behind the falls, one only 8 feet above the pool, and the other much higher up and "hardly more than ten inches back from the main stream of the falling water. Some of the moss of which the nest was constructed appeared green and living, giving the nest a cushiony look."

Joseph S. Dixon (1935) records the first nests found in the southern Sierra Nevada:

We found three nests, but there probably were others in the vicinity, since over a dozen Black Swifts were seen. The three nests were located within a linear distance of twenty feet, so that the species might reasonably be said to have colonial nesting habits, at least in this instance. The nest site was located in the deep granite gorge of the Marble Fork of the Kaweah River. All three nests were located in a shallow cave that had been formed by the falling of a section of the cliff, leaving a broad arch about thirty feet in height. The bare, wet, dark granite wall rose precipitously above a deep pool beside a waterfall, spray from which kept the entire surroundings drenched with mist.

In all three instances the swift nests were made of green resurrection moss, pressed down but not stuck together with saliva, and were placed on and supported by a clump of fragile five-fingered ferns. The first nest was a firm, mossy cup placed about eighteen feet above the water. This nest measured outside 3 by 4 inches in diameter and was 3 inches high. The trampled-down shallow cup was empty, the young bird evidently had just left the nest [August 7].

The latest nesting record comes from Albert Ervin Thompson (1937), who found a nest "near the western boundary of General Grant National Park in Fresno County, California, in the Transition Life Zone at an elevation of five thousand two hundred feet above sea level in the Sierra Nevada Mountains." He says further:

The narrow mountain gorge in which the nest was found is forested with tall sugar and yellow pines, white fir, incense cedar, and giant sequoia, and, because of a steep slope to the northwest, receives very little direct sunlight except during a brief portion of the afternoon. At other times only random shafts of light find their way among the trees.

The nest was built in a hollow of a granite wall, sheltered by an overhanging projection of rock. It was about six feet above the bed of a mountain brook and not more than twelve feet removed from a rushing cascade that boiled down a chute from a cliff above. Because of the smoothness of the sheer face of the rock, the situation was inaccessible to snakes and small mammals. The nest was formed by moist mossy material, imbedded in a natural growth of the same plant. Seeping water and spray from the waterfall kept the site continually moist. For this reason the nest was at first mistaken for that of a water ousel. One egg was laid, but after it hatched the young bird mysteriously disappeared, perhaps devoured by an enemy.

Eggs.—The single egg of the northern black swift is usually, in the six specimens that I have examined, elliptical-ovate in shape, though some are nearly elliptical-oval. The shell is smooth but without gloss. They are dull, pure white in color, but one is somewhat nest-stained. The measurements of 34 eggs average 28.6 by 19.0 millimeters; the eggs showing the four extremes measure **31.5** by 18.3, 28.0 by **20.6**, **24.5** by 19.5, and 28.5 by **17.8** millimeters.

Young.—Nothing seems to be known about the period of incubation or to what extent the two sexes assist in incubation and the feeding of the young, though it seems to be assumed that the female does most of the brooding and feeding. All observers seem to agree that the young swift is fed at infrequent intervals, mainly early in the morning and late at night. Mr. Michael (1927) says: "Most young birds receive food every few minutes, but here we find young birds that go for hours without food. Raking the skies all day long, the old swifts probably return in the evening to pump their young full of concentrated nourishment." Many hours of patient watching yielded very little information on this point, but on August 15—

at 12:30 an old bird arrived. She flew up the canyon and alighted directly on the edge of the nest. Clinging here with her tail appressed and one long wing spread out across the surface of the wall she apparently pumped food into the young bird. She appeared to fairly stuff the young one, pumping food into him ten times in twenty seconds with but slight pauses between times. At first the young one was very eager and squirmed with delight while being fed. Soon, however, he was full and had to be coaxed to take the last two or three helpings.

When through feeding her young one, the mother bird crawled up onto the nest and the young one squirmed and twisted until his head was quite snuggled under his mother's breast. Not an audible sound was uttered during the meal. but just before the parent bird departed she uttered two sharp, squeal-like notes; and then three more as she tumbled backward into space to speed off down the canyon. The young bird stretched and preened and once more settled down. * * * I believe that the female takes upon herself all the duties of incubation and of the feeding of the young.

Miss Smith's (1928) observations at Berry Creek Falls corroborated Mr. Michael's statement that the young birds can, and do, go long hours without food. She writes:

On each visit my chief interest was in finding out how often and when the young birds were fed. Unfortunately, I was not able to spend a whole day with the swifts until August 25, and then the youngest bird was more than two weeks old. I had not seen Primus (so named because he was first discovered) fed during my four previous visits with him. I had, however, seen Secundus fed at about four o'clock in the afternoon, and again the next morning at half past nine. I suppose being a very young bird he was fed more than once on each of these two days. But August 25 they all were fed only at nightfall. That day my sister and I managed to cover the four and one half miles from camp to the falls before a quarter past five o'clock in the morning. As we approached we heard soft, low cheeping notes, and then in the dim light saw birds circling and darting about in the small amphitheatre in front of the falls. It was impossible for the eye to follow them or count them, they flew so swiftly and the light was so faint. One could be seen chasing another, and then we could see several fluttering up the cliff and disappearing behind a log, and almost immediately half a dozen swept by us. By half past five, before it was light enough to see clearly, every bird had left. From then until sunset not one of the swifts returned.

Just before sunset Primus backed out of his nest, and clinging to the threshold of the niche, exercised his long wings. Seven times he vibrated them, with short intervals of rest during which his wonderful wings were stretched wide against the rock. Suddenly, a swift, surprisingly light gray in color, "plastered" itself against the wall below Primus, and motionless watched us for fifteen minutes. Primus, seeing no reason for concern about us, scrambled back onto the nest and waited patiently for his meal. Finally the old bird fluttered up and for two minutes in the fading light we could see it feeding the young one by regurgitation. Then the other parent arrived, darker and seemingly larger, and immediately we guessed it was the mother. She fed the young bird for four minutes with only very short pauses, while the father looked on.

Mr. Dixon (1935) says of the young swift that he observed in Sequoia National Park: "The outstanding feature of the young swift was his aversion to light. He always turned around in the nest so as to face the darkest corner. Another feature was the ease and tenacity with which he clung to the nest with his sharp, strongly-curved claws. When placed against a vertical granite cliff, he had no trouble clinging by one foot, but tucked his head down to avoid the bright light."

Plumages.—Mr. Dixon (1935) says that a recently hatched chick was "bluish black in color. Its eyes were closed, and there was not a bit of natal down on its body." An older young bird, found dead in a nest on July 25, 1912, and now in the Thayer collection, is completely covered with long, soft down, "dusky drab" to "blackish brown"; the down is longest on the back and rump and shortest on the head; the wing coverts are growing, and the primaries have burst their sheaths for over a quarter of an inch.

Frank M. Drew (1882) estimates that four years are necessary for the black swift to acquire its fully adult plumage, which hardly seems likely. Based on a study of ten specimens, collected in Colorado, he describes the succession of plumages as follows:

A young male of the year, taken Sept. 17, was marked as follows. General color dull black, every feather tipped with white, scarcely appreciable on upper back and throat, broader on upper tail coverts and rump. Crissum almost pure white. In birds of the second year the general plumage has a brownish cast; feathers of back tipped with brown, the head whitish, belly feathers yet broadly tipped with white. The third year the color is black, with a very faint edging of white on under tail coverts. In the fourth year pure black, forehead hoary, neck with a brownish wash.

Tail in young of first year, rounded; in second year, slightly rounded; in third year slightly emarginate, feathers becoming more acute. In adult, forked, outer feathers three-eighths of an inch longer than inner.

I have never seen a young black swift, with "every feather tipped with white," but I am inclined to believe that Mr. Drew is correct in describing this as the juvenal plumage. The juvenal plumage apparently has never been described in the manuals, and probably there are no specimens in young juvenal plumage in collections. The downy young, described above, has the incoming feathers of the wing coverts, and the remiges tipped with white. Enid Michael (1933) had a young black swift brought to her on August 10, 1932, that had fallen out of a nest and was unable to fly; from what she had previously learned from her study of young swifts in their nests, she estimated that this bird was about five weeks old; and she says: "Every feather on its back, tail, wings and crown was daintily tipped with white. The tiny feathers of its crown and forehead, being fringed with white, gave its crown, and especially its forehead, a frosted appearance." Mr. Rathbun has sent me the following description of a young black swift picked up dead in the Willamette Valley, Oreg., September 20, 1924: "Seemingly an immature bird— not in good condition of preservation. Back and abdominal feathers tipped with grayish white. Head from bill to crown also with grayish-white-tipped feathers. Primary wing feathers edged in grayish white. Length 7 inches." From the above descriptions, and from what shows in the few published photographs of the young swifts in the nests, it seems fair to assume that the juvenal or first plumage is characterized by the white tips of the body plumage, above and below, and by the white-tipped primaries. How long this plumage is worn, or how soon the white tips wear away, we do not know; but evidently this plumage is worn until after the birds leave for the south.

Considerable discussion has occurred and much has been published on the plumages of the black swift, particularly on the significance of the white spots on the under parts, as sex characters or age characters.

Mr. Ridgway (1911) evidently considered this a sex character, for he says: "All the sexed specimens examined by me, from whatever locality, show that all those with white-tipped feathers on posterior under parts are females and all those without these white-tipped feathers are males." This is not so in a series of 42 specimens, of various ages and sexes, that I have examined. More than one-third of all the birds that showed conspicuous white spots, or more or less white tips, on the feathers of the abdomen and under tail coverts are sexed as males, and less than two-thirds are sexed as females. Perhaps this character is more persistent in females than in males.

Mr. Drew (1882) implies that the sexes are alike in all plumages, and says: "In birds of the second year the general plumage has a brownish cast; feathers of back tipped with brown, the head whitish, belly feathers yet broadly tipped with white." He seems to be substantially correct on both of these points. The white-spotted birds that I examined were collected mainly in June, though two were taken in May, two in July, and one in August. All these birds have square, or slightly emarginate, tails; and none of them white-tipped remiges, which are characteristic of the juvenal plumage, as indicated above. They could not be young birds of the year, for the young birds of the year were still in the nests at the time nearly all of these birds were collected. They agree perfectly with Mr. Drew's description of the second-year bird, and I am inclined to think that that is what they are. They are numerous in collections, as perhaps immature birds may be easier to collect than adults. If this assumption is correct, then the conspicuous characters of the second-year plumage are the absence of white tips on the remiges and the presence, in varying degrees, of white spots or tips on the feathers of the abdomen and under tail coverts. This assumption has been made after giving due consideration to all that has been published on the subject and a lot of data from and correspondence with my friend S. F. Rathbun; he has made an extensive study of the black swift for many years and is inclined to agree with Mr. Ridgway; but it seems to me that all the evidence fits into the theory advanced above and agrees with Mr. Drew's (1882) idea of a second-year plumage.

Mr. Drew's statement, that "four years are necessary for them to acquire their complete plumage," seems open to question. He says that in "the third year the color is black, with a very faint edging of white on under tail coverts." There is great individual variation in the amount of white on the under parts of immature birds, probably due to wear or earlier or later molting in different individuals. It seems fair to assume that the "very faint edging" referred to by Mr. Drew may be only evidence of further advance in second-year birds. Apparently these swifts molt their contour plumage, perhaps their wings and tails, during the early summer. Mr. Rathbun tells me that he has always noticed that summer specimens "appear to have almost fresh plumage"; and Harry S. Swarth (1922) says that the birds he collected in the Stikine region, between August 19 and 30, "had entirely finished the annual molt and were all in the new plumage."

In the adult plumage the sexes are very much alike in coloration, though females average somewhat paler and browner on the under parts, and the female tail is not so deeply emarginate as that of the male. Mr. Drew (1882) says that in the adult the outer tail feathers are three-eighths of an inch longer than the inner feathers, giving the tail a forked appearance; this is undoubtedly true of fully adult males, and perhaps of some very old females. Mr. Rathbun tells me that he can usually distinguish the two sexes in flight by the extent to which the tail is emarginated. In the series that I have examined all the young white-spotted birds have square or slightly emarginate tails, all the adult males have deeply emarginate tails, and all the adult females have only slightly emarginate tails. Major Brooks, who probably has handled more black swifts than anyone in North America, wrote to Mr. Rathbun: "Swarth and myself, together with another observer in the last century, have carefully recorded that some females, probably about 10 percent, are absolutely indistinguishable from the adult male in every external character, emargination of tail, absence of white spots, etc." In a series of black swifts, collected by Mr. Swarth (1912) in southeastern Alaska in June and July 1909, "there is one female that in color and markings is indistinguishable from the males. * * * Like the others, however, it differs from the males in having a square, rather than a forked tail." This particular female contained an egg, almost ready to be laid, so that there was no doubt about the sex.

Mr. Rathbun (1925) writes: "The males are larger and darker than the females. As a rule their sooty underparts from the breast down lack any trace of light tipping on the feathers, and when this does occur the tips are of a brownish tint and very faint. In all our males the under tail coverts are tipped with brownish, rather well defined though much obscured in some individuals. There is a large variation in the amount of hoariness on the forehead."

He tells me that this swift has a complete molt during summer and is in full fresh plumage before leaving in fall.

Food.—The northern black swift feeds entirely on the wing, where it is very successful in catching the flying insects, on which it feeds exclusively; it captures a great variety of insects, and anything in the way of aerial insect life seems to be acceptable to it. Mr. Rathbun (1925) publishes a detailed list of the contents of six stomachs, collected by him near Seattle between June 22 and September 7 and reported on by the Biological Survey. The list is too long to be included here. The stomachs were reported as all full and all containing 100 percent animal matter. Prominent among the contents were caddisflies, Mayflies, crane flies and various other flies, a variety of beetles, many termites and flying ants, numerous plant lice, leafhoppers, treehoppers, wasps, and a few moths and spiders.

Clarence Cottam has sent me the following notes on the contents of 36 stomachs of this swift, as analyzed in the laboratory of the Biological Survey:

"Both in frequency of occurrence and in total percentages of volume, ants, bees, and wasps (Hymenoptera) appear to be the dominant food items taken by the black swift. Ants of the genus *Lasius* were consumed by 6 of the 36 birds here considered and comprised 90 to 100 percent of the total content, averaging about 150 individuals per stomach. The paper wasps (*Vespula*) were ingested by one-sixth of the birds and formed 51 to 87 percent of the food. Traces or small percentages of the Ichneumonidae, or parasitic wasps, occurred in the majority of the stomachs.

"Flies (Diptera) were a close second in importance and formed at least a trace in most of the stomachs; in many they made up 70 to 95 percent of the total content. The principal types met with were the long-legged flies (Dolichipodidae), flesh flies (Sarcophagidae), root maggots (Anthomyiidae), crane flies (Tipulidae), midges (Chironomidae), Ephydridae, and the grass-stem maggots (Chloropoidae). In a series of six birds from King County, Wash., flies of nine genera made up 100 percent of the contents.

"Many species of beetles (Coleoptera) were encountered in the food items, but most of them made up only minor percentages or traces, and in only a few cases did they amount to as much as 6 percent of the total. The chief families of Coleoptera taken were the ground beetles (Carabidae), rove beetles (Staphylinidae), weevils (Curculionidae), leaf beetles (Chrysomelidae), click beetles or wireworms (Elateridae), and scarab beetles (Scarabaeidae).

"Large termites, or white ants (*Thermopsis angusticollis*), also known as Isoptera, were the principal items consumed by four of the 36 swifts and comprised 70 to 99 percent of the contents, with numbers per stomach varying from 15 to 90 individuals. Mayflies (Ephemeridae) and caddiceflies (Trichoptera) were also taken at times and formed 5 to 35 percent of the content."

Behavior.—Mr. Rathbun (1925) writes admiringly of the powers of flight exhibited by the northern black swift:

In all its flight actions this Swift shows a power and an easy grace that win our admiration. It seems to live upon the wing, and to restrict its flight most of the time to a considerable elevation, the height being seemingly influenced by the character of the weather. It is generally the case that during the continuance of a low atmospheric pressure the Swifts will not fly very high, but when this condition ceases they then ascend. At the time of high pressure the Swifts are often at a great height and it is not uncommon to see them gliding at the very limit of vision. At such times so high are some of them that even with the aid of field glasses they show but faintly against the sky. It would be mere surmise as to the height that they attain, several thousand feet certainly, and as some have even disappeared from view, when the glasses were in use, one has no knowledge of the height to which they go. On a bright summer day to see these dark birds circling far above is always captivating. Should the sky happen to have clouds some of which are white and shining, the Swifts as they wheel across their glistening surfaces, are plainly outlined, but seem to fade insensibly from view when in turn they cross the open spaces of the sky. At such times it is the constant shifting view with the seeming change in distance of the gliding Swifts that adds to our interest when watching them. * * *

But this bird has also the power of very rapid flight. Infrequently it happens near the close of day that some will be seen hastening to their mountain retreats, at such times being widely scattered and flying rather low. With strong and rapid wing beats an almost direct course is followed, and but a few seconds elapse from the time one is first seen until after passing it fades from sight in the distance. And when thus observed in full flight, the power shown for fast flying never fails to impress the beholder.

The position of the Black Swift's wings as it glides or circles is dihedrally down. We have never seen any variation from this, and in this respect a contrast is shown by our *Chaetura*, whose wings are often highly elevated when sailing short distances or on entering their nesting places or roosting resorts. This wing position of the Black Swift seems worthy of mention, although it may be possible that it varies at times under conditions with which we are not familiar.

He mentions in his notes an occasion on which the swifts were flying low; he was crossing Lake Washington in a row boat on a rainy day in June: "While crossing, we noticed very many of these birds flying about at quite a low height above the water. Two were taken, and then we proceeded on our way. It was not long before a heavy rain began to fall and this hastened our return; but, when we reached the spot where first the swifts had been observed, suddenly on all sides of the boat were numbers of the birds hawking about quite close to the water's surface, some flying past not more than fifteen or twenty feet away."

Referring to the summer movements of the swifts, about Seattle, Wash., he writes (1925):

The Swifts that remain in this region undoubtedly nest far within the Cascade range, and each morning from their chosen retreats make a trip to the lowlands where they seem to stay most of the day. * * *

By the middle of June, the Swifts instead of associating in such large numbers seemed to have separated into colonies of varying sizes, each of which, during the summer months, appears to follow a certain more or less defined route every day, which the birds used each morning when flying from their mountain resort to the lower country, returning over it with equal regularity as the evening drew near.

These journeys have the appearance of being long excursions, but the wide distances mean little to this Swift with a power of flight to which there seems but little limitation. The valley of the Middle Fork of the Snoqualmie River, some thirty miles almost due east of Seattle, is one such route that we have noticed the Swifts following; and here at various times during several summers we have watched the daily flight of a colony of these birds that numbered nearly one hundred and fifty.

In a valley of one of the mountain rivers, on an afternoon in June, Mr. Rathbun observed a flight behavior, which he describes in his notes as follows: "No swifts were seen until about 5:30 p. m., when a few flew by widely scattered. At 6:30 p. m., more swifts began to straggle past. While watching them, I noticed a dark, dense cloud moving slowly toward where I stood. I expected to see some swifts in company with it. I was not disappointed. There were about 50, and it was of interest to see them gliding around in advance of and below the cloud. By their actions it looked as if they were feeding, and all kept pace with the slow movement of the cloud. None of the swifts were below 400 feet, some much higher. As the cloud passed the swifts kept company with it; and then followed an interval when none were seen. Half an hour or so later another of the heavy clouds rolled up from the west. Only a short distance in front of it were more swifts circling, these soon followed by others gliding about beneath the cloud. In this flight were at least 60 of the birds, and, as in the first instance, they moved along with the cloud until lost to our sight."

M. P. Skinner has sent me the following notes on a flock of swifts that he watched at the Vernal Falls in the Yosemite Valley: "After circling once or twice around at the falls, they flew down the canyon below for half a mile with great swiftness, then whirled in a circle and came back. They repeated this over and over again. They kept in the early morning shade as long as I watched them. Periods of wing beating alternated with gliding on set wings, and both periods varied very much in length."

Ralph Hoffmann (1927) says: "The flight of the Black Swift is amazingly swift; it includes sudden sharp turns, steep downward plunges and hurried upward flights. The long, narrow wings at times 'twinkle' rapidly, or when the bird is sailing, are either held uplifted over the back or curved downward with the tips well below the body. The tail is very slightly forked but in flight it is constantly spread and appears fan-shaped when the bird makes a sudden turn."

I can find no evidence that the northern black swift has ever been seen perching on a tree or wire, or resting on the ground; its regular resting places seem to be the steep, rocky walls, often dripping with moisture, such as they choose for nesting sites. Though their feet are small and light, they have very sharp claws, and are able to cling to the rough surface for long periods. Mrs. Michael (1926) has seen them clinging to the wet walls behind the Vernal Falls and near it. "From the distance of fifty yards the birds appeared to stick as limpets do to the wet rocks of a sea shore." But, on closer examination, she found that "they were not sticking to the wall as limpets, but their bodies were held slightly away from the wall, with not even their tails touching." With one bird, she noted that "his strong toe nails were hooked to some tiny support and his entire tarsus rested firmly against the wall, thus holding his body and tail free." Later (1933) she says of a young black swift that she had in captivity: "When climbing up a sheer surface the swift used its wings, feet, tail and sharply hooked bill. When in repose it lay flat on its belly in the manner of a poor-will. * * * The legs seemed to have swivel joints, and it was strange to see the bird reach up its foot between the body and wing to comb its back and crown feathers."

Voice.—There is not much to be said about the voice of the black swift. All observers agree that it is generally a silent species; its note is seldom heard, except during the mating season and on its breeding grounds. Mr. Rathbun (1925) writes:

During its spring migration and shortly following, a period when the birds are associated in numbers, we have watched them for long spaces of time and always a perfect silence seemed to prevail among them. And this apparently is the case until the time comes when by their actions they show that they are mating. Even now their chatter-like note is but seldom heard, although invariably it is given at the time when one dashes at another, and this often proves the case when a pair may happen to fly in close company. During the midsummer we have heard their rapid notes as the birds passed in flight near the close of day, and in the autumnal migration when rarely one would make a quick dash at another. But these instances are uncommon and the species can properly be regarded as quite silent, being very different in this respect from the Chaeturine Swifts whose shrill twitterings are so frequent as they fly about. And the chatter of the Black Swift somewhat resembles that of the smaller ones; it being as rapid, but smoother in quality and more rolling, in fact rather pleasing to hear.

Grinnell and Storer (1924) describe its note as "a high-pitched twitter, not so shrill or long-continued as that of the White-throated Swift."

Field marks.—The black swift can be recognized by its size and coloration. It is the largest of the three western swifts. The white-throated swift, which most nearly approaches it in size, differs from it in having a well-marked and conspicuous pattern of black and white on the under parts, as well as the white rump patches, which show from above. The black swift appears wholly dark, except under certain conditions of reflected sunlight; the white markings on the immature bird are not conspicuous, except at close range. Vaux's swift is the smallest of the three and does not show in flight the slightly forked and fan-shaped tail of the black swift. Mr. Hoffmann (1927) suggests that "the beginner may take the much commoner Purple Martin for a Black Swift; the deeply notched tail, never spread like a fan, the habit of perching on stubs, the loud, musical notes and the difference in the sexes should readily identify the Martin." Grinnell and Storer (1924) state that, in the black swift, "the fore margin of the two wings as viewed from below is a double convex, and not a single continuous arc as in the White-throated Swift; moreover, the movements of the wings are more deliberate than in that species."

Fall.—Mr. Rathbun says in his notes: "The autumnal migration straggles over a more or less extended period. In the Puget Sound region it begins to take place soon after September 1, and it lasts three weeks or slightly more. I have observed this for many years, and the swifts do not pass by in the large groups that one will see in spring. Day after day in fall they straggle by in small numbers. Very often we have noticed that these groups were in multiples of three, which in our opinion would represent the parent birds with their single young. Invariably associated with the black swifts were the Vaux's swift, and if either was seen you could expect to see the other. And quite often, in company with both species of swifts, would be violet-green and barn swallows, all straggling past at odd times throughout the day."

In the Stikine region Mr. Swarth (1922) observed: "At Sergief Island, August 17 to September 7, black swifts were abundant, though seen only in cloudy or rainy weather. Then large flocks appeared, as many as seventy-five or a hundred being in sight at once flying over the marshes, the individuals moving about in wide circles, and the flock as a whole moving in a definite path. The birds sometimes flew very low, occasionally skimming along just over the tall grass. A flock would appear, circle about overhead awhile, and then vanish. About fifteen or twenty minutes later, others, or perhaps the same flock, would come in sight again."

DISTRIBUTION

Range.—Western North America; closely related nonmigratory races are found in southern Central America and in the West Indies.

Breeding range.—The breeding range of the black swift extends **north** to southeastern Alaska (Portage Cove); and northwestern British Columbia (Telegraph Creek). **East** to British Columbia (Telegraph Creek, Hazelton, and 158-mile House); southwestern Alberta (Banff); probably western Montana (Libby, Glacier National Park, and Stryker); and southwestern Colorado (Howardsville). **South** to southwestern Colorado (Howardsville); and southern California (Cerro Gordo, Sequoia National Park, and Santa Cruz). **West** to California (Santa Cruz, Berry Creek, and Yosemite Valley); western Washington (Seattle and Bellingham); British Columbia (Chilliwack and Okanagan Landing); and southeastern Alaska (Boca de Quadra and Portage Cove).

Winter range.—Unknown. Despite repeated statements that this species spends the winter season in southern Mexico, an examination of the available data fails to substantiate the assertion, the dates of observation or collection being entirely within the seasons of migration. Accordingly, while it is possible that these birds do winter with the resident form in southern Central America, factual evidence is at present lacking.

Spring migration.—Early dates of spring arrival are: Baja California—San Telmo, April 30. California—Haywards, April 19; Grapevine, April 24; Yosemite Valley, May 11. Washington—Seattle, May 16; Simialmoo, May 27. British Columbia—Chilliwack, May 8; Courtenay, May 15; Lulu Island, May 25; Alberni, June 9.

Fall migration.—Late dates of fall departure are: Alaska—Sergief Island, September 7. British Columbia—Hazelton, August 29; Errington, September 20; Okanagan Landing, September 26; Courtenay, September 29. Washington—Bellingham, September 1; Seattle, October 7. Oregon—Albany, September 22. California—Santa Cruz County, September 13; Haywards, October 1.

Casual records.—Among the records of occurrence of the black swift outside the range as above outlined are the following cases: New Mexico, reported from Willis in September 1883 and noted at Lake Burford, on September 28, 1904; Arizona, seen at Flagstaff on August 18, 1920; eastern Colorado, two seen on July 8 and three on July 10, 1910, in Estes Park, several seen near Trinidad, July 8–14, 1892, while a specimen in the collection of George B. Sennett was labeled as taken at Denver on June 26, 1884; and Idaho, taken or observed on the Malade River on August 13, 1834. A specimen came on board the S. S. *Antigua* on September 20, 1933, while the vessel was 84 miles off the coast of Guatemala.

Egg dates.—California: 27 records, June 16 to July 29; 14 records, June 24 to July 9, indicating the height of the season.

CHAETURA PELAGICA (Linnaeus)

CHIMNEY SWIFT

PLATES 44–46

HABITS

CONTRIBUTED BY WINSOR MARRETT TYLER

From its unknown winter quarters, somewhere in Central America or on the South American Continent, the chimney swift comes northward in spring and spreads out over a wide area, which includes a large part of the United States and southern Canada.

Individually the swift is an obscure little bird, with a stumpy, dull-colored body, short bristly tail, and stiff, sharp wings, but it is such a common bird over the greater part of its breeding range and collects in such enormous flocks, notably when it gathers for its autumnal migration, that as a species it is widely known.

The birds also have the habit of continual flight during the hours of daylight throughout the summer, and therefore keep always before our eyes when we look up at the sky. They exemplify speed and tireless energy; they sail and circle on set wings, then with flickering wing beats they are off in a burst of speed, shooting like an arrow through the air, chattering their bright notes as they race along—little arrows "cutting the clouds" over country, town, and woodland.

Spring.—Swifts move up into the northern latitudes only when spring is rather far advanced, not until their aerial insect food is plentiful well above the ground. Therefore their arrival varies a good deal from year to year.

Kopman (1915) reports that the average date of appearance in New Orleans is about March 18. In New England, in an average year, we do not expect the birds for fully 30 days after this date; hence we may infer that they spend a month in moving across a dozen degrees of latitude.

A daylight migrant, solely, so far as is known, we see the first arrivals of this swift commonly in the afternoon, sailing in small companies—perhaps only a single bird—often high in the air. As they fly along, they give an occasional chatter, or a few rather feeble chips, but with none of the energy and volubility characteristic of the breeding season. On cloudy days in spring, when the swifts dip down

over the surface of a pond and feed among the twittering swallows—
a common habit of theirs—they are apt to be silent.

When the birds appear, leisurely drifting up from the south, they
often fly in great loops. They turn slowly aside from their northerly
course, swinging farther and farther around until they are moving
for a time toward the south, then, veering gradually, they resume
their journey, but soon turn again and make another sweeping curve,
each loop carrying them nearer their destination.

An hour before dark, in the lengthening evenings of early May,
we often see a little gathering of New England swifts that have
settled on their nesting grounds but are not occupied as yet with
breeding activities, flying about in company, high over their chosen
chimney, chattering together. The birds may be so high in the air
that the sound of their voices barely reaches our ears. These newly
arrived birds pay little attention to each other and do not approach
near or chase one another as they will in June, yet they keep in a
loose flock, sailing and flickering in a somewhat circular path and
sometimes coast down from their high elevation, and climb up to it
again. Then, as dusk deepens, at about the time the bat appears, they
gather around their chimney and drop into it.

Although swifts, during their spring migration, often collect, before
going to roost, in flocks of considerable numbers, they are less conspicuous at this season than during their impressive gatherings in
autumn. These are described under "Fall."

Courtship.—In June, here in New England, the swifts become very
noisy. Even from within doors we hear their voices as the birds
hurry past not far from our roof. As we listen their chips appear
sharper and faster than they did the week before, more clearly enun-
ciated, and they run in a long series that seems to grow in intensity
as the birds come nearer, reaches a maximum when they pass overhead, and dies away as they rush on.

When we watch the birds at this season we notice also a difference
in their behavior. There is little of the slow, apparently aimless
circling of early spring, when, although the birds gather in small
companies and follow similar paths in the air, they are seemingly
indifferent to one another's presence.

The breeding season is here. Purpose has come into the swift's
brain, and purpose has brought intensity and speed, and concentration
on a mate. Now they fly close together, two birds, three birds, sometimes four in a little bunch. The length of a swift's body scarcely
separates them as they tear along, ripping through space, following
the twists and turns of the bird in the lead.

Soon two birds are left alone, the others circling off for a time.
Both of these birds are chipping sharply, flying fast, close together,

and during their mad dash, one, if not both, uses a peculiar note—a line of chips, a chatter, then the chips again. This combination of notes accompanies the height of the pursuit, and the swifter and closer the chase the sharper and quicker the notes. It seems also that the nearer the birds are to one another, the faster they fly. They may fly sometimes, their wings almost touching, at a pace that seems reckless; then the notes spatter out as if self control were lost, and at last, as the pursuer overtakes his goal, he rises a little above her and lifts up his wings, and there appears to be a moment of contact.

The probability that the nuptial flight leads, at least sometimes, to sexual contact in the air is increased by Sutton's (1928) careful study of the swift. He says: "In this courtship flight, the pair of birds may fly rapidly about, twittering loudly; suddenly the upper bird will lift its wings very high above the back and coast through the air, sometimes for several seconds, while the bird beneath may soar with its wings held in a fixed position below the plane of the body. It may be that this graceful and interesting display is at the culmination of courtship activity."

From the fact that swifts in the courting season so often fly three together when engaged in their pursuits—in the initial part at least, for at the culmination the pair find themselves alone—a surmise has arisen that one male and two females make up the trio and that the swift is polygamous. This surmise, however, is not yet attested by any conclusive evidence.

Nesting.—Of the few North American birds—and they are very few—that were influenced favorably by civilized man when he settled on this continent, the chimney swift received the greatest benefit. Before the coming of man, the swifts had been building their nests for thousands of years in hollow trees, here and there in the American wilderness. Then man came, and unwittingly supplied, within his chimneys, exactly the situation the swift required for nesting, an upright surface inside a cavity, protected from the weather— the equivalent of a hollow tree. Thus the birds' nesting sites were increased a millionfold.

Nowadays the typical site is in a chimney, "from near top to 22 feet below it," Forbush (1927) says. Yet, as the following quotations show, the swift occasionally avails itself for nesting purposes of some other of man's works; also from time to time it is found breeding in its ancestral manner.

The nest itself is a little hammock—half-saucer-shaped—composed solely of dead twigs, which the bird breaks off as it flies past a tree. The twigs are attached to the wall, and the twigs themselves are fastened to one another by the glutinous saliva of the bird, which hardens and fixes the structure so firmly to its support that it withstands, as a rule, the rain of summer storms.

Lewis (1927) reports that "a pair of Chimney Swifts built a nest and hatched a brood of young in an open well near an old deserted farm-house in the southern part of the county [Lawrenceville, Va.]. The nest was typical for the species and was stuck just above a bulge in a rock in the well wall, just as they are stuck to the rocks in a chimney. It was located about 7 feet below the surface of the ground, and 10 feet above the water."

Hyde (1924) found an occupied nest "in an abandoned cistern about one mile east of the town of Magnolia, Putnam County, Ill." He says: "The cistern was half hidden by vegetation. The diameter at the aperture was three feet and at the bottom nine feet. There was water nine feet below the aperture. The nest was in an entirely sheltered position four feet above the water. All these figures being approximate."

Kennard (1895), speaking of a nest in New York State, says: "I found a Chimney Swift's nest placed just under the ridge pole of an old log barn and against the side of one of the logs of which it was constructed. * * * It was within a foot of an enormous hornet's nest. The five young birds which were nearly fledged were clinging to the bark of the logs in the immediate vicinity and seemed to get on much better with the hornets than I did."

Evermann (1889) describes a "peculiar nidification of this species" as follows: "A pair fastened their nest in 1884 upon the inside of the door of an out-house at the Vandalia depot in Camden [Indiana]. The birds entered the building through small holes made in the gables. This building was in daily use, but those who visited it were cautioned by the railroad agent to open the door with care so as not to jar the eggs from the nest. Four eggs were laid, one of which was jostled from the nest, the other three hatched, and the young were reared in safety. The nest was repaired and used again in 1885, and again in 1886, a brood being reared each season."

Most astonishing records of nesting are reported by Moore (1902b) thus: "In this locality [Scotch Lake, New Brunswick], more nests are built inside buildings than there are inside chimneys. The nests are usually glued to the gable end of the building—sometimes barns, sometimes old uninhabited houses are chosen—and one nest, the past summer, was built in a blacksmith shop within fifteen feet of the forge. A number of years ago a pair nested in the upper part of a house in which a family lived, and near to a bed in which children slept every night. In this case the birds entered through a broken window."

Daniel (1902) gives an instance of the nesting of swifts in hollow cypress trees in the Great Dismal Swamp. He says:

Along the southeastern shore, growing in the lake some distance out from the shore line, are a number of large hollow cypresses. The roots or "knees" of these trees extend upward and outward from the surface of the water, curving inward some distance up, and in most of them, between the water and base of the tree proper, there are openings large enough for a canoe to enter. By pushing our canoe in these intervals between the roots, we were able to examine the interiors of the hollow trees. In these we found the swifts nesting in their primitive fashion, the nests being fastened to the interior walls about midway down.

T. E. Musselman wrote me in 1935 that he has noted that swifts are beginning to use silos as nesting sites in the Middle West.

Eggs.—[AUTHOR'S NOTE: The chimney swift lays three to six eggs, more commonly four or five. These are pure white and only moderately glossy. In shape they vary from elliptical-ovate to cylindrical-ovate. The measurements of 56 eggs average 20.10 by 13.24 millimeters; the eggs showing the four extremes measure **21.59** by 13.46, 21.34 by **13.72, 17.53** by 13.72, and 18.29 by **12.70** millimeters.]

Young.—The young swift starts life in a world of danger. It comes from the egg a blind little naked thing, no bigger than your fingernail, lying in a frail cradle of sticks that overhangs a black "drop into nothing." The little swift, however, is equipped to deal with the dangers of its birthplace. Very early in its life it can cling and crawl; it can hide under its nest; it can move about over the walls of the abyss in which it lives; and, when the time for flying comes, it can clamber toward the free air, taking, perhaps, the longest and last walk of its career.

Frederic H. Kennard illustrates in his notes the hardiness of the young swift when it comes from the egg. He says: "On July 15, 1918, somewhere between 9 and 10 a. m. at Duck Lake, Maine, I found among the ashes of the fireplace, in a friend's unoccupied camp, a chimney swift's nest which I had been watching and which, when I had last seen it, the previous noon, in the chimney, had contained two eggs. It had evidently been dislodged from its proper place by a thunderstorm and torrential rain of the night before.

"The nest and both eggshells lay among the ashes, close together, at the back of the large fireplace. Both eggs were broken, and the shells lay just where they had fallen. One of them was evidently addled, while the content of the other was apparently missing.

"Imagine my surprise, when after hunting for some time, I discovered that the content of the other egg was a tiny swiftlet, which, blind and with the back of its skull badly bruised and suffused with blood from its fall down the chimney, had nevertheless made its way out through the ashes, dropping down the thickness of a brick from the fire place proper to the hearth beyond, then across the hearth; and had climbed, in a style worthy of a young hoatzin, and was still clinging in an upright position to the finely woven wire fender that had enclosed the fireplace, but which I had moved aside in order to facilitate inspection.

"Of course this bird might have been hatched the day before, sometime between noon and the time of the storm, which occurred about 10 p. m., but my impression was, from the position of the eggshell as it lay broken in halves among the ashes, that the little fellow ready to hatch had come down either in the shell or in the act of emerging from it. There were no signs of any yolk to be seen. Judged from his size and development he must have been less than a day old. There had been but one nest in the chimney; and there was no possibility of any outside intermeddling, as the camp was kept locked and I had been the only one to enter it in weeks."

Of the young when nearly ready to fly he says: "Found a swift's nest down in Charlie Boyce's boat house on the wall about 5' 9" above the floor, and the four nearly fledged young clinging to the pretty smoothly sawed board wall from 18" to 24" away from the nest. Upon investigating I found that their toenails were long and sharp and that they could flutter up or across the wall at will, though when undisturbed they kept well together in a compact little group, propped up on their tails. When disturbed the young birds squealed loudly something like an exaggerated rattlesnake."

Burns (1921) states that the eyes of the young swift become wide open on the fourteenth day. This accords with the observation of Mary F. Day (1899), who watched at close range the development of a brood of swifts and noted that the incubation period was 19 days; that "even at the tender age that must be reckoned by minutes, these young birds were fed, seemingly, by regurgitation"; that the "two first ventured from home when nineteen days old"; and that they flew from the chimney four weeks after hatching. Speaking of the exercising of the nestlings, she says: "The young aspirants would stand in the nest and for a time vibrate the wings rapidly, so rapidly that the identity of wing was lost." And of the fledglings 26 days after leaving the egg she says: "They take flying exercises up and down the chimney, but I believe have not yet left it."

Carter (1924) studied the feeding of five fledgling swifts at a nest built on the wall of an abandoned cabin in Ontario. He says:

The old birds gained access to the interior of the building through a broken window and were remarkably tame, feeding the young within three feet of the observers, thus giving an excellent opportunity to observe the process of feeding. The parent, with greatly extended cheeks and throat, alighted upon the wall among the young. Immediately there was a great commotion. After a short hesitation a young bird would be fed by forcing some of the food from the mouth of the parent into that of the offspring. After a moment's feeding there was a pause and then the process was repeated, either to the same young or another. As many as three were served at a single visit.

Lewis (1929) describes thus the feeding of a brood of young birds that had fallen when their nest had been dislodged by rain but were clinging to the wall of the chimney:

From the start the old birds did not see me sitting on the hearth, or, seeing they paid little attention. I was much surprized to see that they always fluttered down and lit on the wall a little below the young birds, bracing themselves in the same manner as the young and reaching up to feed them. The young would turn their necks down as far as possible without changing the position of their bodies. The old birds would stretch up, putting the bill inside the gaping mouths of the young, and seemingly feed by regurgitation. This was invariable during the time I spent watching them, which amounted to a number of hours.

The four young clung to the wall without moving noticeably, always side by side, and were fed from daylight until dark at intervals of from 1 to 28 minutes until July 31, when I was obliged to leave home. [The nest had been dislodged on June 25.]

After the nest had fallen, but before the parents came down into the lower part of the chimney to feed their young, the little birds gave a note that Mr. Lewis describes as "a loud, harsh squeal, quite unlike the chattering they always make when being fed."

Townsend (1906) comments on the noisiness of a nestful of chattering swifts he found inside "a small hay barn" at Cape Breton. He says: "The shrill twittering of the young was almost deafening in the small hay loft."

Guy A. Bailey (1905), in a study of a swift's nest built inside a barn near Syracuse, N. Y., shows that the parent bird urges the young to leave the nest even before (according to his photographs) the flight feathers are more than half released from their sheaths. He says:

Generally, after feeding the young, the old bird crawled over to one side of the nest and cautiously insinuated its body behind the young birds. The adult bird kept crowding until all but one or two of the brood of five were forced out of the nest and took up positions on the vertical roost. The remaining birds would sometimes leave the nest of their own accord and follow their mates. This was noticed especially after those clinging to the boards had been fed.

It often happened that the adult birds would remain away from the young as long as twenty minutes, during which time the little ones would return to the nest. Usually, however, one parent would remain with the brood until relieved by the mate. On such occasions there was a period of several minutes when both parents were present.

Plumages.—[AUTHOR'S NOTE: The young swift is hatched naked and blind, but the spinelike quills soon begin to appear, and these develop into a juvenal, or first-winter, plumage, which is much like that of the adult; there are some light edgings on the scapulars and rump, which soon wear away, and the under parts are somewhat darker than in adults, especially on the throat. I have seen young birds acquiring the first winter plumage as early as August 10 and others still in the postnatal molt as late as September 25. This plumage is probably worn through the winter, though no winter specimens have been available for study. Forbush (1927) says that a "complete prenuptial molt beginning in late winter or early spring is followed by a plumage as adult; adults apparently molt twice a year, a complete postnuptial molt in autumn and a partial (possibly complete) molt in spring."]

Food.—Pearson (1911) quotes a letter from W. L. McAtee of the United States Biological Survey: "The bird's food consists almost wholly of insects, and beetles, flies and ants are the principal items. It gets many beetles (Scolytidae), the most serious enemies of our forests, when they are swarming, and takes also the old-fashioned potato beetle (*Lema trilineata*), the tarnished plant-bug (*Lygus pratensis*), and other injurious insects. The bird is, of course, largely beneficial to the agricultural interests of the country."

Knight (1908) says: "The food of the Chimney Swallow consists of almost any of the smaller insects which fill the air of a summer's day."

Behavior.—The relationship between man and the chimney swift is a rather curious one. Although the species spends the summer scattered over a large part of the North American Continent, it never, except by accident, sets foot upon one inch of this vast land. The birds build their "procreant cradle" in the chimneys of thousands of our homes and crisscross for weeks above our gardens and over the streets of our towns and cities, yet, wholly engrossed in their own activities far overhead, they do not appear to notice man at all. Indeed, it is easy to believe that the swift is no more aware of man during the summer, even when it is a denizen of our largest cities, than when in winter it is soaring over the impenetrable jungles of Central America.

How do we regard this bird that does not know we are on earth? We are glad to have swifts breed in our chimney; we like to see them shooting about over our heads, and we enjoy their bright voices, yet, do we feel such friendship for them as we feel for a chipping sparrow, for example, which builds sociably in the vines of our piazza? The little sparrow may be wary, and may fly away if we come too near, but at least it pays us the compliment of recognizing our existence. The swift, however, is not even a semitrustful neighbor; it is a guest that does not know we are its host. We may almost think of it as a machine for catching insects, a mechanical toy, clicking out its sharp notes.

But let us note this fact. Every ten years or so the swifts do not appear about our house in the spring. Something has gone wrong on their journey northward. Our chimney will be empty this year; there will be no dark bows and arrows dashing back and forth above our roof, no quick pursuits and chattering in the evening. All summer something is lacking because there are no swifts to enliven the season. We realize, now that they are gone, how we should miss their active, cheerful presence, if they never came back again. But we may be sure they will come back—next year perhaps—to visit us again, this most welcome "guest of summer."

Bird banding has brought man and the chimney swift for the first time into close association. During the past few years, swifts have been banded in very large numbers. At daybreak, as the birds pour out of the chimneys where they have roosted during their autumnal migration, they are captured in traps placed over the chimney and so ingeniously devised that the outward flow of hundreds of birds is not interrupted. The banders who have handled the birds report that they show little or no fear (or consciousness) of man and appear tame to an extraordinary degree.

The following quotations from Constance and E. A. Everett (1927) illustrate their behavior after being caught. These authors state that: "In less than five minutes, with but one casualty, one hundred sixty-four Chimney Swifts were inside of that cage ['a six-foot house trap'], clinging to its walls of wire mesh like a swarm of bees, except that though densely massed, they were clinging to the wire and not to each other. A few were at all times on the wing, as they changed from one group to another, bewildered, perhaps, but not in the least frightened. Most of them, however, promptly alighted and tucked their heads under the wings and tails of those birds above them, until the inner walls of the cage took on the appearance of being shingled with birds."

When removed from the cage, "these swifts were very quiet, and apparently comfortable at all stages of the game. When held in the hands they would snuggle between the fingers confidingly; and when held against the clothes they would wriggle under the folds of the garments and contentedly go to sleep."

Of the next morning's work they say: "Since there were so few birds, we took the time to enjoy playing with them. Miss Constance and the boys tried wearing them either singly as a brooch, or collectively as a breast plate; and always the birds snuggled down as though perfectly willing to join the game, provided their naps were not interfered with. Finally some passing school girls were adorned with live breast pins to take home for show, while several birds, clinging to Constance's coat rode many blocks in the car, and, scolding, had to be dragged off to their liberty."

These observations were made at Waseca, Minn., on September 8 and 9, 1926.

In flight, the swift, perhaps from necessity because the bird spends so much of the day in the air, relieves its wings from time to time from their quick flickering and sails—the wings held motionless, fully extended from the body. When beating its wings, the bird appears always in a hurry; it seems to be moving them up and down as fast as it can; it often rocks from side to side, as it turns this way and that, and ever seems to be trying to fly a little faster.

Sutton (1928), in an able study of the swift's flight, aided by examination of captive birds, states that "no intermediate, half-spread position [of the wing] was ever maintained in healthy individuals. In fact, such an intermediate position seemed impossible [on account of anatomical structure]. * * *

"It may be stated broadly, therefore, that the Chimney Swift wing, so far as its spreading is concerned, has but two normal positions; one, folded at rest, the other, open for flight, whether that flight be rapid forward flapping, soaring, coasting, or even sudden descent."

One evening Dr. Sutton, standing at the mouth of a chimney while swifts were going to roost, watched the birds enter, within arm's reach. Describing this experience, he says:

I was amazed at their precision and speed. As a rule, they slowed up abruptly just before making the final plunge, this being accomplished by a spreading and lowering of the tail, and by rapid, vigorous, downward and forward strokes of the wings, during which the loosely and widely spread primaries seemed to aid in checking the speed. When a proper point above the mouth of the chimney was reached the birds suddenly pressed the spread tail downward as far as possible, and with outstretched wings high above the back, still loosely fluttering, through an arc of about forty-five degrees, either dropped directly, turned jerkily from side to side, or twirled gracefully downward into the chimney.

Again, in the morning, peering down the chimney as the birds emerged, he says: "I was surprised to see that the birds were flying almost directly forward, but in an upward direction. Their bodies were not in a horizontal position; they were almost vertical, and the whole spectacle gave the impression that the birds were crawling up invisible wires."

For years there has been a controversy concerning the swift's flight. Some observers held that the swift moved its wings simultaneously, like other birds; others believed that the wing beats were alternate, like the strokes of a double-bladed paddle. It is easy to see how confusion between fact and appearance might arise. Swifts *do* appear to fly with alternate wing beats, but chiefly, if not wholly, when the birds tilt to one side in making their quick turns. Then one wing appears to be up and the other down, and as a matter of fact such is the case in reference to an imaginary line drawn across the swift parallel to the ground—one wing is above the line, and the other is below it. But the bird being tilted to one side, in order to show the relative position of one wing to the other, we must allow for the tilting, and we must draw the imaginary line, not parallel to the ground, but through the short axis of the *bird's body*. The observer, standing on the ground, does not make this adjustment, for he does not take into account the instantaneous tilting of the bird.

The question was definitely settled by Myron F. Westover (1932), who demonstrated by motion photography that *"there was no instance where there was any alternation of wing-movement;* the wings move in unison as do those of other species of birds." Dr. Chapman appends an editorial note to the article: "Mr. Westover's film was shown in the American Museum to the members of the Bird Department who agree that it demonstrates beyond question the truth of his conclusions."

There is a difference of opinion also among observers as to whether the swift, when collecting nesting material, breaks off dead twigs with its feet or with its beak. Coues (1897), questioning the correctness of a drawing by Fuertes representing the bird snapping off a twig with its feet, says: "We have always supposed the bird secured the object with its beak, as it dashed past on wing at full speed; or at any rate that has been my own belief for more years than I can remember. But Mr. Fuertes vouched for the correctness of his representation from actual observation. The question being thus raised, I set it forth recently in a query inserted in one of our popular periodicals, asking for information."

There are six replies to Coues' query printed in The Nidologist (vol. 4, pp. 80, 81), five of which are in accord with his opinion, while one is against it, as is one more reply published in The Osprey (vol. 1, p. 122). Dr. Coues declares that "these leave the case still open!"

More recently Shelley (1929), from an ample experience of 13 uninterrupted years of observation of swifts at close range, states unequivocally that they "gather their nesting material * * * *with their feet."* He adds: "I never yet observed a Swift grasp or carry a twig in its beak."

Mr. Shelley's well-weighed opinion added to that of Mr. Fuertes, whose accuracy and skill in observing birds have never been surpassed, should be accepted with confidence until motion photography shall prove or disprove the correctness of their view, although the swift may adopt both methods of collecting nesting material.

We may recall that Audubon (1840) appears to have had no doubt upon the question, for he says: "They throw their body suddenly against the twig, grapple it with their feet, and by an instantaneous jerk, snap it off short, and proceed with it to the place intended for the nest."

Although without much doubt swifts pluck off twigs with their feet, they may find it convenient to arrive at the nest site with their feet free to grasp the wall of the chimney. To gain this end, it is possible that on the way to the nest, the birds may transfer the twig to their beak, for William Brewster (1937b) in his Concord journal says that on June 15, 1905, he saw one "drop into the chimney this evening carrying a short twig held crossways in its *bill*."

An entry in Brewster's Concord journal also indicates that the swift may be more nocturnal in its habits than is commonly believed. He writes under the date August 5, 1893: "At about 2 A. M. I was surprised to hear Chimney Swifts twittering outside the window. There seemed to be a good many of them and the sound of their voices indicated that they first circled about the house several times and then went off towards the South. When I first heard the twittering, there were also several birds making their peculiar rumbling in the chimney, but this soon ceased and was not again repeated. The night was dark and still at the time, with rain falling gently and steadily."

We must remember also that Wilson (1832) states that "the young are fed at intervals during the greater part of the night," and Henry C. Denslow writes to Mr. Bent of "the vivid memory" of an observation of the birds' nocturnal activities. He says that "the chimney swift feeds its young in the middle of the night, going out and in the chimney several times with the usual rumbling of wing beats and the usual chirring sound of the young birds while being fed. I chanced to sleep in a small room with a chimney, near Rochester, N. Y., for several years, and so became familiar with this habit of the bird."

Frederic H. Kennard, in his notes, describes an interesting habit that he observed at very close range at a nest containing young built on the inner wall of a boathouse. He says: "She(?) [a parent bird] sat very close, moving her head only occasionally, panting with the heat, and did not appear to mind me much until her mate flew in, lit on the wall nearby, when she got off the nest and fluttered up and down the wall beside or below the nest, snapping her wings together (apparently behind her), a note of warning or anger, or something of the sort, perhaps to scare me away or to show her displeasure. She would raise her wings slowly until they stood out straight behind her back, parallel and almost touching." And later he adds: "They do not seem to snap their wings except when disturbed by me. There is no snapping when they ordinarily leave their nests. When they do snap they slowly raise their wings until they are straight up from their backs and then snap them a couple of times."

At the same boathouse he "saw one of the swifts fly through a crack in the door just after I had come out and closed it. He didn't slow down at all, never missed a beat, but merely turned on one side and went through, full speed."

Voice.—The notes of the swift remind us of the bird itself—energetic and quick; sharp and hard like the bird's stiff wings. The note most commonly heard as the birds shoot about over our heads is a bright, clear, staccato *chip* or *tsik*—whichever suggests the sharper sound—often repeated in a series and sometimes running off into a rapid chatter. The chip note varies little, if at all, except for the quickness of the notes, and seems to punctuate the bird's ceaseless rush through the air. Sometimes, when the birds are very high in the air, the chattering call comes down to our ears, softened by distance—like sparks slowly falling to the earth after a rocket has burst.

Simple as these notes are, the birds introduce a good deal of variety into them by modifying the interval between them, thereby changing the expression of their lively theme.

One modification, which I have mentioned under "Courtship," having heard it only in the breeding season and only when the birds were under stress of excitement, serves to illustrate this ability and may be regarded as representing the song of the swift. It is made up of a long series of notes in which the birds, after giving several isolated chips, change abruptly to a series of very rapid notes, a sort of chatter, then, with no pause between, change back to the chips, then back again—chips–chatter–chips, and so on. We may term it the "chips and chatter call."

Another modification of the chip note, often heard in summer when the birds are in a comparatively quiet mood, is a long chatter in which the volume increases and lessens, suggesting the sounding of a minute watchman's rattle.

There is one note quite different in quality from the above notes and less frequently heard than any of the variations of the chip. This is a musical monosyllable—sometimes divided into two syllables—a squeal, almost a high whistle with a slight upward inflection, like *eeip*, sometimes repeated once or twice. I have heard it both in spring and fall; hence it cannot be, as I once thought it was, a note of immature birds.

Field marks.—The swift may be distinguished readily from any of the swallows by the shape of its wings and the manner in which it moves them. Swallows' wings are roughly triangular, the triangle seeming to join the bird's body by a fairly wide base, whereas the swift's wings are narrow at the base—they are pointed, and slightly curved like the terminal part of a sickle's blade—and appear to be set on well forward.

The stroke of the swift's wing gives a jerky, hurried effect compared with the more leisurely movement of a swallow, and the tips of the wings are not swept backward, even when the birds are sailing, as they are, in varying degree, in the flight of all the swallows.

The swift has been likened to a winged cigar, tapered at both ends, flying through the air. The resemblance is very close, except when the bird fans out its stumpy tail, as it does from time to time.

The nearly uniform dull color of the swift's under parts and its very short, square tail, combined with its characteristic flight, serve to identify the bird even at a considerable distance.

Enemies.—Because the swift spends a large part of its life moving rapidly through the air, almost never coming to rest except at its nest or when roosting in a chimney or a hollow tree, it is practically out of reach of any mammal that otherwise might prey upon it. And while flying its speed and its erratic course render it almost immune from attack by hawks.

In his notes T. E. Musselman cites an exception to this immunity. He says: "I was watching a flock of about 1,500 swifts circling about a chimney in Quincy, Ill., forming an avian funnel which was dropping into its black depths. It was almost dusk when a sharp-shinned hawk flew from a neighboring sycamore tree to the top of the chimney and seized one of the swifts as it was poised with upturned wings and was just about to drop into its night's sanctuary. The swift squealed as it was being carried away, so I was able to follow the course of the tiny hawk as it flew through the semidarkness back to the tree."

Musselman (1931) also reports an occasion when swifts were overcome by gas while roosting in the chimney of a church in Quincy, Ill. He says: "One cold October night it was necessary to turn on the fire, which resulted in the killing of between 3000 and 5000 Chimney Swifts that had harbored there. Three bushel baskets of dead birds were taken from the flue."

Julian Burroughs (1922) tells of an instance in which a large number of swifts, taking refuge in a chimney, dislodged the soot. Many were smothered in the chimney, while others, several hundred, evidently confused by the soot, continued down into the house where they were found "on all the mouldings and pictures." These were released apparently unharmed. "There were about fifty live ones and fifty dead in the furnace—also ten water-pails full of dead ones in the pipes and bottom of chimney."

The greatest hazard of the swift's life, perhaps, comes in the spring or early summer when, once in a dozen years or so, a prolonged, drenching downpour of rain clears the air of insects, and threatens the local birds with starvation. Brewster (1906), referring to such a storm, says: "The Swifts * * * were seriously reduced in numbers, throughout eastern Massachusetts, during the cold, rainy weather of June, 1903, and the losses which they suffered that season have not as

yet been made good." Since 1903 the birds here in New England have
been decimated by several minor storms but have quickly recovered
their loss.

Fall.—Fall comes early in the yearly cycle of the swift's life. At
the end of the summer there is a long journey before the birds, old
and young, to the warm air of the Tropics where they can find food
throughout the winter months.

Late in July and early in August we often see small groups of
swifts in the air, evidently preparing for migration. These flocks
are doubtless made up of our local birds, those that have spent the
summer in our vicinity, and they are accompanied, presumably, by as
many of their young as are on the wing. They travel such long
distances through the air, often curving round and round a chimney
or church tower, that they derive a good deal of exercise from the
flights—exercise that must serve to strengthen the wings of the young
birds.

Under date of August 7, 1917, my notes mention this habit. "In
these exercising flights, as I take them to be, the birds fly mostly in
long curves; they are really circling, although they may turn at any
time to either side. The birds, a dozen or more of them, are sailing
in a great ring; they suggest bits of wood floating in an eddy of a
slow-moving stream. They are far from one another, flying silently,
mainly on set wings. One veers toward another, which quickens its
pace by rapid, flickering wing beats. A chase is on. One or more
birds join in, giving the long chatter. Now they hurry through the
air, close together. When one comes near another, it may raise its
wings in a V above its back, soaring for a moment. The chases are
soon over, however; the birds seem to lose interest in speed and resume their circular, soaring flight. They often turn out from the
circle, tilting to one side, the outer wing uppermost.

"During the middle of the day I do not see the swifts gathered
about the house; it is chiefly in the morning and evening that they
are most active. This evening two birds, close together, flew slowly
over my head at a low elevation. One gave the long chatter and
chips alternately, but in a quiet way with little staccato quality."

It is at about this time, the first two weeks of August, that we
see evidence of molting in our local swifts. As they fly overhead we
notice a narrow gap in their wings where a flight feather or two
is missing, and in every case the little gap in one wing corresponds
almost exactly with the gap in the other, but this slight bilateral
loss of wing surface seems to hinder the birds' flight little, if at all.
Apparently molting does not cripple them, as it does many woodland birds; indeed, the swift, spending the hours of daylight in the
sky, must not be disabled for even a single day.

The most spectacular event in the swift's life, from our point of view, occurs during the autumnal migration when the birds, late in the afternoon, congregate in a large, wheel-shaped flock and circle about the chimney they have selected as their roosting place for the night. The following quotations describe in detail such gatherings.

Townsend (1912), writing of the bird in the St. John Valley, New Brunswick, says:

At Fredericton, on July 25, I watched a large flock of Swifts enter for the night a chimney on the southwest corner of the Parliament Building. Sun set at about 8 P. M. At 8.24 P. M. one bird set its wings and dropped into the chimney and soon they began dropping in fast, while the flock circled first one way then another or crowded together in a confused mass, twittering loudly all the time. Owing to the proximity of the dome regular circling was somewhat interfered with, but as a rule the birds circled in the direction of the hands of a clock, and individuals would drop out and into the chimney in dozens when the circle passed over it. Occasionally they would all swoop off to the other side of the building, soon to return. At 8.45 P. M. practically all the birds had entered the chimney and I had counted roughly,—at first singly and later by tens,—2200 birds.

The setting of the wings, which Dr. Townsend speaks of, takes place just over the mouth of the chimney. The bird raises its wings above its back and drops into the chimney or very often shies off, like a horse refusing to take a fence and, after making another circuit, tries again.

Linton (1924) gives us a vivid picture of the Swifts "at bedtime," showing a spirit of play among the birds. He writes from Augusta, Ga.:

October 5, 6.5 P. M.: Sky overcast; large numbers of Swifts in the upper air; look like swarm of bees; general direction of flight in circle, counter-clockwise. 6.7: A few began to enter the chimney, when a passing auto frightened them for a short time. 6.8: Entering again, average probably not far from 15 per second, at times many more than this [the flue of this chimney was said to be 3 feet square]; circling continuously counter-clockwise. As the circle approaches the chimney, a column of Swifts, from a point 20 feet above the level of the top of the chimney descends to the chimney. The Swifts in this column which fail to enter continue the circle at a lower level, joining the higher level at the opposite side of the circle, and in a position which makes them contributing parts of the descending column, when they again come to that point. Great swarms of Swifts could be seen in the upper air, their paths apparently crossing and recrossing, but really all flying in circular paths at different levels. Many appeared as minute specks in the upper air. At 6.23 all were in, stopping abruptly; probably no more than a dozen stragglers in the last 5 seconds. It thus took the flock a little over 15 minutes to enter the chimney.

October 8, 6.12 P. M.: Sky clear; 3 or 4 Swifts seen from window. 6.13: 12 or more Swifts in sight. 6.15: 100, more or less, in sight. 6.15:20: 500, more or less, in sight. 6.16: Increasing in numbers rapidly; general course in wide circles, counter-clockwise. 6.17: Seem to be enjoying themselves too much to go to bed; immense numbers; upper air full of them. 6.19:20: Getting closer to chimney; some of them dipping down to within a foot or two of the top. 6.20: Changed their minds for a few seconds; again enjoying themselves in the air.

6.21: Getting closer again. 6.21:30: Changed minds again. 6.22:30: Look as if they were getting ready to go to bed. 6.23: Getting closer; circles variable, 150 to 200 feet in diameter nearest level of top of chimney, lower portion, at times, possibly no more than 50 feet in diameter. 6.23:30: Passing near top of chimney. 6.24: Passing very close to top of chimney. 6.24:30: A few going in. 6.24:40: Entering at rate of 15 or more per second. Same maneuvers as on previous evenings. 6.25:30: Going in very rapidly; 15 per second a very conservative estimate. 6.28: A second or two when they did not go in so rapidly, being disturbed by the puffing of a locomotive on the Georgia Railroad near by. 6.28:30: Going in as rapidly as ever. 6.30: All in; stopped suddenly.

Audubon (1840) gives an interesting account of a large number of swifts he found roosting in a hollow tree in Louisville, Ky. He says:

I found it to be a sycamore, nearly destitute of branches, sixty or seventy feet high, between seven and eight feet in diameter at the base, and about five for the distance of forty feet up, where the stump of a broken hollowed branch, about two feet in diameter, made out from the main stem. * * * Next morning I rose early enough to reach the place long before the least appearance of daylight, and placed my head against the tree. All was silent within. I remained in that posture probably twenty minutes, when suddenly I thought the great tree was giving way, and coming down upon me. Instinctively I sprung from it, but when I looked up to it again, what was my astonishment to see it standing as firm as ever. The Swallows were now pouring out in a black continued stream. I ran back to my post, and listened in amazement to the noise within, which I could compare to nothing else than the sound of a large wheel revolving under a powerful stream. It was yet dusky, so I could hardly see the hour on my watch, but I estimated the time which they took in getting out at more than thirty minutes. * * *

The next day I hired a man, who cut a hole at the base of the tree. * * * Knowing by experience that if the birds should notice the hole below, they would abandon the tree, I had it carefully closed. The Swallows came as usual that night, and I did not disturb them for several days. At last, provided with a dark lantern, I went with my companion about nine in the evening, determined to have a full view of the interior of the tree. The hole was opened with caution. I scrambled up the sides of the mass of exuviae, and my friend followed. All was perfectly silent. Slowly and gradually I brought the light of the lantern to bear on the sides of the hole above us, when we saw the Swallows clinging side by side, covering the whole surface of the excavation. In no instance did I see one above another. Satisfied with the sight, I closed the lantern. We then caught and killed with as much care as possible more than a hundred, stowing them away in our pockets and bosoms, and slid down into the open air. We observed that, while on this visit, not a bird had dropped its dung upon us. Closing the entrance, we marched towards Louisville perfectly elated. On examining the birds which we had procured, a hundred and fifteen in number, we found only six females. Eighty-seven were adult males; of the remaining twenty-two the sex could not be ascertained, and I had no doubt that they were the young of that year's first brood, the flesh and quill-feathers being tender and soft.

Audubon estimates that the number of birds "that roosted in this single tree was 9,000." This investigation took place "in the month of July." He visited the tree again on August 2, after the local young birds "had left their native recesses." Of this visit he says: "I concluded that the numbers resorting to it had not increased; but I found many more females and young than males, among upwards of fifty, which were caught and opened."

Musselman (1926), writing of swifts overtaken by wintry conditions with snow in Quincy, Ill., says: "I discovered that on days when the thermometer indicated an approach to the freezing point the birds remained in the chimneys until about nine o'clock in the morning. During the daytime the birds quickly returned from their feeding over the river, circled but a time or two, and dropped into the chimney until warm. * * *

"The most popular chimneys were those which connected below with the basement, and served, therefore, as warm air flues. In such chimneys the temperature reached 70°. Little wonder that the birds preferred these chimneys on damp and cold nights!"

The two following quotations describe very unusual departures from the swift's regular habit of roosting.

Latham (1920), writing from Orient, Long Island, N. Y., states:

About one P. M. August 17, 1919, while collecting insects near the eastern border of a broad brackish meadow, my attention was attracted to Chimney Swifts (*Chaetura pelagica*) frequently flying slowly in from the west and disappearing in the fringe of vines and shrubs that separated me from the extreme east boundary of the marsh. In this heavy growth, from waist to head high, were elderberry bushes (*Sambucus canadensis*) heavily hung with ripe fruit. I selected a bird for special study. It advanced on descending, hovering flight. About four feet above the tangle, near the farther side, it paused and dropped abruptly into a clump of elderberries. Carefully marking the locality, I worked my passage to a few feet of the spot. The swift was clinging to the cymoid head of the elder eating the fruit. The ease with which the bird took flight from its slender perch, rising directly upward several feet above the cover and dropping rail-like back into it, was interesting and worthy of note.

The cover harbored at the time not less than fifty swifts. Most of them were flushed with more or less difficulty, but some individuals took wing within arm-reach of the observer. No others were noted eating fruit. * * *

It is evident that the birds had established a roosting, or resting place out of the ordinary. It is not satisfactorily settled whether the birds sought the brush to feed on elder-berries or for shelter. The writer is of the opinion that the bird seen eating berries was only an exceptional case where the bird took a berry after alighting within reach of it.

E. K. and D. Campbell (1926) report from Cold Spring, N. Y., an astonishing roosting place for swifts, *the bark of an oak tree*. They state:

At 2.30 P. M. September 5, 1926, we observed an excited flock circling between the house-front and the adjacent oak trees, and above the house-top and back. Their flight seemed to focus at a point 25 feet up on the trunk of a tall oak. The day was dull and we judged there was some sort of food there. Really, however, they were gradually alighting on the bark, as we discovered at 4.30 P. M., when most of the flock was found to have grouped itself in close formation, as shown in the rough sketch. * * *

The birds seemed two or three deep, and several of us estimated well over a hundred of them. They were snuggled together, seemingly to keep warm, and the heads all concealed beneath the wings of those above. This patch of birds was of irregular shape, nearly 5 feet high and 7 to 8 inches wide at the widest part. It was constantly changing, as some birds seemed to lose their grip and fly off and return, so that a dozen or two were on the wing and seeking a place to work into the group. We saw some alight at the edge and work up close, while others lit in the middle of the group and must have reached through with claws to grasp bird or bark, those failing falling back and taking wing. All had their heads concealed but the few upper ones. Toward dusk the birds, matching the moist bark, were invisible, but we examined them again by flashlight after dark, and all was quiet.

Next morning, to our surprise, they were still there, in broad daylight, and some remained through to the afternoon.

Cottam (1932) describes in detail some remarkable gatherings of swifts "at night circling the great dome of our national capitol, feeding on the small insects attracted there by the powerful flood lights." He observed the birds on many evenings, both in spring and fall, once in a flock of "approximately 2,000," circling "the dome—the area of greatest light concentration—where they remained until the lights were turned off shortly after midnight." Of the bird's evolutions, he says:

On the nights when flocking occurred at the capitol, the birds began to arrive in small groups from all directions about sundown, and by the time they normally would have been going to roost they had formed into one great swarm. For the first fifteen or twenty minutes after sundown the birds foraged over the tree tops and flew in all directions without any apparent system to their movements, except that they remained in a rather restricted area. Gradually, as it grew darker, a greater number were seen to fly more or less in the same general circular direction; in other words, there was a distinct impression of group movement. About the time the lights came on or shortly thereafter, all were following a definite course. Each time flocks of incoming birds disrupted the rhythm and unison of the concentric flight there was a momentary disbanding. When they reformed, however, all seemed instinctively to fly in the same direction. Most often the flight was uniformly circular, but occasionally it took the form of a conical cloud somewhat resembling a cyclone funnel. On one occasion it was seen to form a great figure "8" with one loop at a lower elevation than the other.

Frederic H. Kennard (MS.) makes this note of an unusual roosting place at Duck, Maine: "In the evening [August 8, 1924] I was treated to a performance of flocking, roosting chimney swifts, which at sundown flocked up and, flying in circles about one end of the smaller of Charlie Boyce's barns, gradually dribbled into a little window up under the ridgepole of the gable end and there clinging by the hundreds in an almost solid sheet against the gable end of the barn. We climbed up into the hayloft and flashed a light onto them, and they gradually flew out until only perhaps 75 to 100 were left. There must have been 500 or 600 in all, though, of course, difficult to estimate."

Winter.—In 1886 all that was known of the chimney swift in winter was that it passed south of the United States (A. O. U. Check-list of North American Birds, ed. 1, 1886). The third edition, published in 1910, adds that the bird winters "at least to Vera Cruz and Cozumel Island [Yucatan] and probably in Central America." The fourth edition, 1931, extends the probable winter range to Amazonia.

Chapman (1931) cites two specimens of the chimney swift, taken late in autumn in West Panama at a time when many South American bound migrants were passing through this region. He says:

If we may assume that they [the chimney swifts] winter in a forested, rather than an arid region it is not improbable that they were bound for Amazonia, where the presence as permanent residents of five species of *Chaetura* shows that the region offers a favorable habitat for birds of this genus. From at least two of the Brazilian species, *pelagica* could not certainly be distinguished in the air. Sight identification, therefore, is out of the question, and until a specimen is secured we shall not know where the Chimney Swift winters. But, as every collector of birds in tropical America knows, to see a Swift is one thing, to get it quite another. Native collectors are not willing to expend the ammunition required to capture Swifts, and even visiting naturalists secure comparatively few. With our attention directed toward Amazonia as the possible winter quarters of the North American species it may be long, therefore, before our theory is confirmed by specimens.

DISTRIBUTION

Range.—Temperate North America east of the Rocky Mountains, wintering probably in northeastern South America.

Breeding range.—The breeding range of the chimney swift extends **north** to probably southeastern Saskatchewan (Indian Head); southern Manitoba (probably Carberry, Portage la Prairie, Winnipeg, and Indian Bay); southern Ontario (Goulais Bay, Sault Ste. Marie, Algonquin Park, Kirks Ferry, and Ottawa); and southern Quebec (Montreal, Quebec City, probably rarely Godbout, and Grande Greve). From this northeastern point the range extends southward along the coast of the Maritime Provinces of Canada and the United States to Florida (St. Augustine, Daytona Beach, and Orlando). **South** to Florida (Orlando, Tarpon Springs, St. Marks, Chipley, and Pensacola); southern Mississippi (Biloxi); southern Louisiana (New Orleans, Thibodaux, and New Iberia); and southeastern Texas (Houston). **West** to eastern Texas (Houston, Troup, and Commerce); Oklahoma (Norman, Oklahoma City, Tulsa, and Copan); eastern Kansas (Wichita, Topeka, and Onaga); Nebraska (Neligh and Cody); eastern South Dakota (Sioux Falls, Dell Rapids, and Fort Sisseton); central North Dakota (Bismarck and Devils Lake); and probably southeastern Saskatchewan (Indian Head).

Winter range.—Unknown, but probably over the dense rain forest of the Amazon Valley, in Brazil. During the winter of 1937–38, however, two of these birds remained on the campus of the Louisiana State University, at Baton Rouge.

Spring migration.—Early dates of spring arrival are: Florida—Pensacola, March 24; Orlando, March 30. Alabama—Autaugaville, March 28. Georgia—Savannah, March 19; Atlanta, April 4. South Carolina—Charleston, March 18; Columbia, March 26. North Carolina—April 4; Hendersonville, April 5. Virginia—New Market, April 7. District of Columbia—Washington, April 5. Maryland—Cambridge, April 15. West Virginia—White Sulphur Springs, April 20. Pennsylvania—Philadelphia, April 2; Beaver, April 14. New Jersey—Morristown, April 18; Vineland, April 22. New York—Geneva, April 19; New York City, April 20; Syracuse, April 23. Connecticut—Jewett City, April 19; Hartford, April 23. Massachusetts—Boston, April 21; Northampton, April 23. Vermont—Rutland, April 18; Wells River, April 26. New Hampshire—Hanover, April 20; Tilton, April 24. Maine—Portland, May 1; Phillips, May 3. Nova Scotia—Wolfville, May 4; Pictou, May 10. New Brunswick—Chatham, April 29; St. John, May 8. Prince Edward Island—North River, May 19. Quebec—Quebec City, April 25; Montreal, April 27. Louisiana—New Orleans, March 13. Mississippi—Biloxi, March 23. Arkansas—Monticello, March 17; Helena, March 21. Tennessee—Athens, March 29; Knoxville, April 10. Kentucky—Lexington, April 2. Missouri—Concordia, April 2; St. Louis, April 4. Illinois—Odin, April 8; Chicago, April 10. Indiana—Richmond, April 1; Fort Wayne, April 5. Ohio—Columbus, April 7; Youngstown, April 8. Michigan—Ann Arbor, April 9; Sault Ste. Marie, April 20. Ontario—London, April 16; Ottawa, April 22. Iowa—Keokuk, April 7; Iowa City, April 17. Wisconsin—La Crosse, April 15; Madison, April 21. Minnesota—Minneapolis, April 26. Texas—Houston, March 24; Bonham, April 2. Kansas—Ottawa, April 3; Manhattan, April 10. Nebraska—Omaha, April 27. South Dakota—Vermillion, April 24. North Dakota—Fargo, May 6; Grafton, May 8. Manitoba—Pilot Mound, May 14.

A swift banded at Charlottesville, Va., on May 2 was found dead on May 19 at Cape May, N. J.; while two birds taken in eastern Massachusetts in May and July had been banded the preceding October at Tuskegee, Ala., and Hattiesburg, Miss., respectively.

Fall migration.—Late dates of fall departure are: Manitoba—Winnipeg, August 27. North Dakota—Grafton, September 5. South Dakota—Sioux Falls, September 11; Yankton, September 26. Ne-

braska—Dunbar, September 28; Omaha, October 15.   Kansas—Lawrence, October 11; Ottawa, October 12.   Texas—Bonham, October 20.
Minnesota—Lanesboro, September 18.   Wisconsin—Madison, October
12.   Iowa—Keokuk, October 18.   Ontario—Toronto, September 30;
Ottawa, October 3.   Michigan—Detroit, October 2.   Ohio—Youngstown, October 17; Oberlin, October 23.   Indiana—Fort Wayne, October 21; Richmond, November 13.   Illinois—Chicago, October 6; Rantoul, October 11.   Missouri—Concordia, October 11; St. Louis, October
19.   Kentucky—Eubank, October 9; Lexington, October 19.   Tennessee—Knoxville, October 23; Athens, October 29.   Arkansas—Helena, October 19.   Mississippi—Biloxi, October 20.   Louisiana—New
Orleans, November 4.   Quebec—Montreal, September 10; Quebec
City, September 30.   Prince Edward Island—North River, September 11.   New Brunswick—Scotch Lake, September 11; St. John, September 18.   Nova Scotia—Wolfville, September 15; Sable Island,
September 30.   Maine—Phillips, September 11; Orono, September
17.   New Hampshire—Tilton, September 10.   Vermont—St. Johnsbury, September 1.   Massachusetts—Boston, September 20; Harvard,
September 28.   Rhode Island—Providence, October 9.   Connecticut—
Hartford, October 19.   New York—Ballston Spa, October 9; New
York City, October 11.   New Jersey—Morristown, October 17; Pennsylvania—Beaver, October 8; Philadelphia, October 29.   District of
Columbia—Washington, October 25.   Maryland—Hagerstown, October 16.   Virginia—Naruna, October 11; Newport News, October 14.
North Carolina—Raleigh, October 4; Hendersonville, October 11.
South Carolina—Columbia, October 28; Charleston, November 5.
Georgia—Atlanta, October 12; Savannah, October 26.   Alabama—
Autaugaville, October 27.   Florida—Orlando, October 23; Pensacola,
November 2.

Further insight into the fall migration of the chimney swift is
provided by the consideration of a few of the several hundred banding records that have been accumulated.   One banded at Lexington,
Mo., on September 23 was recaptured at Baton Rouge, La., on September 27; one banded at Newark, Ohio, on September 20 was retaken
at Nashville, Tenn., on September 27; while a third, banded on
August 23 at Kents Island, New Brunswick, was retrapped at Opelika, Ala., on September 20.   A swift banded at 5:30 a. m. on September 22 at Glasgow, Ky., was taken that same evening in a chimney
at Nashville, Tenn., 90 miles from the point of banding.   Another
record, which seems to indicate the direction of the movement along
the Gulf coast, is of a bird banded at Sanford, Fla., on August 9 and
found with a broken wing near Tallulah, La., on September 25.

Casual records.—Some of the following records in Latin America
probably indicate the migration route of this species, but lack of

intermediate data makes it appear desirable to list them under this heading.

Panama: Two specimens were obtained on the Caribbean coast near the Colombian border on April 24 and 25, 1934; a specimen was taken at Bocas del Toro on October 28, 1927; another was taken at Almirante Bay, on October 24, 1926; while Dr. Frank M. Chapman saw a flock of about 40 at sea, some 10 miles north of the mainland near Porto Bello, on April 18, 1937. Costa Rica: About 30 were seen and a specimen was obtained at Villa Quesada on October 24, 1933. Nicaragua: Two specimens were taken at Eden on April 1, 1922. Guatemala: There is said to be a specimen in the British Museum (Natural History) taken in this country, but details are lacking. British Honduras: A specimen was taken (accidentally destroyed) in March 1905. Mexico: A specimen was obtained at Presidio, Veracruz, on May 6, 1925, while another was obtained on April 4, 1902, at Pueblo Viejo in this State, the collector reporting that swifts were crossing the lagoon all day, headed north; one was obtained at Rio Givicia, Oaxaca, on March 21, 1906; one was taken in Nuevo Leon on April 24, 1911; and the species also is believed to have been taken on Cozumel Island, Quintana Roo. Haiti: Several were seen over Port-au-Prince on April 19, 1917; a specimen was taken at Tortue Island, on May 18, 1917; a flock of 40–50 was seen over Morne La Selle on April 15, 1927; it was noted at Hinche on April 23, 1927; and several were observed at Belladere, on April 30, 1927. Dominican Republic: Several were seen at Comendador on May 1, 1927.

A specimen was taken on September 13, 1849, in Bermuda; several others were seen in the same locality on the 24th of that month; and one was collected there in September 1874. There seems to be no authenticated record for Newfoundland, but one was taken at Sukkertoppen, Greenland, in 1863. One was collected at Anticosti Island on June 9, 1901; in western North Dakota two were seen at Sanish on July 27, 1918, and a pair were noted at Charlson during the summer of 1923; four were seen at Miles City, Mont., on May 20, 1917, and two specimens were collected in Custer County on July 17, and 27, 1919; a specimen was found dead at Indian Head, Saskatchewan, on October 11, 1905, and they were seen in that locality on September 2, 1897; two were noted at Edmonton, Alberta, on May 17, 1897; and in New Mexico a specimen was taken at Rinconada on March 1, 1904, and another on the Mimbres River on May 22, 1921.

Egg dates.—Illinois: 6 records, May 15 to July 3.

New York: 17 records, May 27 to July 5; 9 records, June 8 to 20, indicating the height of the season.

Quebec: 5 records, June 14 to July 3.

Virginia: 11 records, May 27 to July 13.

HABITS

This, the smallest of the North American swifts, replaces in the northwestern part of our continent the common chimney swift of the eastern States. It breeds from southeastern Alaska and central British Columbia southward to the Santa Cruz Mountains of California and eastward to Montana and Nevada; but it is rare east of the Cascades and the Sierra Nevada.

Throughout most of its range it is much less numerous than the chimney swift is in the East. Most observers speak of it as rare during the breeding season, but S. F. Rathbun tells me that in the vicinity of Seattle, Wash., "the little Vaux's swift is more or less a common bird. It arrives late in April and, though widely distributed, is more apt to be seen in the river valleys, somewhat open, in which are tall, dead trees; and quite likely one reason for this is that among such trees are some that are hollow and will afford nesting places for the birds."

Spring.—While migrating, or when preparing to migrate, this little swift often gathers into immense flocks. The following observation by H. H. Sheldon (1922b), made at Santa Barbara, Calif., illustrates this point: "On April 29, 1922, about 7 P. M., the largest flock of Vaux Swift (*Chaetura vauxi*) I have ever seen or, in fact, heard of, circled over my house several times. By careful estimate I judged the number to be very nearly six hundred individuals. My observations of the Vaux Swift have heretofore been made only within its breeding range; while this is my first observation of a migrating flock, such an immense gathering of this rather rare wilderness dweller is no doubt a most unusual occurrence."

Courtship.—Mr. Rathbun writes to me: "This swift does not appear to be mated when it comes, but after a short time some change is noted in its actions. As they fly about, suddenly with a shrill twitter one of the swifts makes a dash or a dive at another, and away both rush, each striving to out-fly or out-dodge the other, the chase brought to an end only when one escapes, or, as often is the case, both fly off in company. As it appears to be quite playful, these actions may be partly in sport, though at this particular time some must have an earnest intent, for the courtship of this little swift evidently takes place upon the wing."

Nesting.—He says in his notes: "It begins to nest quite soon after it has mated. Its nest is built inside a hollow tree, as in this respect the bird chiefly follows the ancient habit of its kind. But with the arrival of man changes have taken place in some of the primitive sections where this swift is found, and it seems to have begun to adapt itself to these, for on occasions it is known to build a nest in some disused chimney, a practice of its eastern relative, the chimney swift, which so commonly uses a like place in which to nest.

"The nest of Vaux's swift is a small, rather saucer-shaped affair. It is attached to the inner wall of a hollow tree, or on rare occasions in a chimney, and usually some distance from the top. It is made of small pieces of twigs stuck together with a gluey saliva of the bird, the twigs broken off from the tips of dead limbs of trees by the swift as in flight it passes the branches. It does not seem to be quickly made, as shown by an instance when we found a pair of these birds nesting in a chimney. A few years ago, on a day in early June, we went to a little schoolhouse near the Snoqualmie River in the foothills of the Cascade Mountains, to find out whether the chimney of the building was in use as a nesting place by Vaux's swift. This was about 40 miles east of Seattle. When we reached the spot no swifts were to be seen, but after a wait of a half hour or so a pair of the swifts appeared and flew in circles about the chimney. Without warning one of the birds dived into it so quickly the eye could scarcely follow it. After a brief stay within the swift came out of the chimney and was joined by its mate, and for a short time both flew around in the vicinity, then ascended very high to mingle with some swallows. Nearly an hour elapsed before one of the swifts returned. It circled the chimney several times, then dropped into it so quickly as to resemble a dark streak. This time it remained in the chimney at least ten minutes. After another long wait both of the swifts returned, one entered the chimney, and several minutes elapsed before it came out. From these actions we assumed that the one that went into the chimney was making a nest, and invariably each time it flew out it gave a sharp twitter. For some time thereafter we stayed in this locality, but although a number of these swifts were seen none entered the chimney.

"Eleven days later we once more visited the schoolhouse. It was about 10 o'clock in the morning when we reached the place, but no swifts were in the locality. After a short time a pair of the birds arrived, both circled the top of the chimney six times, and then one entered by a straight-down dive. The other, which had remained outside, flew away but returned five minutes later and twittered. Immediately the swift in the chimney came out, and in company both left the vicinity. Forty-five minutes elapsed before the pair came back. With rapid twittering notes they swiftly circled the chimney a number of times, then flew from sight. We went on the roof of the building and looked down the mouth of the chimney but could see no sign of any nest. Next we entered the schoolhouse and, as the large stovepipe hole in the side of the chimney was high above the floor, we stood upon a table, stuck our head through the hole, and carefully looked at the inside of the chimney. A good sight of its upper part was had because of the light, but its lower part was dim, and no nest could be seen. Then we went to the lower part of the building into which the chimney extended to the ground, and by the removal of a few loose bricks from one of its sides we had a good view of the lower part of the inside of the chimney. Here we found the nest. It was about 5 feet from the bottom of the chimney and firmly attached to the wall in the angle of the southeast corner, which might give some protection from the rain, as usually this comes with a wind from some point south. The nest was a small, slightly shallow structure, compact and well made, but it contained no eggs. We left the locality soon after but returned later in the day, and during our brief stay one of the swifts came back and went into the chimney.

"A few days later we again went to the schoolhouse to see if any eggs were in the swift's nest. In this we were disappointed, for since our preceding visit the building had become occupied by a family who, of course, made use of the chimney for its ordinary purposes; for, while we were there, smoke issued from it, and evidently the swifts had deserted their nest as it still lacked eggs. We remained some long time in the vicinity of the schoolhouse, but no signs of any swifts were seen at all."

D. E. Brown writes to me that "on July 8, 1924, a nest was found in an old chimney near Seattle that contained young birds. I could not tell whether there were four or five young birds. On June 30, 1925, a nest with four eggs was found in an unused chimney of a fireplace in Seattle. The nest was 6 feet from the bottom of the fireplace, and the female bird was on the nest. The eggs were slightly incubated at this date."

Although there are other records of nesting in chimneys, the great majority of Vaux's swifts apparently still cling to the ancestral habit of nesting in hollow trees. The trees chosen are usually tall, dead stubs, frequently charred by forest fires and often hollow nearly or quite down to the ground level, and the nest is generally well down from the top, or even near the ground level. W. L. Dawson (1923) says: "Almost invariably the birds nest within twenty inches or such a matter of the bottom of the cavity, no matter how elevated the orifice. * * * The Vaux Swift also nests, according to Mr. C. Irvin Clay, of Eureka, in the stumps of logged-off redwood lands. The birds enter by weather fissures, and since the stumps are almost always undermined by fire, it sometimes happens that the nest is found beneath the level of the ground."

There are four nests of this swift in the Thayer collection in Cambridge, all from Eureka, Calif. One nest is made of pine needles, glued together, and was fastened to the inner wall of a hollow stub and only 2 feet above the ground level. Another was made of spruce twigs and needles and was placed in a burnt redwood stub, 20 feet high; the nest was 12 feet down from the top on the inside. Three of these nests are very small and narrow, so that the eggs had to be laid in two parallel rows; and the bird must have incubated lengthwise of the nest, for two of the nests held six eggs each, one five and one four. One larger, well-made nest was constructed of spruce and fir twigs and was profusely lined with spruce and fir needles, smoothly laid; this nest was 3 feet from the ground inside a hollow redwood stub 18 feet high. The other nest was taken from a redwood stub 60 feet high and about 10 feet in diameter at the base; it was burned black on the outside, but the inside was smooth and unburned; a V-shaped break on one side afforded an entrance to the hollow 20 feet below the top of the stub; the cavity below this opening was 14 feet deep, and the nest was placed only 8 inches from the bottom of the cavity.

Some unusual nesting sites have been reported. Charles A. Allen (1880), of Nicasio, Calif., writes: "They are to be found only on the highest hills or mountains, where there are plenty of pines. In these trees they construct their nests, which they build in old holes excavated by the California Woodpecker. They invariably select old, decayed trees, and build at great heights, so that it is impossible to get their eggs." As Mr. Allen evidently did not actually see a nest in such a situation, his statement is subject to confirmation and is offered here only as a suggestion.

J. A. Munro (1918) says: "Mr. T. L. Thacker sent me a nestling in the flesh, from Yale, B. C. It had fallen from a nest that was built under the roof of the C. P. R. water tank. There are a number of small openings under the eaves, and Mr. Thacker tells me that several pairs breed there every year."

William L. Finley (1924) tells of a still more remarkable nesting site: "At Wiedemann Brothers' nursery, is an engine house with a metal smokestack sixty feet tall and thirty inches in diameter. The lower end of the flue broadens out and opens into the front of the boiler. A pair of Vaux Swifts dropped down the metal flue sixty-two feet and built their nest on the front of this metal boiler. * * *

"Mr. Wiedemann did not find the nest until he heard squeakings in the boiler and thought some bats had taken possession. Opening the metal doors of the boiler, there he saw the parent Vaux Swift with her four young birds. He saw her go and come and even caught her, but she did not object, for when she flew out of the door she was soon back through the top of the stack with more food."

Eggs.—Vaux's swift lays three to six eggs; four, five, and six seem to be the commonest numbers. The eggs are usually elliptical-ovate or elongate-ovate, rarely ovate. They are pure dead white, without gloss, or sometimes faintly creamy white in color. The measurements of 51 eggs average 18.5 by 12.4 millimeters; the eggs showing the four extremes measure 19.8 by 12.2, 18.5 by 13.5, 16.8 by 12.0, and 18.8 by 11.8 millimeters.

Young.—Mr. Finley (1924) watched the feeding of the young swifts in the nest described above, of which he writes:

I stood outside at twelve o'clock, noon, and saw one of the parent Swifts come flitting along just above the chimney top, suddenly swerve and drop in. He, or she, whichever it was, was feeding every fifteen or twenty minutes. I went below and with the aid of an electric light, I could see the bird feed her young. Sometimes she would light on one side of the nest and sometimes on the other, to feed. Once I saw her clutch the edge of the nest and brace herself with her tail underneath, and she jabbed her bill in the mouth of a young bird and fed by regurgitation. As she started up the long climb, she quivered her wings, hooked her sharp toes in the sooty side of the stack and walked right up as if she were going up a ladder.

William B. Davis (1937) made some observations on a nest located in a brick chimney, and about 12 inches below the roof of the building, in Bellingham, Wash.; on August 2, between 9:37 and 11:15 a. m., the parent, or parents, made eight trips to the nest to feed the young. He writes:

When I first looked into the chimney, I was greeted by the clamor of the young. Their calls consisted of series of rasping notes uttered in rapid succession. The young were perched on the edge of the nest, each with its posterior end projecting over the edge and with its head directed toward the corner of the chimney. Below the nest the chimney was streaked with excrement, a circumstance which indicated the young were not defecating in the nest. This probably explains the clean condition in which Edson found the empty nest when it was collected two days later. No evidence was obtained that the parent bird removed the fecal sacks of the young, although one can infer that it probably did when the young were smaller and unable to perch on the edge of the nest. Each time the parent returned from a trip afield, the young became vociferous, their calls lasting until the old bird left. By listening for the calls of the young, one could mark the coming and going of the adult.

After the parent had returned from its sixth trip, I moved close to the chimney and witnessed the feeding of the young. When first observed, the old bird was clinging to the chimney beside the nest, supported partly by the stiff tail feathers. The young were facing her (?), each with its mouth wide open clamoring for food and vying with its nest mates. I was led to wonder what relation existed between lustiness of voice and the chance of being fed at that particular visit. Later, after additional observations, I learned that proximity to the parent determined to a large extent which of the young was fed. At succeeding visits, the old bird alighted first at one side of the nest and then at the other, feeding the one, or ones, closest. The food, consisting of insects, largely leaf hoppers (as determined by gullet examination of the young), was placed far back in the open mouth of each young one. * * *

After the parent bird had fed one of the young, it caught sight of me and dropped to a lower level in the chimney where it alighted out of sight. I moved closer and placed my head directly over the opening to get a better view. As I did so, I heard the rapid beating of wings and, thinking the bird was coming out, I instinctively jerked my head to one side to avoid being hit. It did not appear, so I looked in a second time and again I heard wing beats. This time I kept my position, and after my eyes had become adjusted to the darkness, I observed its stunt several times. The bird would let go its hold on the wall, and, by rapidly beating its wings, suspend itself in the middle of the chimney and at the same time produce the br-r-r-r-ing sound. Apparently the sound was produced by the beating of the wings themselves, for I could not observe them touching the sides of the chimney. During these performances the young were quiet. I interpreted this behavior as a means employed to intimidate the intruder, much as does the hissing of the chickadee or the swooping dive of the Red-tailed Hawk.

Plumages.—As far as I can learn from the rather scanty material examined, the sequence of plumages and molts in Vaux's swift is about the same as in the closely related eastern chimney swift. The spiny quills of the nestling develop into a juvenal, or first winter, plumage that is much like that of the adult. The narrow whitish edgings on the scapulars of the young bird soon wear away; and adults will average paler on the throat and under parts.

I have seen adults molting the contour feathers and primaries in August, but the molt of the primaries must be very gradual in a bird that spends so much of its life on the wing. Mr. Rathbun tells me that this swift has a complete molt during summer.

Food.—Almost nothing has been published on the food of Vaux's swift, beyond the statement by Mr. Davis (1937) that the food fed to the young consisted of insects, largely leafhoppers. Probably its food consists wholly of small flying insects, such as mosquitoes, gnats, various flies, and perhaps small beetles. On dull, damp days much of its food is gathered at low levels, but on clear hot days, when the insects fly high, it ascends to great heights in pursuit. I can find no record of stomach contents.

Behavior.—Mr. Rathbun says in his notes that "Vaux's swift flies at all heights, at times just above the surface of the ground, and again it will be seen high against the sky. Its flight need not be mistaken for any swallow. It is fast, lacks a certain smoothness, and is apt to fly more directly, circle less; also, it has at times somewhat of a darting movement, erratic as it were, which brings to mind the actions of a bat. In fact, this bird is always in a hurry."

Ralph Hoffmann (1927) notes a marked difference in flight between this swift and the swallows: "A close observation of the tail shows that it never displays a forked tip; it either ends in a point like a cigar or is spread like a fan when the bird makes a sudden turn.

* * * The Swift takes a number of very rapid strokes, its wings fairly twinkling through the air, and then sails with the long narrow wings curved backward and slightly downward."

Vaux's swift shares with its eastern relative the social habit of roosting in chimneys in large numbers at certain seasons. Mr. Rathbun has described this very well in the following elaborate notes: "About the middle of August the actions of this swift show the time is near when it intends to leave the region for its winter home. Now the social trait of this bird is much in evidence. For late in each day the swifts begin to assemble in the vicinity of some hollow tree of size, or some good-sized chimney not in use, within which they aim to pass the night. We have watched this action on the part of the birds from its commencement to the close. In one case where a large, tall chimney was used, 25 days elapsed from the time when first they began to use it until the last of the swifts ceased to do so. The swifts began to resort to the chimney about the middle of August, and each evening thereafter for the next 10 days showed an increase in their number until at least 500 made use of it. Then for 16 days the number of birds steadily grew less until only three swifts entered the chimney to pass the night, and after this for several days no more were seen to use the place.

"The swifts began to come to the locality where the chimney stood an hour or two before sunset. Usually they flew about the chimney or quite close to it. From time to time there were arrivals, which mingled with those in flight, all forming a long and narrow flock of flying swifts that swept around the top of the chimney, their twittering so loud and ceaseless as to be heard some distance. At times a few would leave the flock and enter the chimney, but the constant arrival of others seemed to keep the flock entire. As they circled some made feints to enter, and this appeared to be a sign that soon an entrance would be made by all. Usually these actions lasted for more than half an hour, but ceased when the twilight reached a certain stage. For then the swifts would suddenly enter their retreat, and while this act was taking place, it bore a likeness to a long black rope one end of which dangled in the chimney's mouth.

"Each evening the performance was much the same, but sometimes an incident would be connected with it. Once when the swifts were racing, a pigeon hawk appeared and dashed at them. Instantly the birds scattered, with the hawk in chase of one it had singled from the flock, but as it made no capture it returned and perched for a short time in a tree not far distant from the chimney. But when it left the swifts at once returned in close formation, hung above the chimney for an instant, and then appeared to fall therein. Not one wavered in the act, all seemed to have a single aim—to get inside the chimney just as quickly as they could.

"But this we noticed: that the temperature and the amount of light prevailing each evening influenced the swifts as to the time they would enter the chimney. On the cooler and darker ones the entrance would be made much earlier, whereas on the warmer and fairer evenings they would enter it quite late."

Dr. S. A. Watson (1933) made the following observation on another method of roosting at Whittier, Calif., during the spring migration:

On the evening of May 12, 1933, large numbers of Vaux Swifts (*Chaetura vauxi*) were noticed circling around the barns of Mr. John Gregg near Whittier. As night came on they began flying into a hay loft where they would cling to the walls and to each other. At places they would cover large sections of the wall five or six deep. It was estimated that at least three thousand swifts found shelter in the barn that night.

Next morning the birds began leaving the barn at about eight o'clock. They would fly out, a few at a time, circle around a while and then fly off in groups. They returned again the next two nights in about the same numbers, and for the two nights following these the numbers decreased rapidly, and on the sixth night they failed to return. The birds were heavily parasitized with lice and seemed weak and emaciated. A dozen or more were found dead each morning during the period they were taking refuge in the barn.

Since there was considerable snow in the mountains when the swifts were staying over, it is assumed that the unfavorable weather barrier caused them to accumulate here until warmer days and better feeding conditions called them farther north.

Voice.—Mr. Rathbun tells me that "its note is a rapid twitter, given often as it dashes through the air with other swifts and sometimes with the swallows, for it is a bird fond of company, though at times only one or two are seen." Charles A. Allen (1880) says that the note is different from that of the chimney swift: "They do not utter the sharp, rattling chipper of that species, but have a weak, lisping note, which is, as near as I can imitate it, *chip-chip-chip-cheweet-cheweet*, and this is only to be heard during the pairing season, when two, probably the male and female, are chasing each other." Mr. Hoffmann (1927) says: "On the breeding ground pairs of Vaux Swifts pursue each other with a faint *chip-chip-chip*."

Field marks.—Vaux's swift looks and acts like a small chimney swift. It might be mistaken at a distance for the black swift, but it is much smaller and much lighter in coloration below. It can be easily distinguished from the white-throated swift, as it lacks the conspicuous white areas on the breast and the flanks. Its flight, as described above, is different from either of the other western swifts.

Fall.—Mr. Rathbun's notes from the vicinity of Seattle, Wash., containing the following observations on the migration through that

State: "Throughout the first three weeks in September we have observed Vaux's swift to pass by in its flight toward the south. The birds will be seen at intervals all day and at times even at twilight. They fly at all heights, singly or in groups, and as a rule quite rapidly. It is not uncommon to see them in the company of other birds: black swifts, nighthawks, and certain of the swallows, species that are on the wing southward at the same time. Even when migrating the playfulness of this little swift is seen, for often one will pursue another of its kind. And on occasions we have seen it make a dash at a black swift, or a nighthawk, though when this took place no notice was taken of the act by either of these birds.

"On one occasion in fall we observed a large number of Vaux's swifts in flight whose actions were quite different. It was at the west coast of this State, along the ocean beach. When first seen, the swifts were 'milling' in the air within a narrow limit, the sight bearing a resemblance to a swarm of bees about a hive. Again and again this action was repeated. At times the birds would suddenly scatter as if a wind had strewn them, but soon they reunited and once more began to mill, though meanwhile the flock slowly drifted southward and at last was lost to view. On this occasion in company with the Vaux's were a number of the black swifts. These were at some height above the smaller swifts, and their graceful circling flight was in marked contrast to that of the Vaux's."

Winter.—The winter range of Vaux's swift is imperfectly known but is supposed to be in Central America. An important addition to our knowledge has been recently made by George H. Lowery, Jr., who found this swift wintering on the campus of the Louisiana State University, East Baton Rouge Parish, La. He has kindly lent me his unpublished manuscript on the subject, from which I quote as follows:

"Swifts were first observed in Louisiana outside of the regular seasons of occurrence during the winter of 1937–38, when two individuals were recorded almost daily from November through February. One of them was captured and banded on February 16, 1938.

"During November 1938 swifts were again noted in the same chimney on the university campus. This time a larger number, 5 to 10, were found. They were observed almost daily from November through February. Six specimens were caught, five of which were banded and released; the sixth was prepared as a study skin. Only after being placed alongside specimens of *C. pelagica* in the Museum of Zoology collection was it noted that the bird differed from that species. Being smaller and paler, it was immediately suspected of being *C. vauxi*. The question arose as to whether the five birds banded and released were the same species as the one made into a skin. These were recaptured on February 15, along with four additional unbanded birds, and all proved to be of the smaller and paler variety. The four unbanded birds were retained as museum specimens, and the others were released.

"After careful comparison with material kindly lent by the Museum of Vertebrate Zoology of the University of California and by the Bureau of Biological Survey, it is obvious that the five specimens taken at Louisiana State University in February belong to *Chaetura vauxi*. Both Dr. H. C. Oberholser and George Willett have examined the specimens and confirmed this identification. It is therefore probable that the specimen captured and released in February 1938 was also of this species."

DISTRIBUTION

Range.—Western North America.

Breeding range.—The breeding range of Vaux's swift extends **north** to southeastern Alaska (probably Baranof Island and probably Thomas Bay); and northern British Columbia (probably Flood Glacier and probably Telegraph Creek). **East** to British Columbia (probably Telegraph Creek, Hazelton, Lac la Hache, Vernon, Edgewood, and Newgate); western Montana (probably Glacier National Park, probably Kalispell, and Red Lodge); west-central Oregon (Fort Klamath and Mount McLoughton); and eastern California (Meadow Valley, probably Campbells Hot Springs, and probably Kenawyers). **South** to central California (probably Kenawyers, and Santa Cruz). **West** to the coastal regions of California (Santa Cruz, San Rafael, Sebastopol, and Eureka); Oregon (Tillamook and Beaverton); Washington (Tacoma, Seattle, Crescent Lake, and Bellingham); British Columbia (Chilliwack, Comox, and Courtenay); and southeastern Alaska (Chickamin River and probably Baranof Island).

Winter range.—Imperfectly known. At this season the species has been detected north to East Baton Rouge Parish, La. (see above), Taxco, State of Guerrero, and Leguna del Rosario, State of Tlaxcala, Mexico; and south to San Lucas and Mazatenango, Guatemala.

Spring migration.—Early dates of spring arrival are: Arizona—Chiricahua Mountains, April 13; Agua Caliente, April 22. California—Eureka, April 10; Buena Park, April 14; Redwood City, April 16; Azusa, April 23. Oregon—Mercer, April 29; Beaverton, April 30; Fort Klamath, May 6. Washington—Nisqually, April 11; Tacoma, April 23; Clallam Bay, May 3. Idaho—Coeur d'Alene, May 6; Rose Lake, May 11. British Columbia—Chilliwack, April 26; Arrow Lakes, April 28; Revelstoke, May 12.

Fall migration.—Late dates of fall departure are: Alaska—Cascade Bay, September 9. British Columbia—Kispiox Valley, September 3; Errington, September 15; Okanagan Landing, September 15. Idaho—Priest River, September 10; Trestle Creek, September 11. Washington—Mount Rainier National Park, September 16; Seattle, September 25; Tacoma, October 1. California—Nicasio, September 24; Buena Park, September 24; Santa Cruz, October 5; Los Angeles, October 14. Arizona—Tombstone, September 20; Pima Indian Reservation, September 26; Santa Catalina Mountains, October 6.

Casual records.—Two individuals were recorded in Jasper National Park, Alberta, on July 6, 1918. The British Museum (Natural History) has two specimens taken in Costa Rica, one at Los Cuadros de Laguna, in July 1898, and the other at Carrillo on November 7, 1898. This institution also lists a specimen from Honduras without exact locality or date of collection, but it seems probable that all three of these examples may be referable to the form resident in southern Central America.

Egg dates.—California: 44 records, May 7 to July 9; 22 records, June 12 to 30, indicating the height of the season.

MICROPUS PACIFICUS PACIFICUS (Latham)

WHITE-RUMPED SWIFT

CONTRIBUTED BY FRANCIS CHARLES ROBERT JOURDAIN

HABITS

The first and, up to the present, only record of this species within our limits is that of a female that was obtained on St. George Island, Alaska, on August 1, 1920. It was observed flying over the tundra and along the cliffs by G. D. Hanna and was recorded by Mailliard and Hanna (1921).

Like most of the swifts, this is a bird of extremely powerful flight and has an enormous range, breeding in eastern Siberia west to the Altai range and east to the Pacific, as well as in the Japanese and other island groups of the northwest Pacific Ocean. Southward its breeding range extends to the northwest Himalayas, where it is represented by a local race, *Micropus pacificus leuconyx*, and to Burma, where another form is found nesting, *M. p. cooki*. In all probability these two races are resident, or at any rate do not migrate far, and have not been proved to leave the Asiatic Continent. The typical race, with which we are concerned, on the other hand migrates by way of the Malay Archipelago to Australia.

The white-rumped swift was first described by Latham in 1801 under the name of *Hirundo pacifica*, not from the bird but from the celebrated Watling drawings, which were executed in Australia (New South Wales). Nothing was known at that time as to its breeding

grounds, but when Pallas' great work on the zoology of Asiatic Russia
appeared in 1811, he described a variety of the common swift under
the name of "*Hirundo apus*, var. B. *leucopyga*," which was subsequently proved to be the same species that Latham had described
ten years previously. John Gould later named it *Cypselus australis*,
and Jardine and Selby introduced a fourth name, *C. vittatus*, but
finally it was recognized that Latham's name had priority, and it
has been generally accepted ever since.

The Himalayan bird, *M. pacificus leuconyx*, was first described by
Blyth in 1845. It is considerably smaller than the typical race and
the feet are flesh-colored, instead of blackish, but it is treated as a
subspecies of *M. pacificus* in the second edition of "The Fauna of
British India." A third form, *M. pacificus cooki*, was described in
1918 from the northern Shan States in Burma by the late Maj. H. H.
Harington. This is also a small race, with black feet and dark shaft
stripes to the feathers of the chin and with dark mantle. More recently Domaniewski has suggested the separation of the northern
birds into three more races—the typical form (*M. p. pacificus*) from
Vladivostok; the Japanese race (*M. p. kurodae*), said to be much
darker; and the Kamchatkan bird (*M. p. kamtschaticus*), from
Petropaulovsk. It may prove to be necessary to accept some of these
new forms, but without an adequate series of skins for comparison
it seems at present desirable to let the matter remain as it is and
to treat the Japanese, Chinese, and Siberian birds under one heading.

Spring.—In Japan and eastern Asia this species is a summer resident. As there is some doubt with regard to the Burmese and Himalayan subspecies as to whether they are partially migratory or not,
it is best to confine our attention to the dates of arrival in the countries
north of India and the Malay Peninsula. J. D. D. La Touche (1931),
writing on the birds of eastern China, gives its distribution as follows:
"China Coast, Shaweishan Is. (migrant). Islands off Fohkien coast,
Shantung coast and Is. (summer). Chihli (summer and migrant).
Yangtse Valley to Szechuen (summer and migrant)." He does not,
however, give any data as to the time of arrival of the migrants
from Australia, but the gap can be partially filled from other sources.
The same writer, in an article on spring migration at Chinwangtao,
on the coast of Chihli, quotes as the earliest date April 14 (2), 1913.
Another was obtained in Fohkien on April 22. The next date is May
9, 1913, when two more were seen, and flocks were observed subsequently in May and June, the latter probably merely visits from
adjoining breeding places. There are, moreover, earlier dates of
specimens obtained, for there is a specimen in the Hume collection
(British Museum) from Takow, China, dated March 22, obtained
by Swinhoe, and he also states (1870) that he secured a specimen from

a large flock in Nychow Harbor, Hainan, apparently on March 19.
T. H. Shaw (1936), writing on Hopei Province, says that it is a regu-
lar migrant to the plains, arriving in April. R. E. Vaughan and
K. H. Jones (1913) record the first arrival on March 26, but most
come in April. In the Japanese Islands specimens in the British
Museum collection were obtained at Nagasaki on March 18 and May
30 by P. Ringer, and from "Japan" in May (Hume collection). In
Sakhalin, L. Munsterhjelm (1922) records the date of first arrival as
June 4, when three birds were seen.

C. Ingram (1908) saw one near Kioto, Japan, on May 4 and
several at Lake Kawaguchi on May 23. Blakiston and Pryer (1878)
also record it as present in May. The late Alan Owston noticed the
date of first arrival in Japan for two consecutive seasons on May 15.
In Siberia it is recorded as arriving in the second half of May; at
Darasun in Dauria it was first noted on May 24 by Dybowski, but
Przewalski records its arrival in southeast Mongolia on April 12,
1872, a very early date.

Nesting.—Accounts of the nesting of this species differ very considerably, and there is no doubt that the species adapts its habits to its
surroundings. R. Swinhoe's (1860) statement that these swifts were
breeding among the huts of a coastal village on Lamyit Island in the
Formosa Channel receives some confirmation from the accounts of
nesting in Siberia, but it does not seem to have been authenticated on
the spot. At Chefoo (Shantung Province), however, he (1874) obtained a dozen birds, caught on the nests on June 22 by his collector,
on a small rocky islet about 15 miles out to sea. Here the swifts were
breeding in numbers in crannies of the rocks, and out of the 12 birds
captured 5 were males and 7 were females, showing that both sexes
take part in incubation. A nest of the year was like a shallow saucer,
nearly 4 inches broad, thicker behind than in front, and constructed
of refuse straw and a few bits of catkins and feathers, all agglutinated
with the bird's saliva. In another case, six nests had been built in
successive years on top of one another and strongly glued together.
From the same coast, off the Shantung littoral, we have an excellent
account of a breeding colony by Capt. H. L. Cochrane (1914) near
Wei-Hai-Wei. After stating that one breeding colony on a rocky islet
had been destroyed by an army of hungry rats, he adds:

Nevertheless, it was a considerable surprise to find a small colony of *Micropus
pacificus* established on an unpretentious rock of the most modest dimensions,
both in length and height. This particular rock, much broken up, some 50 yards
long, and at its highest point 39 feet high, is situated 1400 yards from the
mainland, and 400 yards from a respectably sized island, which latter is un-
tenanted by Swifts of any description. Of limestone foundation, the rock is
seamed with deep fissures and long narrow crannies, and it is in these recesses
that the White-rumped Swift was found breeding in such elevated situations

that sea and spray, in their most angry moments, are ineffective to disturb the tranquility of the site chosen. On landing upon the rock and commencing to climb over it, not a sign of any bird life was visible, with the single exception of a solitary shag (*Phalacrocorax pelagicus*) which flew off hurriedly from the far side of the rock near the water's edge, where it had been dreaming away the hot summer afternoon. Altogether seven Swift's nests were found; of these two were in vertical crannies, the remainder in horizontal fissures, and all a full arm's length in. Only two nests contained eggs (June 6th), and only three Swifts were seen on the rock. The first nest found contained two eggs. The female bird was on the nest, and the male bird underneath the nest, clinging to it with both feet. So narrow was the cleft, that the birds were constrained to remain in one position, turning round being out of the question. The nest itself, wedged between the rock faces, was a small, perfectly round plate of straw, three and a half inches in extreme diameter, thickest at the rim and very slightly dished in the centre. A few feathers had been worked into the outer part of it, which was hardened with glutinous matter produced by the bird. The two birds at the first nest made no attempt to fly, and allowed themselves to be drawn out, a somewhat difficult operation. They clung very tenaciously to the fingers with exceedingly sharp claws, but when thrown into the air, immediately flew off with a strong swinging flight. A single bird flew from the second nest discovered, which was two feet down in a horizontal crack, and was similar in all respects to the first nest and contained three eggs. The eggs of the *Micropus pacificus* are typical Swift's eggs—pure white in colour and elongated in shape. Three apparently new nests were found close to each other in the same cranny, a long narrow aperture between two boulders. The remaining two nests were adjacent but separated, the whole area for the purpose being very restricted.

The rock was again visited five days later. All the nests now contained eggs, three of them one apiece only. No other nest beside that previously mentioned contained three eggs. One additional nest was discovered containing two eggs; this made eight nests in all. A Swift was found on each nest, but both birds at only two nests. Three Swifts made their appearance when the rock was approached on the latter occasion, and continued to fly around during the visit.

Captain Cochrane's excellent paper is illustrated by a plate showing the rocks, with deep fissures, and the nest and eggs in position within the cleft.

From Japan we have a few all too scanty notes from Alan Owston, who informed A. J. Campbell (1901) that on a yachting cruise he visited an island called Ukishima, about half a mile long, 200 feet high, and about 20 miles south of Yokohama. Here he explored some caves on the south side of the island, where he roughly estimated that there must have been not less than 2,000 of these birds nesting. There is also a well-known breeding place (which is shared with the spine-tailed swift, *Chaetura caudacuta*) behind the Kegon waterfall, near Nikko, Japan. Here the rocks consist of alternate hard and soft strata, making a series of shelves, and between these the swifts place their nests. Since the outer edges of the ledges are weathered and so rotten that they will not bear the weight of a man, the place is practically inaccessible.

In Sakhalin, Marquis Yamashima describes nests found on the rocky coast as being built of seaweeds, fallen leaves, and *Usnea longissima*, stuck together with saliva and forming a dish-shaped nest, 7 to 12 centimeters in outside diameter and 1 to 4 centimeters in depth.

In Siberia and Mongolia most of the breeding places appear to be in cavities and recesses among rocks, not only in the lower zones, but even at 12,000 feet or more. Madame Kozlova (1932) describes the nests as sometimes placed in cavities and at other times built openly under a prominent ridge. At Yakutsk, however, R. Hall (Hartert and Hall, 1904) states that these swifts nest on beams under the market-place verandas and among them but do not breed in close company. The inhabitants have a superstitious fear about disturbing them, so it was only through the good offices of the chief of police that Mr. Hall was able to secure two specimens of adults and two full-grown nestlings at dusk from a quiet corner of the market place by the help of a local youth. The nest consisted of a few straws and feathers cemented together by saliva, and the grasp of the bird's claws was strong enough to pierce the fingers and draw blood.

Eggs.—The clutch is composed of two or three eggs, which closely resemble those of other species of swift, being "cylindrical-ovate" and dull white without gloss. In the new work in course of publication on the eggs of Japanese birds, by K. Kobayashi and T. Ishizawa, two eggs of the Kobayashi collection are figured, taken on Mount Fuji, Hondo. It is here stated that in Japan the normal clutch is two, but that three have been recorded. The average of 17 Japanese eggs is given as 26.76 by 17.44; maxima, 29 by 17.7 and 28.7 by 18.4; minima, 25.2 by 18.2 and 25.5 by 17.6 millimeters. Twenty eggs from Siberia, China, and Formosa (14 measured by the writer and 6 by Dybowski) average 26.06 by 16.61; maxima, 28.1 by 17.1 and 26.1 by 17.5; minimum, 23.5 by 15.6 millimeters; Japanese eggs, therefore, seem to be slightly larger. The average weight of 10 Japanese eggs is 4.4 grams (Kobayashi).

Plumages.—R. Hall notes that in the two nestlings the feet were reddish brown, and E. Hartert (1904) states that the juvenile plumage is similar to that of the adult. T. H. Shaw (1936) says the upper parts are browner, feathers with whitish edges; wing coverts and inner webs of inner primaries bordered with white.

Adult: Upper parts blackish brown; back, upper tail coverts, almost black with faint gloss; chin, throat, and broad band across rump white, with narrow black shaft stripes to feathers; under parts otherwise dark brown, each feather with broad white tips and sub-terminal blackish band. Iris deep brown; bill black, feet purplish black. Weight, 32–39 grams (Shaw).

Measurements (in millimeters) : Exposed culmen, 6–7; tarsus, 10; wing, 166–173 (Shaw), 176–184.5 (Hartert). Tail deeply forked, 77–79 (Shaw), 72–84 (Hartert).

Food.—Entirely insects, taken on the wing, but little definitely recorded. J. C. Kershaw (1904), however, says that on the Kwangtung coast it feeds largely on a species of beetle that infests the "paddy" (rice).

Behavior.—All writers call attention to its extraordinary powers of flight, often at great heights, coming down to lower levels in thundery and stormy weather. Przewalski describes it as spending whole days on the wing, shooting through the air and among the rocks, but in morning and evening coursing low over the steppes and feeding.

Voice.—On the whole it is not a particularly noisy bird. Cochrane (1914) speaks of "a moderate amount of subdued screaming" while hunting. C. Ingram (1908) also, comparing it with *M. apus*, says it has very similar habits, but is a much more silent bird and more sparing of its screamlike cry; and La Touche (1931) also speaks of it as extremely silent, only a faint scream being now and then audible.

Field marks.—At close quarters the white rump, taken in connection with the large size, renders identification easy, as the white-rumped swifts of the *affinis* group are much smaller. It is frequently seen on the wing in company with the large spine-tailed swift (*Chaetura caudacuta*), from which it is readily distinguishable by the difference in the shape of the tail, square in *Chaetura* and deeply forked in *M. pacificus*.

Fall.—Toward the end of August the flocks disappear from Mongolia, but in Japan they seem to linger till October, and an extraordinary incident occurred in 1897, when Mr. Owston saw more than a dozen on December 26, when they should have been in Australia, as related in A. J. Campbell's work (1901). It may be a coincidence, but this was the year of the great bush fires in Tasmania and Australia, the smoke from which covered thousands of miles at land and also at sea. Swinhoe obtained a specimen at Amoy in November, now in the British Museum, and at Hongkong departure takes place early in September. It arrives in India about September, but the bulk of the migrant horde comes in October and November.

Winter.—From the Asiatic mainland and the islands of the North Pacific this species migrates across the Pacific Ocean to Australia and also in smaller numbers to Tasmania. On the way it has been recorded from Borneo by Salvadori; also from New Guinea by the same author, R. B. Sharpe, and O. Finsch; it winters in Australia, rarely visiting Tasmania. During its stay in Australia it is usually seen on the wing, coming down only in stormy weather.

A. J. Campbell (1901) states that he has only two records of this species perching; one a case of an apparently over-fatigued bird, which settled for a moment on the ground; the other, by Dr. W. Macgillivray, who reports a passage of thousands of these birds at Portland on February 14, 1899; he was informed that a flock took up their quarters for the night in a large gum tree, where their constant twittering could be heard till quite dark.

DISTRIBUTION

Breeding range.—In the North Pacific: Kurile Islands, Hokkaido, Seven Islands of Izu, Quelpart Island, Tanegashima, Yakushima, Tokuroshima, Loochoo (Riu-kiu) Isles, Botel Tobago, Sakhalin, and Formosa.

On the Asiatic mainland: Kamchatka, east Siberia west to the Altai, Manchuria, Mongolia, Korea, China, Kansu, and Tibet. Replaced in Burma by *M. p. cooki* and in the northwest Himalayas by *M. p. leuconyx.*

Migration range.—Southeastern Asiatic mainland, passing through India and Malay Peninsula, through the Malay Archipelago, Papua, etc., to Australia generally and occasionally also Tasmania.

Egg dates.—China, 8 nests with 1 to 3 eggs between June 6 and 11 (Weihai-Wei).

Japan, June and July; June 19 (Hondo, Kobayashi).

Siberia, fresh clutches in Dauria June 14 (Dybowski), also July 17; also Makutsk, June 19.

AERONAUTES SAXATALIS SAXATALIS (Woodhouse)

WHITE-THROATED SWIFT

PLATES 47, 48

HABITS

In the mountainous regions of the far west, especially where precipitous, rocky cliffs tower above deep canyons, one may catch a glimpse of these little winged meteors darting about far overhead. It was in the Huachuca Mountains in Arizona where I first saw this marvelous swift; a mountain brook flows swiftly over its rocky bed through a steep and narrow canyon, known as "the box," so narrow that in some places one can almost touch both sides of it at once; on each side the rocky cliffs rise to a height of 100 or 200 feet, almost shutting out the light of day; and far above us we could see these swifts darting in and out of crevices in the rocks, or cleaving the sky in their rapid gyrations. Swifts are well named, for, in proportion to their size, they are the swiftest birds that fly, and this species is one of the swiftest of them all. I am tempted to quote the following appreciation from the writings of Dr. George M. Sutton (1935) : "The White-throated Swift belongs to the heavens, not to earth. Beautiful as the creature is, when seen lying among the rocks where it has fallen, or on your hand, it somehow is no longer a White-throated Swift at all. Like a fish from the deep sea that has burst in shallow water, it is only a mass of flesh already starting to decay—of feathers that so recently had pushed aside the thin atmosphere of dizzy heights; feathers that twanged and rustled as the bird shot forward a hundred yards in a twinkling; feathers that knew nothing of the shadows of forests, that knew only the shadows of clouds, the full blaze of the sun, the coolness of clean unscaled pinnacles."

Courtship.—Courtship seems to be performed largely, if not wholly, on the wing. W. L. Dawson (1923) writes: "That most friendly of encounters, the nuptial embrace, appears to take place, also, in the air. In this the birds come together from opposite directions, engage with the axes of their bodies held at a decided angle laterally, and begin to tumble slowly downward, turning over and over the while for several seconds, or until earth impends, whereupon they separate without further ado."

Enid Michael (1926) says: "White-throated Swifts we have seen cling together and pin-wheel down through the air for a distance of five hundred feet."

Several others have noted a similar performance; and Frederick C. Lincoln has twice collected, with a single shot, two birds in the act, which in both cases proved to be a male and a female (Bradbury, 1918).

But coition may take place in the nesting crevices also, for James B. Dixon says in his notes: "The males are so amative that when we would take the females out of the cracks they would pounce onto them while in our hands; and we actually caught a pair in this way while hanging onto a ladder in front of the nest crack."

Nesting.—The white-throated swift nests in cracks and crevices in almost or quite inaccessible rocky cliffs on the sea coasts on rocky islands off the coast, and in the mountains up to elevations of 10,000 to 13,000 feet. Much has been written about the difficulties encountered in reaching the nests of these birds, for the nesting cliffs are difficult, or impossible, to scale, and when the nesting crevice is reached the nest is placed so far back in a narrow crack that it is often beyond reach and sometimes even out of sight. Some few nests have been found in niches at a comparatively low height in a cliff, but usually a climb on a rope for 75 or 100 feet from the top or the base of a cliff is necessary to reach the nests. This swift is evidently one of the most successful of birds in placing its nest beyond the reach of predatory animals and birds, not excepting the human egg collector.

James B. Dixon has sent me the following notes: "This bird is a common breeder in the rougher, more mountainous sections of the whole of southern California, as I have found them nesting in every county south of Tehacipi, and from the ocean cliffs to the highest peaks up to 6,500 feet above sea level. I have seen them nesting in the dug-out holes of rough-winged swallows and right in the middle of a large colony of swallows, where it was extremely difficult to tell which one of a myriad of holes the swifts were inhabiting.

"Usually the nests are very flimsily built of feathers glued together into one complete structure. The nest naturally takes the shape of the crack in which it is located and therefore takes all kinds of shapes; but where they have room they will build a nice, round, well-cupped nest that is so well stuck together that it can be dropped from the cliff and not a feather will be lost. Nest building begins very early in spring and continues for a long time. I have seen birds enter the cracks in a cliff early in March with feathers in their bills, which they must have carried for miles, as the feathers were chicken feathers and there were no poultry yards nearer than 6 or 8 miles in an air line.

"In 1915 I made a special effort to collect several sets of eggs. As we did not know when the eggs would be laid and had seen them building their nests so early, we started operations in April. At this time we found the females sitting on their nests and still building by adding occasional feathers. We inspected these locations week by week from early in April until the last of May before any eggs were laid. The females were in the nests the better part of the time, and the minute a female left a nest every male within sight would take after her.

"The main colony of about 12 pairs was located in the center of a 400-foot hard granite cliff. Here we located three nests that could be reached; the others were too far back to be seen, although the sitting birds could be heard twittering and giving their typical shrill calls."

There is a set of four eggs, with the nest, collected by J. B. Dixon and C. T. Schnack, in the Thayer collection in Cambridge, which came from the same nesting site. In the elaborate data that came with it they state that the nest was located on a large granite cliff in a steep, narrow canyon near San Pasqual, San Diego County, Calif. It was taken on May 25, 1913, from a diagonal crack on the face of the cliff, 175 feet from the top and on a projecting point of the cliff. The nest is a compact wad of white plant down, mixed with feathers, all securely glued together, and is lined with white, brown, buff, and black feathers, with a few small, bright-yellow feathers; it measures about 4 inches in longest diameter and is hollowed to a depth of about three-quarters of an inch; the eggs are badly "flyspected," as seems to be frequently the case in nests of this species.

There is another interesting nest of this species in the collection, perhaps a different subspecies, taken by Gerald B. Thomas in the Coxcomb Mountains of British Honduras on May 27, 1906. It was located in a cave, 50 feet from the ground, in a high cliff; it was glued to the wall of the cave 10 feet from its mouth. The nest resembles that of the chimney swift in shape and size, being almost too small for the five eggs it contained; it is made of weed stems glued together into a firm basket, and is profusely lined with small feathers, dark brown and white, which look as if they might have come from the parent bird.

Wilson C. Hanna has published two interesting accounts (1909 and 1917) of the nesting habits of the white-throated swift in a quarry on Slover Mountain in the San Bernardino Valley, Calif. He describes the difficulties involved in securing the eggs, shows photographs of the nests, and gives a series of measurements of both the nests and the eggs. In his second paper, he says of the nests:

Both the vertical and the horizontal cracks are used as nesting sites, but with the exception of set no. 5, all that I took were from vertical cracks. It is almost impossible to take nests from horizontal fissures without destruction of the eggs and in the exception noted, a rock weighing at least 35 tons was removed. * * * The location of nest no. 6 was rather unusual, being reached by going into a vertical crack about three feet, then up eighteen inches, then to the side about eight inches. * * *

Nests are constructed, for the most part, of chicken feathers and grasses cemented together and to the rocks, probably by saliva. They vary in size to suit the space between the walls of rock and are usually shallow and narrow. * * *

All nests that I have examined have been infested with numerous "bugs." In the two nests where birds could be seen while incubating, the insects could be observed crawling on the birds' heads. The eggs, in every case, were more or less spotted as a result of the insects, depending upon how long they had been in the nest.

William C. Bradbury (1918) made some elaborate preparations and, with the help of three young men, collected several sets of eggs near Hot Sulphur Springs in Grand County, Colo. He writes:

The cliffs where the birds were seen, bordering the Grand River, east of Sulphur Springs, are of a mixed lava formation, with some parts of hard, ringing material, and others of cracked, crumbling formation, intermixed with seams and deposits of soft lava ash, through which the river has cut its way in ages past. The visible base of the cliffs is at the top of a steep slope of debris, extending to the Grand River several hundred feet below. * * *

The first available prospect, located by Niedrach through the presence of excrement about eight feet up, and to which he was able to climb, was in a horizontal crevice about two and one-half inches in width, sloping slightly downward and partly filled, in places, with lava, sand and vegetable matter evidently deposited by the wind. Upon reaching the crevice a Swift darted forth nearly in his face, and he caught sight of its mate retreating back into the crevice, from which it was not seen to emerge. Less than an hour's work resulted in collecting, from a point about eighteen inches back, our first nest, containing four fresh eggs.

Florence Merriam Bailey (1907) made the interesting discovery that white-throated swifts were nesting in cracks in the walls of the old mission building at San Juan Capistrano, Calif. She located four nests by seeing the birds enter the cracks; but only one nest was actually seen, of which she says: "The nest behind the end of the stone arch was the only one seen and this—as it was ten feet from the ground—only by climbing and peering up the crack. The crack, as seen in the photograph, was behind the capitol of the pilaster on which one end of the arch rested, the capitol having been jarred away from the wall by an earthquake—doubtless that of 1812. About ten inches up this crack the nest could be seen tightly wedged in between walls less than two inches apart. As well as could be seen without destroying the nest, it was made of bark, feathers, grass, and wool."

Eggs.—The white-throated swift lays three to six eggs, oftenest four and frequently five. The eggs vary from elongate-ovate to cylindrical-ovate, or almost narrowly elliptical. They are dead white to pale creamy white and without gloss. As mentioned above, the eggs are often more or less spotted with the excrement of the insects with which the nests are often badly infested. The measurements of 50 eggs average 21.24 by 13.74 millimeters; the eggs showing the four extremes measure 25 by 15, **19.1** by 12.9, and 21.9 by **12.7** millimeters.

Young.—Enid Michael (1926) had a young swift in captivity that she kept alive for ten days.

This captive swift slept much of the time, but during his wakeful hours he was a very active bird; shoving and flopping along on his breast he could move rapidly. He was kept in a wooden box with a screened cover, where there were folded flannels into which he could snuggle away and sleep. When awakened he would set out at once to explore his box. He could crawl up the vertical wall of the box without the least difficulty, and one of his favorite stunts was to race about, back down, on the under side of the cover screen. This screen was ordinary mosquito-proof netting. When the screen cover was removed he would scurry up the wall of the box and topple headlong onto the floor. No sooner had he hit the floor than he would begin to skid about on his breast, using his feet as propellers. He had a fancy for dark cracks, and if he should find such a place he would surely disappear. Best of all, he loved to crawl up one's sleeve to snuggle warmly under one's arm. He had very strong feet and claws like a mammal. When attached to one's garments he clung tenaciously, and each hooked toe nail had to be pried loose before he could be removed.

Plumages.—I have seen no very young white-throated swifts, but birds in the juvenal plumage show the same color pattern as the adults, though the colors are duller and less clearly defined. The long, curved claws are highly developed for climbing.

Food.—As the food of this swift is obtained wholly on the wing, it probably feeds on whatever small flying insects it can capture. Mrs. Bailey (1928) lists "winged ants and other hymenoptera, bugs, flies, dung beetles, engraver beetles, clover root weevils, leafhoppers, etc."

Clarence Cottam contributes the following report on the stomach contents of white-throated swifts: "In 21 stomachs of the white-throated swift analyzed in the food-habits laboratory of the Biological Survey, the dominant food items appear to be flies (Diptera), the root maggots (Anthomyiidae) being the most important, with the long-legged flies (Dolichipodidae), the flesh flies (Sarcophagidae), and the March flies (Bibionidae) occurring in lesser numbers. March flies make up 100 percent of the food of a bird from Wyoming but did not occur in any of the remaining 20 stomachs. Flies were present in nearly every stomach and formed from 6 to 100 percent of the total contents.

"Beetles (Coleoptera) were well represented, especially the dung beetles (*Aphodius*), and entered into the diet of ten of the birds with amounts varying from 2 to 84 percent, although they averaged about 10 percent of the total content. Other Coleoptera identified were weevils (Curculionidae), hister beetles (Histeridae), leaf beetles (Chrysomelidae), rove beetles (Staphylinidae), skin or larder beetles (Dermestidae), bark beetles (Scolytidae), and the antlike flower beetles (Anthicidae).

"Bees, wasps, and ants (Hymenoptera) entered prominently into the bill of fare of about a fourth of the birds and were present as traces in three-fourths of stomachs examined. Bees were found to represent from 1 percent to as much as 86 percent of the total content, and ants in two cases formed over 90 percent of the food.

"The true bugs were moderately abundant, the most important being stink bugs (Pentatomidae), treehoppers (Membracidae), leafhoppers (Cicadellidae), and squash bugs (Coreidae); of the last named family, 50 specimens in one stomach formed 67 percent of the content."

Behavior.—The one striking characteristic of the white-throated swift is its dashing, exceedingly rapid, and erratic flight. Of the three western swifts, Vaux's may be swift, and the black swift swifter, but the white-throated is certainly the swiftest of the three. S. F. Rathbun writes to me: "If there is a faster-flying bird than the white-throated swift, I would like to see it. Always it appears to fly at top speed. At times the velocity of its flight seems beyond belief. The flight of this swift is often more or less direct, but it darts and swoops, and turns so quickly as it flies that the eye is not quick enough to see how the reversal in the direction of its flight takes place. You watch one as it passes, almost disappears, and in an instant it returns and flashes by. Its flight is so unpredictable that one never knows what next it will do. At rare times, we have seen the white-throated and the black swift in company, and this gave us an opportunity to compare the flight actions of the two. Always the flight of the former is dashing, whereas that of the latter is easy and graceful, as it glides around."

Mr. Hanna (1917) writes:

It is claimed by some that these birds do not use their wings in unison, but I am of the opinion that they do flap both wings at the same time, at least part of the time if not always. When flying about feeding upon insects, usually at several hundred feet elevation above the ground, they make a few rapid beats with the wings, then soar a little while, then beat their wings rapidly for a few moments and so on. They vary their flight by sharp darts in other directions, probably to catch insects. When returning to the cliffs they often keep their wings beating fairly steadily. Both when penetrating and leaving the crevices they seem to use both their wings and feet as aids to locomotion. * * *

During the heavy rains of January, 1916, quite a number of swifts were found on the ground in a helpless condition. It seems that some of the crevices had become flooded with water which had drenched the birds, causing them to attempt to escape, but it was impossible for them to fly with wet feathers. Several of these birds were kept in a warm place till their feathers were dry enough for them to fly away.

The white-throated swift has well been called the rock swift, for it lives its life in the rocky cliffs and in the air. So far as I know, no one has ever seen one alight on the ground, on a tree, or on any kind of perch. Its feet are not well formed for walking or perching, but they are well adapted, with long, strong claws, for climbing about in the caves and crevices in the cliffs. Mr. Dixon says in his notes: "Their legs are so malformed from nonuse as to be almost nothing but claws, to propel them through the cracks; and they can climb around much the same as bats or mice in such a location."

The photograph and the diagram published by Enid Michael (1926) illustrate this character.

Dr. Gayle Pickwell (1937) gives an interesting account of the roosting habits of this swift in Santa Clara County, Calif.:

The niche in which the swifts quartered themselves in 1931, and throughout the observations here reported upon, consists of a recess of unknown depth extending beneath a rock face that lies at an angle a little short of the vertical. It is about fifteen feet immediately above Sycamore Canyon Road. The crevice through which the swifts enter and leave measures, it is estimated, from two to three inches in width and about two and one-half feet in length. All the swifts noted, during the dates specified, used this aperture and this one only.

On August 3, the swifts were flying about in the canyon when first observed just at sunset. A crude estimate made of their numbers in the air gave from one hundred to two hundred individuals. Prior to entering the night roost the birds streamed in a procession into the shadows by it and then turned out into the light of the canyon. Shortly thereafter they entered the rock, streaming in with unbelievable rapidity. Three or four struck the crevice simultaneously, and now and then they struck one another. Twenty or more entered in an interval of one or two seconds. The entire flock was housed between 7:20 and 7:25 p. m., and a constant chattering thenceforth welled from the rock face. The sun had set some time previously, and deep shadows filled the gorge of the canyon.

On September 21, a similar performance was witnessed, but the number had decreased to approximately 49 birds; these all entered the rock in exactly two minutes, between 6:30 and 6:32 p. m. On October 24, "the birds went into the roosting niche as fast as shot poured through a funnel; faster than the tongue could waggle in an attempt to count." They all entered within a space of ten seconds. Later observations were made in November and in January; at the latter time only about a dozen swifts were seen to use the roost.

Voice.—Dr. Alexander Wetmore (1920) says: "The call note of this bird is a shrill laughing *he he he he* heard usually when two or three are coursing along together." Ralph Hoffmann (1927) writes: "In spring and during the breeding season while pursuing each other about the cliffs in which they nest they utter a shrill twitter, suggesting the syllables *tee-dee, dee, dee, dee.*" Mr. Hanna (1909) describes the vocal powers more fully, as follows: "The swifts do not seem to have any musical ability, but their notes or calls are pleasing, especially to one who is studying them. One series of peculiar shrieks is given while the bird is in rapid flight and is suggestive of joyous freedom. Another series of notes is given when the birds are in the crevices, which sound very much like the twitterings of small chickens as they cuddle under their mother's wings, only the swifts' notes are much louder. These twitterings are quite a contrast to the wild shrieks, and they cannot help but suggest comfort and satisfaction."

Field marks.—White-throated swifts are very apt to be associated with violet-green swallows, when insects are flying low and the birds are coursing about at no great height above the ground; at such times it is often confusing to try to pick out the swifts, as they dart about among the swallows. But the shape of the swift is very distinctive, with its long, narrow wings set, as it sails, in the form of a cross; and its wing strokes, as it flies, are much more rapid than those of the swallow. Moreover, the swallow is all white on the under parts, whereas the swift looks mainly black, except for the conspicuous white throat, a central streak of white on the breast, and a white patch on each side of the rump. These white markings will easily distinguish the white-throated from the other two western swifts.

Winter.—At least a few white-throated swifts attempt to spend the winter as far north as west-central California, although some of them evidently perish in the attempt, for lack of food or from the effects of the cold. Dr. Gayle Pickwell's (1937) observers reported that during January 1937 only about a dozen swifts were seen entering the roosting place in the rock in Santa Clara County, referred to above, and that two or three dead birds were found on the ground below the rock.

Mr. Hanna (1917) reports that "during the extremely cold wave of early January, 1913, eight, to me perfectly healthy, swifts were taken out of a crevice where they, with many others, seemed to be roosting in a dazed or numb state. They were kept in a room for about six hours and then turned loose, one at a time, a few hundred feet from the point where they were captured. All flew away in a dazed fashion and nearer the ground than usual and none were observed to return to the place where they were captured. * * * The facts are that these birds are not observed for many days in the coldest weather, yet are found to be plentiful within the rocks, in a dormant state."

DISTRIBUTION

Range.—Western North America north to southern British Columbia.

Breeding range.—The breeding range of the white-throated swift extends **north** to southern British Columbia (Vaseux Lake); Montana (Libby, Columbia Falls, Yogo Creek, and Billings); and northwestern South Dakota (Slim Buttes). **East** to western South Dakota (Slim Buttes, Elk Mountains, and Hot Springs); northwestern Nebraska (West Monroe Canyon); southeastern Wyoming (Goshen Hole Rim); eastern Colorado (Chimney Canyon, Golden, and Garden of the Gods); New Mexico (Lake Burford, Cañon el Diablo, Anton Chico, and Capitan Mountains); western Texas (Davis Mountains and Chisos Mountains); Tamaulipas (Jaumave); Hidalgo (Chico); and El Salvador (Los Esesmiles). **South** to El Salvador (Los Esesmiles); western Guatemala (Duenas); southwestern Chihuahua (Jesus Maria); and Baja California (Guadalupe Island). **West** to Baja California (Guadalupe Island, San Fernando, San Ysidro, and Los Coronados Islands); western California (Escondido, San Juan Capistrano, Santa Cruz Island, Santa Barbara, San Luis Obispo, Pine Canyon, and probably Mount Lassen); central Washington (Lake Chelan); and British Columbia (Fair View and Vaseux Lake).

The range above outlined is for the entire species, but a southern subspecies (*A. s. nigrior*), apparently resident in the southern part of the range, is now recognized.

Winter range.—In winter these swifts are found **north** to California (Alum Rock Canyon, Santa Clara County, Redlands, Indio, and Salton Sea); casually central Arizona (Big Sandy Creek and Phoenix); and southwestern New Mexico (15 miles southwest of Hachita and Chloride). From these northern limits the winter range extends southward, probably to Guatemala and El Salvador.

Spring migration.—Early dates of spring arrival are: New Mexico—Chloride, March 6. Colorado—Colorado Springs, March 20; Durango, April 4; Palisades, April 25. Wyoming—Laramie, April 24; Midwest, April 28. South Dakota—Sioux National Forest, May 12. Montana—Billings, April 23. Arizona—Tucson, March 9; Paradise, March 14; Grand Canyon, March 25. Utah—Salt Lake, May 1. Washington—Everett, May 10.

Fall migration.—Late dates of fall departure are: Utah—Willard, September 4. Arizona—Grand Canyon, October 6. South Dakota—Hot Springs, September 9. Wyoming—Laramie, September 9. Colorado—Boulder, October 2.

Casual records.—A specimen of this species was captured alive at Hillsdale, Mich., in August 1926; and another was obtained at Hot Springs National Park, Ark., on May 4, 1935.

Egg dates.—California: 86 records, May 8 to June 21; 43 records, May 21 to June 3, indicating the height of the season.

Family TROCHILIDAE: Hummingbirds

EUGENES FULGENS (Swainson)

RIVOLI'S HUMMINGBIRD

PLATES 49, 50

HABITS

This fine, large hummingbird is the largest of our North American hummingbirds, though the blue-throated hummingbird closely approaches it in size, the two appearing about equally large as seen in life. It is also one of the handsomest, although not so brilliantly colored as some of the smaller species. In the male the crown is a rich metallic violet-blue, and the throat a brilliant emerald-green, abruptly contrasted with the glossy-black breast and the bronzy green of the back; this color pattern is so arranged that every change in the bird's position brings a different color into view.

It is mainly a Central American species, ranging as far south as Nicaragua, through the tablelands of Guatemala and Mexico, and barely crossing our southern border into the mountains of southern Arizona and New Mexico. It was added to our fauna by Henry W. Henshaw (1875), who took the first specimen at Camp Grant, Ariz., in 1873. Since then, as he expected, it has been found to be a fairly common summer resident in various other mountain canyons.

We found it in the Huachuca Mountains, Ariz., in several of the canyons, where its favorite haunts seemed to be among the maples along the mountain streams, and where it ranges from 5,000 feet up to 7,500 feet on the slopes just below the main pine belt, where there were scattering yellow pines. Otho C. Poling (1890) says of its haunts in this same region:

It arrives in May, but is nowhere plentiful until the mescal shrubs begin to blossom, about the middle of June. From this time on during the entire summer one may observe on almost any hillside below the pine belt large clusters of bright red or yellow flowers spreading out from stalks ten or fifteen feet high. There are many varieties of this plant and all are favorite feeding resorts of the Rivoli Hummer. I have shot as many as a dozen in a day simply by sitting down and watching for them to come and feed. It is necessary to select a well-matured plant, and at the proper elevation, as well as in good surroundings of spruce pines. While feeding, these birds range from 4,500 to 8,000 feet altitude or up to the pine belt, their favorite grounds being where the pines end on the downward slope.

Bendire (1895) quotes from some notes given him by Dr. A. K. Fisher, as follows:

The Rivoli Hummer was not met with by us in the Chiricahua Mountains until we made camp in the upper part of Ruckers Canyon, among the yellow pines (*Pinus ponderosa*). On the morning of June 5, 1894, an adult male dashed through the camp, paused a moment over a flower spike of a scarlet *Pentstemon*, and then disappeared up the canyon as rapidly as it had come. No more were seen until we reached the high mountains at Fly Park. * * * They were usually found in the more open parts of the forest where fire had killed a portion of the evergreens, and a deciduous undergrowth of aspens and shrubs thrived about the cool springs and little rivulets. A boreal honeysuckle (*Lonicera involucrata*) was abundant and just coming into bloom. All the Hummers in the vicinity, the Rivoli Hummer among them, delighted to glean from the flowers and to sit half concealed among the large leaves of this shrub."

Dickey and van Rossem (1938) say of its haunts in El Salvador: "Rivoli's hummingbird was found only among the oaks and pines and among the scrubby, flowering growths between 7,000 and 8,000 feet on the south slope of Los Esesmiles, and about some flowering agave plants scattered over rocky portions of the summit of Volcán de Santa Ana at 7,200 feet."

Nesting.—Mr. Henshaw (1875) seems to have reported the first nest discovered, of which he says:

A very beautiful nest was discovered, which, save in its large size, resembles in its construction the best efforts of the little Eastern Rubythroat. It is composed of mosses nicely woven into an almost circular cup, the interior possessing a lining of the softest and downiest feathers, while the exterior is elaborately covered with lichens, which are securely bound on by a network of the finest silk from spiders' webs. It was saddled on the horizontal limb of an alder, about twenty feet above the bed of a running mountain stream, in a glen which was overarched and shadowed by several huge spruces, making it one of the most shady and retired little nooks that could be imagined. * * * The dimensions of the nest are as follows: depth, externally, 1.50; internally, 0.75; greatest external diameter, 2.25; internal diameter, 1.15.

Major Bendire (1895) received two nests from W. W. Price, taken in the Huachuca Mountains, Arizona: "The best preserved one of the two measures 2¼ inches in outer diameter by 2 inches in depth; its inner diameter is 1½ by 1¼ inches in depth. It is composed of soft, silky plant fibers, and is thickly coated exteriorly with small pieces of lichen, and lined with fine down and one or two soft, fluffy feathers, apparently those of a species of Titmouse. It resembles the nest of the Ruby-throated Hummingbird very closely in its general make up, but is naturally considerably larger. It was found by Mr. L. Miller on June 22, 1894, at an elevation of about 7,000 feet, saddled on a walnut branch about 10 feet from the ground, and contained one young nearly able to fly."

Apparently this hummingbird does not like to have its nest location observed, for, on May 28, 1922, as we were walking up through the narrow, rocky canyon known as "the box," we happened to see a partially built nest on a horizontal branch of a maple overhanging the stream. While we were watching it the female came to the nest with building material and evidently saw us. On our return, a few hours later, we were surprised to find that the nest had been entirely removed, and it was never again rebuilt in that same spot.

On the following day we found another nest in Miller Canyon, in the same general region in the Huachuca Mountains. It was about 30 feet from the ground, saddled on a horizontal branch of a maple over the trail, and so far out on the branch that it could be reached only with the aid of a rope. My companion, Frank C. Willard, succeeded in securing it for me, however. It was a beautiful nest, much like those described above, made of plant down and other soft substances, covered with lichens on the outside, and all bound together with cobwebs. This, and other nests that I have seen, though suggesting those of the rubythroat, are proportionately broader and not so high.

Mr. Willard records seven other nests in his notes, all found in the Huachuca Mountains. Five of these were in maples at heights ranging from 20 to 55 feet above ground; one was 40 feet up on a horizontal branch of a large pine and 20 feet out from the trunk; the other was placed 40 feet from the ground in a sycamore near the tip of a branch at the top of the tree. Of this last nest he says: "The nest appeared to be built in an old western wood pewee's nest, and was made of sycamore down, covered with lichens. The female sat in the nest until I reached the branch, and then flew, returning again almost immediately and sitting on the nest until I almost touched her with the net; she tried to get under the net while I was taking the eggs out, and finally settled right in the net. After the eggs were taken she returned and rearranged some of the lining while I was cutting off the branch." All these nests were found at altitudes ranging from 5,000 to 8,500 feet, mostly nearer the former level. Bendire (1895) says that they range up to 10,000 feet.

Mr. Willard, in his published article (1899), describes the bird's actions in building its nest:

Returning the next day, what looked like the beginning of a nest could be seen; so I sat down to watch. The bird soon came with something in her bill which she stopped just a second to place in position, then flew off through the branches of a large pine nearby. On her return I could see nothing in her beak, but she evidently had some spider web, for she laid something on one side of the nest and then, turning around, reached under the branch and took hold of it and pulled it under and up, fastening it in place by a stroking motion with the side of her bill. This work continued with great regularity during the hour spent in watching her, nearly every other trip seeming to be after spider web. Once a short stop for rest was made, and several expeditions against neighboring Wood Pewees or an inquisitive Jay relieved her labors. Just a week was required to build the nest and lay two eggs.

Of the behavior of the bird at another nest, he writes in the same paper: "While I was trying to get within reach the female made numerous dashes at me. She would fly from an oak a few rods distant, straight as an arrow right at my head, turning off and upward at a sharp angle when within two or three feet of me. I instinctively dodged several times, she came so close. During the last few feet of her flight the wings were held perfectly steady, not vibrating in the least until after she had turned. The humming of her wings was like that made by an immense beetle or a bumblebee, lacking the sharpness of that of small hummingbirds."

Eggs.—The Rivoli's hummingbird lays almost invariably two eggs. These are like other hummingbirds' eggs, pure white, without gloss, and varying from oval to elliptical-oval, sometimes slightly elliptical-ovate. The measurements of 43 eggs average 15.4 by 10.0 millimeters; the eggs showing the four extremes measure **16.5** by 10.4, 15.3 by **11.4**, **14.0** by 10.0, and 15.1 by **9.4** millimeters.

Plumages.—I have seen no nestlings and can find no description of them. Ridgway (1892) says that the immature male is "intermediate in coloration between the adult male and female, * * * the crown only partly violet, the throat only partly green, chest slightly mixed with black, etc., the tail exactly intermediate both in form and color." And that the young female is "similar to the adult female, but all the contour feathers of the upper parts margined with pale buffy-grayish, and under parts darker, with entire sides distinctly glossed with bronze-green." These characters are well shown in a large series that I have examined. Four young males, collected in July, all show more or less green in the throat, but only one, taken July 25, shows any violet in the crown. Others, taken in September and on November 1, show further progress toward maturity; and two young males, taken July 9 and 12, are still in first winter plumage.

Food.—Not much has been published on the food of Rivoli's hummingbird. Bendire (1895) mentions a boreal honeysuckle (*Lonicera involucrata*) as one of the plants from which Dr. Fisher saw them gleaning food, and says: "They are said to be especially fond of hovering about the blossoms of the mescal (*Agave americana*); these are generally infested by numerous small insects, on which they feed, and, like all our hummingbirds, they are exceedingly greedy and quarrelsome, chasing each other constantly from one flower stalk to another."

He quotes Mr. Price as saying that "during the flowering season it feeds extensively in the flowers of the *Agave parryi* in the Huachuca Mountains. In the Chiricahuas I have found it early in the mornings in open glades, feeding on the flowers of an iris." Mr. Poling (1890) mentions its fondness for the bright red and yellow flowers of the mescal on the slopes of the Huachucas.

Probably any brightly colored flowers, to which insects are attracted, are resorted to by this and other hummingbirds, the insects feeding on the nectar and the hummingbirds feeding on both insects and nectar. Mr. Fowler (1903) saw it feeding "among some scarlet geraniums in a large flower-bed."

Three stomachs examined by Cottam and Knappen (1939) contained leaf bugs, plant lice, leafhoppers, parasitic wasps, beetles, flies, fragments of a moth, and undetermined insects and spiders. "No fewer than eight species of insects and spiders were noted in one stomach." Spiders made up 31.66 percent and flies 26 percent of the whole food.

Behavior.—While I was collecting birds with Frank Willard in the Huachuca Mountains, he asked me not to shoot any blue-throated hummingbirds, as they were so rare, and I agreed to respect his wishes. One morning we were sitting on a steep hillside watching some large hummingbirds that were chasing each other about in the tops of some tall pine trees on the slope below us. I wanted a Rivoli very much, so he pointed out one that I could shoot, but, much to his disgust, when we picked it up, it proved to be a male bluethroat. This illustrates the similarity of the two species in general appearance.

The flight of Rivoli's hummingbird is somewhat different from that of the small hummers that I have seen. It is a large, heavily bodied bird, and its flight, though swift, is somewhat slower in proportion to its size than that of the smaller species; its wing strokes are less rapid, and it indulges in occasional periods of sailing on set wings, much after the manner of a swift.

F. H. Fowler (1903) writes of one that he saw: "Its motions are unlike any other hummer I have ever seen as its wings did not hum in the manner that has given this family its name, but cut the air with strong, firm, wing beats. Its flight was erratic, like that of the hummingbird moth, and at times like that of a bat. It would even soar, or sail for a few feet. It was not very shy, but when it made up its mind to go it would flit away on an erratic course without the slightest warning."

Mr. Poling (1890) observes that "their flight is exceedingly rapid at times but they often fly slowly so that the wings can be easily seen during the beats. The noise made by this bird's wings during a rapid flight is not like the buzzing of the small Hummer's wings, the beats being more slow and distinct, without any buzzing noise."

Like many other hummingbirds, the Rivoli is very quarrelsome; those that we watched, as mentioned above, were evidently quarreling with the bluethroats. And Mr. Ridgway (1892) quotes the following remarks of Mr. Salvin, who was trying to collect a specimen of this species: "Another Humming Bird rushes in, knocks the one I covet off his perch, and the two go fighting and screaming away at a pace hardly to be followed by the eye. Another time this flying fight is sustained in midair, the belligerents, mounting higher and higher till the one worsted in battle darts away seeking shelter, followed by the victor, who never relinquishes the pursuit till the vanquished, by doubling and hiding, succeeds in making his escape. These fierce raids are not waged alone between members of the same species. *Eugenes fulgens* attacks with equal ferocity *Amazilia dumerilii*, and, animated by no high-souled generosity, scruples not to tilt with the little *Trochilus colubris*."

Voice.—Mr. Poling (1890) says that their "note is a twittering sound, louder, not so shrill, and uttered more slowly than those of the small Hummers."

Field marks.—The large size of Rivoli's hummingbird and its manner of flight will distinguish it from all except the blue-throated hummingbird. The adult males of these two species may be easily distinguished by the different color patterns, if the bird is near enough; the bluish-purple crown, the brilliant green throat, and the glossy black breast of the Rivoli are very different from the greenish crown, dull blue throat, and grayish-brown breast of the blue-throated. More conspicuous at a greater distance are the broad white tips of the three outer tail feathers of the blue-throated, as compared with the uniformly dark, greenish-bronze tail of the male Rivoli. The females of the two species are more alike but can be recognized by the tails; the female Rivoli has the three outer feathers tipped with grayish, whereas in the blue-throated these tips are white.

DISTRIBUTION

Range.—Southern New Mexico and Arizona; south to Nicaragua.

Breeding range.—Rivoli's hummingbird breeds **north** to southeastern Arizona (Santa Catalina Mountains and Fort Huachuca); southwestern New Mexico (Chiricahua Mountains and San Luis Mountains); and Nuevo Leon (Bravo). **East** to Nuevo Leon (Bravo); western Tamaulipas (Rampahuilla); and Guatemala (Momostenango and Tecpam). **South** to Guatemala (Tecpam, San Lucas, and probably Santa Marta); and Guerrero (Omilteme). **West** to Guerrero (Omilteme); State of Mexico (Volcano of Toluca); Durango (Arroyo del Buey); western Chihuahua (Pinos Altos); eastern Sonora (Oposura); and southeastern Arizona (Huachuca Mountains, Santa Rita Mountains, and Santa Catalina Mountains).

Winter range.—Present information does not permit exact delineation of the winter range, but at this season it apparently is not found north of Guerrero (Taxco). From this point it occurs southward casually to Nicaragua (San Rafael).

Migration.—Early dates of spring arrival in Arizona are: Huachuca Mountains, April 24; Tombstone, May 9. No data are available for the fall migration.

Egg dates.—Arizona: 24 records, May 6 to July 28; 12 records, June 14 to July 14, indicating the height of the season.

LAMPORNIS CLEMENCIAE BESSOPHILUS (Oberholser)

ARIZONA BLUE-THROATED HUMMINGBIRD

PLATES 51–52

HABITS

Although the blue-throated hummingbird had been known for more than half a century, as a Mexican bird, it was not until 1884 that it was introduced to our fauna. William Brewster received the first specimen, which was taken by Frank Stephens's assistant in the Santa Catalina Mountains, Ariz., on May 14, 1884. Since then it has been found in the Huachuca, Chiricahua, and Santa Rita Mountains in Arizona and in the San Luis Mountains in New Mexico; it probably will be found to occur in summer in some of the other mountain ranges in that general region. This race of the species also is found in the Sierra Madre of western Mexico.

The species was split into two subspecies by Dr. H. C. Oberholser (1918), who named the northern race *Cyanolaemus clemenciae bessophilus* and described it as "similar to *Cyanolaemus clemenciae clemenciae*, but bill shorter; male with upper parts duller, particularly on the rump, which is more washed with grayish; lower surface decidedly paler; and throat duller. Female duller above and paler below than the female of *Cyanolaemus clemenciae clemenciae*." The difference in the length of the bill between the two races is not very impressive; in typical *clemenciae*, the average for eight males is 23.8, and for two females 26.7 millimeters; whereas in *bessophilus*, the average for ten males is 22.2, and for two females 24 millimeters; however, there seems to be no overlapping in the list of measurements given.

The Arizona blue-throated hummingbird will always be associated in my mind with Ramsay Canyon, that interesting bird paradise on the eastern slope of the Huachuca Mountains in southeastern Arizona. The approach to it lies across some gently sloping, grassy plains, which rise to an elevation of about 4,500 feet at the base of the mountains; from here the trail in the canyon slopes upward to a height of about 9,000 feet at the summit of the divide. Around the mouth of the canyon an open parklike grove of large black-jack oaks furnishes a congenial home for a number of noisy and conspicuous Arizona jays. The lower and wider portion of the canyon, along the bed of the stream, is heavily wooded with giant, picturesque sycamores and various oaks, maples, ashes, walnuts, alders, and locusts; while on the drier slopes are dense thickets of scrubby oaks and various thorny bushes, with scattered red-stemmed manzanitas and small alligator-bark cedars; and on the hillsides the rounded head of a handsome madrone towers occasionally above the forest.

The canyon is well watered by a clear, cool mountain stream that comes bounding down through a narrow, rocky gorge, furnishes the water supply for a summer colony, and finally disappears below ground in the washes out on the plains. We made our headquarters at Berner's place, at an elevation of about 5,000 feet, a cool and delightful place in the wider part of the canyon, where a number of neat cottages and small gardens are maintained for the summer colony. Here the stream ran almost under our cabin; and here we often heard the loud buzzing of the blue-throated hummingbird or observed its direct and rapid flight, as it whizzed by our doorway along the stream. It seemed never to wander far from the narrow confines of this mountain gorge and always seemed to feel perfectly at home and unafraid among the cottages and gardens.

Courtship.—Once we saw two males contending for the affections of an observant female; they were chasing each other about in the treetops and displaying their widespread, long tails, with the conspicuous white tips on the outer feathers; perhaps the bluethroats were more in evidence than they appeared to us. They saw us and departed before the ceremony was completed.

Nesting.—One of our main objectives in Arizona was to find the nest of the blue-throated hummingbird; but all our efforts were in vain, for we never succeeded in finding an occupied nest. We did, however, find some old nests in two entirely different situations. There was an open dancing pavilion, roofed over but open on all four sides, that stood close to the stream. My companion, Frank C. Willard, told me that this hummer had nested under the roof of this building in the past, and he pointed out to me the remains of two nests of previous seasons on a dead branch that extended under the eaves. We saw the hummer near this pavilion several times, but, up to the time that we left, she had not built another nest there.

We had been told that the blue-throated hummingbird had been known to build its nests on the stems of some flowering plants that grow in clusters on the rocks, above the pools or waterfalls, in a narrow rocky gorge, known as "the box," a short distance above our cabin. While passing through this gorge on several occasions we had heard or seen this hummer flying past us, and had looked for its nest in vain. But one day, while examining a large clump of cardinal monkeyflower (*Mimulus cardinalis*) growing on a sloping ledge near a little waterfall, we found a last year's nest of this hummer attached to the stem of one of these plants and not over a foot above the ledge.

George F. Breninger (Childs, 1906a) found and collected a nest and two eggs of this hummer, which came into the collection of John Lewis Childs, who published a colored plate of it in The Warbler. The nest was found on May 29, 1897, in the gorge where we found the nest referred to above. It was attached to some of the taller stems in a large clump of maidenhair ferns, "which grew in the side of a wall of rock in a cut worn by water." It was a large nest, apparently about three inches high and about two inches wide; it was "composed of oak catkins, green moss and spiders' webs."

Frank C. Willard (1911) has found several nests of the Arizona hummingbird, of which he writes:

In July, 1899, I located a nest built in an old Black Phoebe's nest on a rock overhanging a shallow pool. * * *

Although I made repeated efforts I failed to locate another nest until the season of 1910. I made my headquarters at Berner's ranch in Ramsay Canyon.

He has a flower and fruit garden, with several small greenhouses for winter use. Hanging from a nail in the roof of one of these was the handle of a lard bucket, and built upon the lower crook was a many-storied hummer's nest, some four inches high. It contained one newly hatched young. The tell-tale "squeaks" of an unseen bird identified my find and by keeping out of sight, and quiet, I was able to get a good look at the female parent. Later I saw very frequently both parents feeding among the flowers and occasionally within arm's length of me. * * *

During the last few days of my previous visit, I had seen the female in a bunkhouse that had formerly been used as a greenhouse. A piece of baling wire was wound around a nail in a rafter and formed a sort of hook. When I found the young one gone, I went at once to this bunkhouse and found the female sitting on a completed nest. She flew as I entered the room. I secured a ladder and soon held the nest and two fresh eggs in my hand. Some children were occupying this room so I did not dare leave the nest for further notes. I put another wire up, however, to furnish another nesting site.

June 21, the nest where the young had been seemed to be receiving additions, and the sides were somewhat built up, but I could not see the birds around. June 25 the nest contained one egg and the next morning there were two. A visitor told me that it was liable to be taken by some small boys who were there, so again I was afraid to leave it for observation and collected the nest and set, first taking a picture of it, showing the eggs. * * *

The nest is made largely of oak blossom hulls, and stems of the same, with a small amount of plant down intermixed. The whole is well tied together with cobwebs. The nest cavity is shallow and the edges are not incurved, differing in both these respects from the nests of other hummingbirds with which I am familiar.

There is a nest, with a set of two eggs, of this hummer in the Thayer collection in Cambridge that was taken by Mr. Willard in the same locality on May 31, 1913. It was placed "on a wire hanging from the ceiling of an old barn; this pair had already raised one brood of young this season." It is a large and roughly made nest, nearly 3 inches high by 2½ inches in diameter and the inner cavity nearly an inch deep. It is made of a great variety of plant material, as described above, felted closely into a compact structure, reinforced with coarse straws and weed stems, bound together with fine fibers and cobwebs, and lined with finer pieces of similar material. The material used reminds me of the kind used in bushtits' nests. Similar materials were used in the nest we found in the *Mimulus cardinalis*, referred to above.

Milton S. and Rose Carolyn Ray (1925) found a nest in a narrow canyon in the Huachuca Mountains on May 28, 1924. It was "suspended on a wire hanging from one of the rafters" in a small deserted building. Mr. Ray says of it: "The nest is beautifully woven of moss, plant down and cottony fibers, webbed together on the exterior and decorated there with bits of very bright green moss and pale green lichens. The lining of the nest consists almost entirely of cottony fibers and down. It is unusually large for a hummingbird, measuring 3¼ inches high by 2⅜ across. The cavity is 1¾ across by 1⅛ deep."

Eggs.—The Arizona blue-throated hummingbird lays either one or two eggs, normally two. These are like other hummers' eggs, elliptical-oval, pure white, and without gloss. The measurements of eight eggs average 15.1 by 10.0 millimeters; the eggs showing the four extremes measure **16.8** by 10.0, 15.0 by **10.4**, and **13.8** by **9.7** millimeters.

Plumages.—I have seen no naked young and no partially fledged nestlings. In the young male the forehead and more or less of the crown are brownish gray, with no green feathers; the green feathers of the upper parts are margined with gray; the postocular and rictal stripes are less clearly defined than in adults; and the blue throat is only partially developed. I have seen birds in this plumage in July, August, and September. Probably the fully adult plumage is not assumed until the following summer, for I have seen birds in this plumage in March and April and as late as June 12.

Food.—In Ramsay Canyon, this hummingbird feeds regularly and fearlessly at the flowers in the gardens about the cottages and even in the greenhouses, where it doubtless secures small insects as well as the nectar from the flowers. Mrs. Bailey (1928) says that, in New Mexico, its food consists of "insects from flowers of the shrubby honey-suckle, gilia, agave, and other plants."

In the summary of the contents of three stomachs, Cottam and Knappen (1939) include fragments of true bugs (Hemiptera), small beetles, flies, wasps, spiders, daddy-longlegs, pollen grains, and plant fiber. In two stomachs 10 percent and 15 percent, respectively, of the food was pollen. "One bird had made 92 percent of its meal on seven specimens of a fly (*Hypocera johnsoni*), which is rare in collections."

Behavior.—The flight of the blue-throated hummingbird seemed to us to be exceedingly swift, as it whizzed by us up or down the stream, uttering at intervals its squeaking note. It always seemed to fly directly over or along the stream; and it was gone almost as soon as it appeared. It was not at all shy and seemed to pay little attention to human beings, coming into the gardens freely while people were about. It would often alight within a few feet of a quiet observer and seemed to spend much time perched quietly on some dead twig, treetop, or other open perch.

Voice.—The only note we heard was the squeaking note, which was repeated every few minutes; Mr. Willard (1911) noted that the second note is higher pitched than the first, and the third note lower than either of the other two. Mr. Ray (see Rose Carolyn Ray, 1925) refers to it as "a rather far-reaching but not overloud alarm note, 'seek'-'seek'-'seek'." Dr. Alexander Wetmore (1932) says: "The birds utter sharp, squeaking calls, and the male has a simple song of three or four notes, repeated at short intervals while the singer perches upright with head elevated."

Field marks.—This large hummer is not likely to be confused with any other hummingbird except the almost equally large Rivoli's. The most conspicuous field mark of the blue-throated is the long, broad tail, with the prominent white tips of the three outer rectrices, recognizable in both sexes and at all ages; only the female Rivoli's has light tipped outer rectrices, and these are gray rather than white. The blue throat of the male is not conspicuous, except at short range and in good light, but the white postocular and rictal stripes are more easily seen at short distances, especially the former.

DISTRIBUTION

Range.—Southern Arizona, New Mexico, and Texas south to southern Mexico.

Breeding range.—The blue-throated hummingbird breeds **north** to southeastern Arizona (Santa Catalina Mountains, Paradise, and the Chiricahua Mountains); southwestern New Mexico (San Luis Mountains); southwestern Texas (Chisos Mountains); and Nuevo Leon (Bravo). **East** to Nuevo Leon (Bravo and Galindo); and Veracruz (Las Minas, Las Vigas, and Huamantla). **South** to southern Veracruz (Huamantla); State of Mexico (Mexico and the Volcano of Toluca); and Guerrero (Omilteme). **West** to central Guerrero (Omilteme); Durango (Arroyo del Buey); western Chihuahua (Jesus Maria and Pinos Altos); eastern Sonora (Oposura); and southeastern Arizona (Ramsay Canyon, Tombstone, and Santa Catalina Mountains).

Winter range.—During the winter season the species is apparently concentrated in southern Mexico, chiefly in the States of Michoacan (Nahuatzen and Mount Tancitaro); and Guerrero (Taxco and Chilpancingo).

The range as outlined is for the entire species, which has been separated into two subspecies. The Texas blue-throated hummingbird (*L. c. clemenciae*) ranges from southern Mexico north to western Texas, while the Arizona blue-throated hummingbird (*L. c. bessophilus*) is found through the Sierra Madre of western Mexico north to Arizona and New Mexico.

Migration.—Very little is known about the migrations of these birds, but they have been observed to arrive in the spring at Tucson, Ariz., as early as April 21.

Egg dates.—Arizona: 7 records, May 14 to July 17.

Mexico: 2 records, February 17 and September 9.

LAMPORNIS CLEMENCIAE CLEMENCIAE (Lesson)

TEXAS BLUE-THROATED HUMMINGBIRD

HABITS

Since Dr. Oberholser (1918) has described the Arizona bird as subspecifically distinct from the Mexican bird of the earlier authors, this type race of the species has been restricted in its distribution to central and southern Mexico from Michoacan and Oaxaca northward to the Chisos Mountains in western Texas. It would seem as if this race might more properly be called the Mexican blue-throated hummingbird, as most of its range is in Mexico; furthermore the birds from the Chisos Mountains do not seem to be quite typical of the southern race; Dr. Oberholser (1918) remarks that these birds "show in some specimens a tendency toward typical *Cyanolaemus clemenciae clemenciae*, but are decidedly referable to *Cyanolaemus clemenciae bessophilus*." On the other hand, Van Tyne and Sutton (1937) refer the Chisos Mountains birds to the Mexican race, *Lampornis clemenciae clemenciae*.

Typical *clemenciae*, the subject of this sketch, has a somewhat longer bill, darker under parts, a slightly more brilliant blue throat, and more extensive as well as brighter green on the upper parts and flanks, than the Arizona bird.

Nesting.—Dr. E. W. Nelson wrote to Major Bendire (1895) as follows:

Coeligena clemenciae is a sparingly distributed summer resident of all the mountain regions of south central Mexico, between 7,500 and 12,000 feet. They are rather quiet birds, often found perched on the tips of large maguey leaves. In the forests of pines of the higher slopes they are not often seen except as they dash by among the trees. On the 9th of September, 1893, a nest containing two eggs was found at an altitude of 11,500 feet on the north slope of the volcano of Toluca, in the State of Mexico. At this time the nights had already become quite frosty here. The nest was built in the fork of a small shrub, growing out of the face of a cliff about 30 feet above its base, on the side of a canyon, in the pine and fir forest. The nest was discovered by seeing the parent approach its vicinity. She flew quietly close up to the nest, and then, turning so that she faced out from the cliff and away from the nest, she moved backward several inches and settled lightly on the eggs. She was easily alarmed, darting away through the forest, and was not seen again. The nest was nearly inaccessible, and one egg was thrown out and broken in securing it.

Major Bendire (1895) says of the nest:

This nest, No. 26332, United States National Museum collection, now before me, is a handsome and rather bulky structure, which is apparently composed entirely of fine mosses, the whole evenly quilted together into a smooth, homogeneous mass, and bound firmly together with silk from cocoons and spiders' webs. It is saddled in a tripronged fork of a small twig, the three stems being incorporated in the walls of the nest, holding it firmly in position, the main stem being only one-twelfth of an inch in diameter. It measures 2¾ inches in outer diameter by 3 inches in depth; the inner cup is 1¼ inches in diameter by three-fourths of an inch deep. The walls of the nest are three-fourths of an inch thick, and the inner cup appears very small for the large size of the nest. It looks like a warm and cozy structure, and it needs to be so. As the eggs were only slightly incubated when found, the young would probably have hatched by September 20, and would scarcely have been large enough to leave the nest before October 12, by which time one might reasonably look for snowstorms at such an altitude. There is but very little inner lining, not enough to hide the moss, which looks to me like the down from willow catkins. Two eggs are laid to a set, and probably two broods are raised in a season.

At the other end of the breeding season, Josiah H. Clark (1900) found a nest on February 16, 1899, near Las Vigas, Veracruz, Mexico, in a canyon at an elevation of about 4,500 feet, of which he writes these interesting circumstances:

On February 12 we had snow, with the thermometer down to 32° F. at 4 p. m., and on February 13, at 7 a. m., down to 29° F. All the plants and trees were covered with ice, and the leaves of almost everything were killed; we found many frozen birds, and that was the fate of the owner of this nest. We only had two cold days, but that was enough to destroy many birds.

The nest was fastened to a vine one tenth of an inch in diameter and about three feet above a small stream of water. The vine hung from a large rock, and would have been sheltered from rain by the overhanging rock. The nest is of bulky structure, and is perhaps a new nest built on top of an old one. It is composed of fine moss massed together, and bound with spiders' webs or similar material. It measures, outer diameter, 2¾ inches, depth 4 inches; inside diameter, 1¼ inches, depth, ¾ inch. There is very little lining, only enough for the eggs to rest on, consisting of down from some fern.

Eggs.—The only two sets of eggs of this hummingbird of which I have any record consisted of two eggs each. The eggs are indistinguishable from those of the Arizona race, dull white and elliptical-oval. The measurements of the only egg I have been able to locate, in the United States National Museum, are 16.26 by 12.45 millimeters.

The food, behavior, voice, and general habits of this subspecies do not differ materially from those of the Arizona race.

ARCHILOCHUS COLUBRIS (Linnaeus)

RUBY-THROATED HUMMINGBIRD

PLATES 53–57

HABITS

CONTRIBUTED BY WINSOR MARRETT TYLER

The ruby-throated hummingbird is the only species of hummingbird that enters the eastern two-thirds of the United States. A minute spritelike bird, scarcely bigger than a good-sized insect, it is white below and burnished, sparkling green on the back. The adult male has a gorgeous flaming throat, which, when the sun strikes it, flashes back a deep, glowing orange or red.

The hummingbird moves its wings with such extraordinary rapidity that it seems to be moving through the air between two wisps of mist. Its buzzing wings hold it steady in the air. We see it poised before a flower, most often alone, its body motionless, its tail swaying, as firmly fixed in space as if it were standing on a perch. We see it dart adroitly from one blossom to another, and another—an inch away, six feet away—pausing exactly in front of each one, probing it with its beak, starting and stopping with a jerk, almost, turning at any angle with a sudden twist; or it may shoot off and away, bounding along at full speed. A remarkable power, unbirdlike, more like an overgrown bee.

Spring.—In spring the ruby-throated hummingbird leaves its tropical or semitropical winter quarters and presses northward, keeping pace as the season advances with the opening of its favorite flowers. The bird's preference for some of these is so marked that it seems oftentimes to regulate its migration so as to arrive on the very day of their blossoming. For example, Austin Paul Smith (1915), writing of the Boston Mountains, Ark., says: "The arrival of the 'ruby-throat' and the blossoming of the dwarf buckeye (*Aesculus parviflora*) were found to be coincident. For it is upon the flowers of this shrub that the ruby-throat finds most of its subsistence for the first two weeks after arrival."

At the start of the northward journey many of the tiny birds fly over a wide stretch of the Gulf of Mexico on their way to the southernmost States. They cross these dangerous waters with little concern, apparently, for W. E. D. Scott (1890) speaks of seeing them "at considerable distance from land" while he was fishing off the Dry Tortugas. "One morning" he says, "I counted six pass by the boat. * * * At such times their flight was direct and very rapid and all were going in a northerly direction. They flew about twenty-five feet above the water and did not appear in any way fatigued, nor show any desire to alight on the boat, as small birds crossing the water so frequently do."

Even in the Southern States hummingbirds run the danger of late, killing frosts. "Didymus" (1891) tells thus of the calamity that overcame them in Florida. "It was a warm winter and the early opening of spring brought out the flowers and started myriads of these little creatures on their journey toward the north. Then came that blighting frost—which they could stand, but the 'death of the flowers' was too much for them and they were picked up dead and dying everywhere. They came in unusual numbers and seemed to be nearly all males. After the frost but few were seen. * * *"

On the other hand, Charles B. Floyd (1937) describes an occasion in which some hummingbirds withstood prolonged low temperature and even snow:

The following observations with Hummingbirds * * * made in the Laurentian Mountains of Canada during the last two weeks of May, 1936, are of interest. * * *

On May 20th the temperature in the early morning was 22 degrees Fahrenheit above zero after a snowfall during the night of six inches. This snow did not completely melt until late in the afternoon. The temperature the following night was 28 degrees above zero. Early on the following morning the temperature was again 22 degrees. Ice formed in water-pails and a cold wind blew all day. * * *

During the morning of May 20th the ground and trees were covered with six inches of heavy, wet snow. I spent several hours paddling along the lake-shore on which our camp was located, observing the Hummingbirds and warblers that came there to feed. * * * All these appeared sluggish with the cold, and the Hummingbirds fluttered about on the underside of the snow-covered leaves, which were about half-developed, apparently capturing minute insects (probably aphids), on which they fed, occasionally dropping to the logs that floated along the shore to secure something so small that I could not determine what it was they were eating. * * *

All the birds permitted so close an approach that I could not use field-glasses during these observations. The last day of my stay the Hummingbirds were observed in their usual feeding places and apparently survived the cold weather unharmed.

Usually in spring we meet hummingbirds singly, or at most two or three together, but once in a while we come upon a gathering of migrating birds—almost always of one sex—collected sometimes in a single favored tree. About noon on May 22, 1936, I came upon such a gathering. The birds were in a good-sized red horse-chestnut tree in full flower. They must have numbered more than a dozen, perhaps twice this number. As I came near the tree there burst out a long series of short, sharp, high, jerky notes, the pitch rising and falling, the volume increasing and decreasing. The individual notes had a squeaky quality suggested by the letters *sk*, but in spite of this I was reminded of the house wren's chatter. By direct comparison, however, the wren's voice was much more mellow, and the delivery more indolent, if one may use the word in reference to that sprightly bird.

Looking in among the branches, I could see here and there two or three birds flying about, making darts at each other. Sometimes a bird or two birds, one chasing the other, flew out and, after flying around the tree a little way, shot in among the branches again. The tree seemed swarming with hummingbirds. Soon the activity calmed down, and the birds perched motionless on small branches, here and there.

The sound quieted also, but rose again energetically when the birds resumed their activity. They probed the blossoms, evidently feeding, but for the most part seemed interested in one another—playfully, or with little hostility. Once I saw two birds fly straight up in the air, close together like mating bees or a swallow feeding its young on the wing, strike at each other, I think, then turn and dive head-downward into the tree. Again a bird flies out from the tree at an approaching bird, utters *zzzt-zzz*, and drives it off.

The notes varied a good deal. Sometimes a note was so fine, high, and drawn out that it was only a hiss; generally they were very short and clearly cut, either single or double; sometimes they took on a rhythmic form and were repeated over and over, for example, *z, z, z, z, z, z, zzt,* the last note emphasized; and often they came in a long series—single, double, and triple notes all intermixed like a telegraph instrument in action.

It was difficult, owing to their activity among the dense branches, to see the birds clearly, and impossible to count them accurately, but I believe that most, if not all, of them were males, their throats in the dark shadow of the branches appearing black.

On the 24th there were fewer birds in the tree—the petals were falling to the ground—and on the 25th only two or three remained.

Jane L. Hine (1894) reports a similar gathering of female birds. She says: "About nine o'clock one spring morning, when lilacs were in bloom, we discovered that the old lilac bush by the well was 'swarming' with Hummingbirds—just come; we knew they were not there a few minutes before. There are five large lilacs on our premises and those of a near neighbor. On investigation I found four of these bushes alive, as it were, with Hummers—all females. The fifth bush, a Persian, they did not favor."

From these observations, and several more in the literature, we may infer that the sexes do not as a rule migrate together, and according to the opinion of many observers the males always precede the females.

Courtship.—In his courtship display the male rubythroat makes use of his marvelous proficiency in flight as well as of the brilliantly glowing feathers of his throat. As we watch him performing such flights as are described below, swinging back and forth along the arc of a wide circle, we get the impression of a bird upheld by a swaying wire; his swings are so accurate and precise that they suggest a geometric figure drawn in the air rather than the flight of a bird. Carl W. Schlag (1930), speaking of the courtship flight, says:

It is comparable to the strutting actions of various species of birds. It is performed several times daily during the breeding season. While the female is quietly feeding from flower to flower, the male will go through this performance, calculated no doubt to impress her more fully with all his charms. Rising up about eight or ten feet above and five or six to one side of her, he will suddenly swoop down, wings and tail outspread, right at her, passing within a few inches of her, the wings and tail making a terrific buzz for a bird so small. Passing her, he rises to an equal height on the opposite side, and turning comes down again in the same way, describing an inverted arc, with that surprisingly loud buzz just as he gets nearest to her. He keeps up this continuous swooping, as I term it, as long as half a minute, at times; at the conclusion of which he usually flies to some near-by perch and rests. During this performance the female feeds quietly at the same cluster of blossoms, not moving any distance away, and sometimes resting on a flower-stalk until he is through.

Mrs. Charles W. Melcher, of Homosassa Springs, Fla., describes a flight that, from its formal, regular character, was probably a variant of the usual courtship display, although there was no dipping—the bird progressing on a level line back and forth—and although Mrs. Melcher did not see a female bird in the vicinity. She writes to Mr. Bent: "Instead of the circular flight he flew in a straight line. Facing the north, he hovered, then moved eastward about 3 feet, then hovered, then moved eastward again for the same distance, continuing thus until he had covered perhaps 25 feet. Then, still facing north, he moved toward the west in the same manner, back to his starting point. I saw him cover the distance four times, twice east and twice west. The fact that he seemed to move sideways makes this a fantastic story, but I think that I have seen the birds that come to our feeders move in almost every direction.

"My attention was first attracted to this flight by the *regularity* of a humming sound out in the garden. There was a hum, then a second's pause, then another hum, each humming and each pause being of equal length. The humming was made, of course, while he hovered, and lasted perhaps three or four seconds. The pause was very short, just the time it took him to move 3 or 4 feet. The sounds of humming and twittering were so different from usual that I went to the door expecting to see some sort of flight that was out of the ordinary.

"Another performance we witnessed lasted two or three minutes. A male and a female were flying up and down. They were facing each other with tails spread, and there was much twittering. They covered a distance of 5 or 6 feet, and their flight was almost vertical. When he was at the top of his flight she was at the bottom of hers, and when she was at the top he was at the bottom. They were about 2½ feet apart. There was no thrusting at each other until, at the last, they came together for an instant on the windowsill. I was too far away to see if the contact was friendly."

Charles L. Whittle (1937) presents a full account of the actions of a male hummingbird during several weeks before egg-laying time— nine days of watching for a mate, weeks of courtship after she arrived, and after the culmination of his wooing, the almost immediate cessation of display. The bird came to his station in Peterboro, N. H., on May 21 "and began a long vigil lasting until May 30th, believed to be a search for a female." He continues:

This vigil took place from three observation posts overlooking a circular garden, one on an aerial, one on a dead branch of an elm, and a third on a dead twig at the top of an apple tree, all these perches being from fifteen to twenty feet from the ground. For the major portion of each day he occupied these perches, moving from one to another, and while perching he continually moved his head from side to side through an arc of 60–70 degrees. One cannot well escape the conclusion that he was searching for a female, since the habit was immediately discontinued upon the arrival of a female at the station on May 30th. Now, for a period of about a month, his attention was devoted to the female and consisted of the usual zooming before her whenever she appeared. * * * On July 2nd a male and a female were seen facing each other in the air about eight or ten inches apart, ascending and descending vertically to a height of about ten feet, and occasionally dropping to the ground for a moment. At other times their flights were more or less spiral in character, and such exhibitions were frequent up to July 7th, when Mrs. Whittle observed a pair drop to the ground beside our driveway, where copulation took place. From this time on the males were seen zooming only occasionally, and vertical flights ceased entirely after the first week in July. * * *

Mating, in the ordinary sense of the word, that is, pairing off well in advance of nest-building and continuing during nidification and raising of the young birds, as far as any evidence observable at this station is concerned, appears not to take place. No preference for a male on the part of a female is indicated until *just prior to egg-laying*, a period seemingly of three or four days. I have found no evidence that a male's interest in a female one day is manifested towards the same female the following day. All the pretty ways common among many species of mated pairs, often lasting two months at least, are entirely lacking among Hummingbirds. The male appears to be a free lance whose intimate interest in the female is confined to the short period just before and during egg-laying.

Nesting.—The hummingbird's nest, "a model of artistic workmanship," Torrey (1892) calls it, is a little compact mass about an inch deep and an inch across, firm in texture, lined with soft plant down, and covered over on the outside with tiny bits of lichen. It is commonly saddled on a limb, usually a small, down-sloping one, often near, and sometimes directly over, water. Wilson (1831) aptly describes the nest when viewed from below as "a mere mossy knot, or accidental protuberance."

Aretas A. Saunders (1936), who made an extensive study of the hummingbird in New York State, describes the situation of the nest thus:

In Allegany Park, the nesting site seems to be always along a brook valley, and in most cases the nest is on a limb that overhangs the brook. Eight nests that I have seen in Allegany Park were on limbs less than an inch in diameter, and one was on a limb a little more than a quarter of an inch through. The limb, in my experience, always slants a little downward from the tree. It is never so high in the tree that it is not sheltered above by other limbs or leafy branches. * * *

I do not suppose that the proximity of the brook has any particular significance in the Humming Bird's nesting except that its favorite flowers grow along the brook and the stream affords an open space. * * *

The [small] size of the limb and its downward slant seem to be aids in protection against possible tree-climbing enemies * * *

The protection from above is possibly to screen the nest from flying enemies, but chiefly to protect it against heavy storms * * *

Various kinds of trees are used for nesting, but in Allegany Park the majority of nests found have been in Hornbeams. Of the 11 nests I have observed, and one other reported to me, six were in Hornbeams, two in Yellow Birch, and one each in Sugar Maple, Red Maple and Beech.   I have seen nests in Hemlocks in other regions * * *

The nests found have ranged from five to 18 feet from the ground or water, all but two of them being actually over water.

Saunders (1936) also points out that "the distribution of Humming Birds in Quaker Run valley is governed primarily by the occurrence of Bee Balm, *Monarda didyma*, the flower upon which they depend chiefly for nectar at the beginning of their breeding season in this region."

Bendire (1895) states that the height of the nest varies "from 6 to 50 feet high, usually from 10 to 20 feet from the ground."   Of the nest itself Saunders (1936) says:

The nesting materials are of four kinds, bud scales, plant down, lichens and spider silk * * *. The bud scales make up the bulk of the nest, but by the time it is finished they are entirely covered by the lichens and plant down. * * *

Lichens * * * are put on the outside before the plant down is put in. The lining, in one case at least, was not put into the nest at all until some days after the eggs were laid and incubation begun.   The bird continues adding lining material to the nest after the young are hatched, in one case gathering Fireweed down and taking it to the nest when the young were two weeks old. The plants from which down is gathered in Allegany Park are Fireweed, Canada Thistle, Orange Hawkweed and Rattlesnake Root.   Possibly others such as Milkweed and various Composites are used also, but the Fireweed seems to be the most commonly used lining material.   The bird gathers thistle down that is flying about in the air, but in the case of Fireweed gathers it directly from the plant * * *

I have never seen the Hummingbird gathering or working with the spider silk which holds the nest together and fastens it to its limb.   The fastening of the nest to the limb is probably an early step in the nest building.   But the spider silk is an important item, and in one nest I have seen, was run out and wrapped along two or three twigs that branched out from the point where the nest was fastened, to a distance of 15 inches.

A. Dawes DuBois, in a letter to Mr. Bent, describing the behavior of a female bird while weaving her nest, says: "I stationed myself close to the nest (which was 12 feet from the ground) and watched the bird come and go.   She always flew off in the same direction and sometimes was away for five minutes or more.   On returning with a tiny tuft of down in her bill, she alighted at once upon the nest and began to tuck the material into its walls on the inner side, using her delicate bill like a needle; then she vigorously worked her body up and down, and round-about thereby enlarging and shaping the cavity. Afterward she tucked or adjusted more securely the lichens on the outside.   The male bird was not seen at any time."

H. E. Wheeler (1922) says that "the behavior of the female will invariably betray her home.   It is easier still to locate the 'house' if the birds are building * * * for the birds keep their territory pretty well cleared of intruding visitors. On one occasion the female Ruby-throat left her nest repeatedly to torment a family of Carolina Wrens, and to pay her respects to a Tufted Titmouse. Otherwise I think I should have never located the tiny nest situated 50 feet above ground, and so thoroughly concealed from view."

In the experience of almost all observers the female parent builds the nest and rears the young unaided by her mate. Bradford Torrey (1892) long ago called attention to this habit in two delightful essays, and Saunders (1936) states in corroboration that "male Humming Birds do not seem to stay in the Quaker Run valley through the nesting season. They are rarely if ever seen after the middle of August."

It is very rare to find any deviation from this habit; hence the following is a very exceptional observation, and it may be that the male's attendance at this nest was merely perfunctory. W. A. Welter (1935), speaking of a nest found in Kentucky, says:

The entire nest, with the exception of bits of lichens that were added later, was built in one day. It is interesting to note that both birds, male and female, worked on this nest that first day. The male evidently was doing his share of the work. This seems to be an unusual circumstance, as ordinarily the male is supposed to scorn such menial duties. * * *

It would seem that the time consumed in nest building diminishes as the season progresses. Perhaps haste is necessary in order that the potential young may be completely developed by the time of fall migration. This need for haste may also have been the stimulant which caused the male in the last case to assist in nidification.

Bendire (1895) says: "I believe two broods are frequently raised in a season, occasionally three perhaps, as fresh eggs have been found as late as August 7. An old nest is sometimes occupied for several seasons and remodeled each year; and should the nest and eggs be taken or destroyed, a second and occasionally even a third and fourth attempt at nesting is made within about a week, and sometimes these subsequent nests are built in the same tree again, or in others close by."

Eggs.—[Author's note: Like other hummingbirds, the rubythroat regularly lays two eggs; I have no record of more or fewer. An interval of one day is said by Bendire (1895) to occur between the laying of the two eggs; he says also that the eggs are often laid before the nest is completed. The eggs are pure dead white without gloss and usually elliptical-oval in shape, though occasionally approaching elliptical-ovate, with one end slightly more pointed than the other. The measurements of 52 eggs average 12.9 by 8.5 millimeters; the eggs showing the four extremes measure 14.5 by 9.1, 11.5 by 8.2, and 12.7 by 7.8 millimeters.]

Young.—Bradford Torrey (1892) describing the young hummingbirds newly hatched from eggs no bigger than a pea, says: "Two lifeless-looking things lay in the bottom of the nest, their heads tucked out of sight, and their bodies almost or quite naked, except for a line of grayish down along the middle of the back." Isabella McC. Lemmon (1901) speaks of the young birds as "dark slate-color, with a little yellowish fuzz on the bodies, exceedingly thin necks, three-cornered heads and short yellow bills," and of birds slightly older, Brewster (1890) says: "Their bills were perhaps a quarter of an inch long, wide at the base, and in general shape not unlike the bill of a *Dendroica*, but more depressed."

Bendire (1895) states that the young "are born blind, and do not open their eyes until they are about a week old." These minute, naked, helpless bits of life grow, as Bendire (1895) says, "amazingly fast, and when about ten days old they are about as large as their parents." Torrey (1892), however, speaks of the brood which he watched closely until after they left the nest, as developing more slowly. He says: "Though at least eleven days old, the tiny birds * * * were still far from filling the cup." He describes thus the behavior of the parent as she brooded her young a few days after they had hatched: "It was noticeable that, while sitting upon the young, she kept up an almost incessant motion, as if seeking to warm them, or perhaps to develop their muscles by a kind of massage treatment. A measure of such hitchings and fidgetings might have meant nothing more than an attempt to secure for herself a comfortable seat; but when they were persisted in for fifteen minutes together, it was difficult not to believe that she had some different end in view. Possibly, as human infants get exercise by dandling on the mother's knee, the baby humming-bird gets his by this parental kneading process."

Torrey's birds were hatched on June 30. "On the 12th [of July]," he writes, "just after the little ones had been fed, one of them got his wings for the first time above the wall of the nest, and fluttered them with much spirit." On July 19 the first young bird left the nest. Mr. Torrey continues:

I was standing on the wall with my glass leveled upon the nest, when I saw him exercising his wings. The action was little more pronounced than had been noticed at intervals during the last three or four days, except that he was more decidedly on his feet. Suddenly, without making use of the rim of the nest, as I should have expected him to do, he was in the air, hovering in the prettiest fashion, and in a moment more had alighted on a leafless twig slightly above the level of the nest, and perhaps a yard from it * * * [Soon] the youngster was again on the wing. It was wonderful how much at home he seemed—poising, backing, soaring, and alighting with all the ease and grace of an old hand.

Illustrating the activity which precedes the flight from the nest, Mr. Torrey says of the other young bird: "He grew more and more restless; as my companion—a learned man—expressed it, he began to 'ramp around.' Once he actually mounted the rim of the nest, a thing which his more precocious brother had never been seen to do, * * * exercising his wings till they made a cloud about him."

C. J. Pennock, in a letter to Mr. Bent, describes a young bird "standing erect on the rim of the nest moving his wings *slowly*—so slowly that I could see the wings distinctly—then rapidly again."

Of the length of time the young birds remain in the nest Forbush (1927) says that it "has been given by different writers as from 6 to 18 days. It may be possible that in the south or during a hot wave in the north, when the female can safely leave her young without danger of chilling them, that she may procure enough food for them to develop wings to the flight stage in a short time; but my New England records of this period run from 14 to 28 days."

During this long period of time the young are fed by regurgitation. Torrey (1892) gives a vivid description of the operation, viewed from close at hand: "The feeding process, which I had been so desirous to see, was of a sort to make the spectator shiver. The mother, standing on the edge of the nest, with her tail braced against its side, like a woodpecker or a creeper, took a rigidly erect position, and craned her neck until her bill was in a perpendicular line above the short, wide-open, upraised beak of the little one, who, it must be remembered, was at this time hardly bigger than a humble-bee. Then she thrust her bill for its full length down into his throat, a frightful-looking act, followed by a series of murderous gesticulations, which fairly made one observer's blood run cold."

When the young bird grew larger, and its beak longer, the parent's beak, Mr. Torrey says, "was thrust into his mouth at right angles," and later, after the young had left the nest, she sometimes passed food directly from her beak to the young bird. "If she found a choice collection of spiders, for instance, she brought them in her throat (as cedar-birds carry cherries), to save trips; if she had only one or two, she retained them between her mandibles."

Carl W. Schlag (1930) says: "In cleaning the nest the humming-bird placed the droppings of the young in a line on the same branch, just above the nest."

Dr. Arthur A. Allen (1930) states that during the first few days after hatching the female feeds the young by merely inserting her tongue into the nestlings' throats and squirting them full of nectar and tiny insects.

Burns (1915) gives the period of incubation as 14 days. Wilbur F. Smith (1920), however, says of a closely watched nest: "On June 2 * * * the first egg was laid, and, after an interval of a day, the second was laid * * *. The young hatched on June 15, after eleven days' incubation, during which time the nest was built higher."

Plumages.—[AUTHOR'S NOTE: The young hummingbird is hatched naked, but pinfeathers soon appear, and the young bird is practically fully grown and fully feathered in the juvenal plumage before it leaves the nest. The sexes are unlike in the juvenal plumage. The young male closely resembles the adult female, with the white tips on the three outer tail feathers; but the feathers of the upper parts are narrowly edged with grayish buff, the throat is marked with narrow dusky streaks, and the sides and flanks are strongly tinged with brownish buff. The young female is like the young male but lacks the dusky streaks on the throat. Young males begin to acquire one or more ruby feathers on the throat in August and September, but no great progress in this direction is made before they leave for the south, and the adult plumage is assumed before they return in the spring. Dickey and van Rossem (1938) say: "In February and March both adults and young go through a complete molt, and at this time the young males acquire the red throat of maturity. Most individuals have completed this molt by the first week in March."]

Food.—The hummingbird is popularly regarded solely as a sipper of nectar, as it buzzes from flower to flower; as one who might say with Ariel, "Where the bee sucks, there suck I"; but when it comes down to the examination of stomach contents, it is proved that a considerable part of the bird's food consists of insects, chiefly those that come to the flowers the hummingbird visits. Frederic A. Lucas (1893), after examining the contents of 29 stomachs of several species of hummingbirds, comes to the following conclusion:

It would seem to be safe to assume that the main food of Hummingbirds is small insects, mainly diptera and hymenoptera. Homoptera are usually present, and small spiders form an important article of food, while hemiptera and coleoptera are now and then found. The small size of the insects may be inferred from the fact that one stomach contained remains of not less than fifty individuals, probably more.

Most of the insects found occur in or about flowers, and my own views agree with those of Mr. Clute, that it is usually insects, and not honey, that attract Hummingbirds to flowers * * *.

In view, however, of the testimony cited at the beginning of this paper, it would seem unquestionable that Hummingbirds do to some extent feed on the nectar of flowers and the sap of trees * * *.

I am much inclined to believe with Dr. Shufeldt that Hummingbirds first visited flowers for insects and that the taste for sweets has been incidentally acquired.

This taste for sweets is very well known to the many observers who have supplied hummingbirds with sugar and water placed about their gardens in artificial flowers. Miss Althea R. Sherman (1913), for example, who has experimented in feeding hummingbirds during seven summers, estimated that a single bird consumed "two teaspoonfuls of sugar daily."

Hummingbirds also avail themselves of the sap flowing from holes drilled by sapsuckers. In the article quoted under the yellow-bellied sapsucker, Frank Bolles (1894) speaks of the hummingbirds as constant and numerous visitors to the sapsucker's "orchards."

In order to attract hummingbirds to our gardens Dr. Arthur A. Allen (1930) suggests planting "caragana, pelargonium, tritoma; * * * tiger lilies, painted cups, bee-balms, scarlet salvias, azaleas, and gladiolus; * * * scarlet runners and trumpet vines; * * * horse-chestnuts and buckeyes."

Prof. O. A. Stevens writes to Mr. Bent from Fargo, N. Dak., as follows: "About the earliest flower that the hummingbirds visit here is *Ribes odoratum*, cultivated from the Missouri River region. The next one, and the one where I always watch for them about May 20–25, is *Caragana arborescens*, an introduced shrub that is much planted here. A little later the native *Aquilegia canadensis* and *Lonicera dioica* are available. On a specimen of the latter some of the flowers drooped to the ground, and, as I watched the bird at them, he rested on the ground for a few moments while he probed several flowers. Early in fall the cannas and gladioli are, of course, their favorites. The most natural summer flower seems to be the native *Impatiens*, and I believe that the hummingbirds' nesting grounds are closely associated with these plants."

Caroline G. Soule (1900) speaks of the activities of a male hummingbird about a bed of nasturtiums. She writes: "Most of his time was spent in slashing off the spurs of the nasturtiums to get at their nectar. We had hardly one perfect nasturtium flower all summer long, owing to his attacks."

Wilson (1831) charmingly notes his experience with the hummingbird as a flycatcher thus: "I have seen the humming bird, for half an hour at a time, darting at those little groups of insects that dance in the air in a fine summer evening, retiring to an adjoining twig to rest, and renewing the attack with a dexterity that sets all our other flycatchers at defiance."

Behavior.—The ruby-throated hummingbird gives the impression of being a nervous, high-strung, irritable little bird. It often resents the presence of other species of birds, however innocent their design may be. It is intolerant also to members of its own species to such a degree that, as a rule, the more hummingbirds there are together, the more excited and hostile they become.

I once saw a hummingbird attack a chimney swift—a strange bird to arouse the hummer's venom. My notes say: "August 2, 1909. This evening I saw Greek meet Greek—a hummingbird chasing a swift. The birds flew overhead rapidly, well above the treetops, the hummingbird a little behind and above. I saw it make a dive at the swift, who avoided the attack by a spurt that carried him well in advance. The hummingbird soon overtook his enemy and made a second swoop down toward him. By this time the birds were so far away that I lost sight of them."

Toward man, however, hummingbirds are usually complaisant, almost to the point of tameness. There are many instances recorded of their being attracted, sometimes in large numbers, to gardens where tubes of sugar and water are put out for their entertainment.

One of the most successful of these feeding stations is the garden of the late Mrs. Laurence J. Webster in Holderness, N. H. Here, for many years, Mrs. Webster studied the birds and provided them with such a bountiful supply of food that, apparently, all the hummingbirds in the vicinity resorted to her garden throughout the summer. She told me that she came to recognize some of the individual birds and, in a few instances, noticed that certain birds would take a long flight, always in the same direction, when they left her garden, and would not return for a long time—evidently visitors from a considerable distance—whereas other birds were in and out of the garden all day. She accustomed the birds to associate the sound of her voice with the presence of food and often called them to a vial she held in her hand by whistling the "phoebe" note of the chickadee.

Her garden on August 5, 1937, when Mr. Bent and I visited her, was whirring with hummingbirds—at least 40, we thought. Mrs. Webster covered the scattered feeding tubes and, seated at an open window beside Mr. Bent, who held a filled tube in his hand, gave the chickadee call. A bird came up out of the garden, poised a moment, then alighted on Mr. Bent's finger.

All day a deep hum sounds through her garden, rising or falling in intensity as birds come together or feed from the vials undisturbed, alone. At dusk, as one by one the birds leave the garden, the pitch of the whirring wings lowers, gradually dying down to a dull, tranquil sound, until "at twilight's hush" the last bird has gone.

It was in this garden that the motion pictures, described below, were taken.

The remarkable flight of the hummingbird, during which the wings move so rapidly that they are practically invisible, has attracted a great deal of interest and conjecture. Some observers maintained that the birds sometimes fly backward when leaving a flower—Bradford Torrey, for example, seemed to have had no doubt on the subject (see above); other observers, however, objected on mechanical grounds that no bird can fly backward. It remained for motion photography to settle the question.

That the hummingbird does fly backward has been definitely proved, and the manner in which backward flight is accomplished has been demonstrated by means of motion pictures taken in 1936 by a new application of photography. Dr. Harold E. Edgerton took advantage of the intermittent flashes in a low-pressure tube in which the flashes occur for 1/100,000 of a second with a period of darkness between them lasting 1/500 of a second. He used a constantly moving film, geared so that a new bit of film came opposite the lens of the camera at each flash, and thus secured about 540 pictures a second. Pictures of hummingbirds in flight taken in this way, when thrown on a screen, apparently reduce the speed of the birds' wing beats to that of a leisurely flying gull and make it possible to study the flight of the bird in detail.

Dr. Charles H. Blake examined with great care the films taken of hummingbirds in flight and found that the birds beat their wings 55 times (completed strokes) a second when hovering, 61 a second when backing, and as rapidly as 75 a second when progressing straightaway. Probably this last figure would be found to increase as the bird gained speed, if the camera could keep the bird in focus. Dr. Blake calculated that, during hovering, the wing tips moved at the rate of 20 miles an hour, and he also learned that the bird is in flight *before* it leaves its perch (the takeoff took 0.07 second) and pulls the perch after it a little way, a phenomenon that Mrs. Webster had suspected from feeling the birds leave her hand.

Dr. Blake kindly explained to me the mechanism of backward flying thus: In backing away from a flower or feeding tube the hummingbird stands almost vertically in the air with its tail pointing downward and a little forward. In this pose its wings beat horizontally, and what would be the downward half of each complete wing stroke if the bird's long axis were parallel to the ground forces the air forward, away from the bird's breast in its upright position, and *drives the bird backward*. Then, on the return half-stroke, the whole wing is rotated at the shoulder joint so that its *upper surface* strikes the air, and, driving it downward, balances the pull of gravity. Dr. Blake also points out that the distribution of weight in the hummingbird's wing is evidently favorable to a very low inertia upon which the quick reversal of motion depends, the weight being concentrated close to the body by reason of the short, heavy humerus.

The following quotation shows the high rate of speed the hummingbird may attain by the lightninglike strokes of its wings. H. A. Allard (1934), who was making a fast trip by auto out of Washington, D. C., says: "Not far out of Warrenton we had settled down to a speed of fifty miles per hour on highway 211, when a Ruby-throated Hummingbird (*Archilochus colubris*) suddenly paralleled our course along the side of the roadway as if deliberately racing with us. It actually passed us for a short distance keeping straight with our course, then swerved away. Its speed appeared to be somewhere between 55–60 miles per hour."

Hummingbirds have been seen so frequently hovering before the brilliant red flowers in our gardens—trumpet vines clambering over the porch, salvias gleaming scarlet in the flower beds—that it has been assumed the birds have a preference for the color red. However, the extensive investigations of Andrew L. Pickens (1930) bring out the fact that it is the brightness of color—its conspicuousness against the background—that draws the hummingbird to a flower. He says:

It is easy to perceive that Hummingbirds prefer the intensity of color shades rather than the paleness of color hues * * *

[But] the question is one that cannot be decided by mere rule of spectrum or pigments. There is so to speak a relativity of colors. * * *

Red being the complement of green is the most conspicuous color that a flower can show. * * *

Orange, while not so brilliant, is more showy in deeply shaded swamps and woods than is red * * *.

Green flowers are too inconspicuous among foliage. In certain contrasting desert backgrounds, or on the sere dry-season prairies it should have value. Thus, while no green Hummingbird flowers are known in the East, *Nicotiana paniculata* one of the greenest large flowers I know, is much frequented in the west during the dry season at least * * *.

Complete lists [of flowers] would probably show red, the sharpest contrast to green, a favorite everywhere, with orange in some favor in tree-shaded regions and a neglected color like green rising in sun-browned territory.

Experiments made by Miss Althea R. Sherman (1913) to test the "supposedly erroneous theory which had been published to the effect that Hummingbirds show a preference for red flowers" indicated conclusively that hummingbirds visited the bottles she placed about her garden *if they contained syrup*, whether or not they simulated a flower in shape or color. The birds associated even an untrimmed bottle with food, just as they soon came to recognize Miss Sherman herself as a supplier of food.

Speaking of pollination Saunders (1936) says that the bee balm "is the most important Humming Bird flower in Allegany Park. The anthers and stigma brush the crown of the Humming Bird's head as the bird probes the flower. The pollen is bright yellow, so that most summer Humming Birds appear to have yellow crowns."

Pickens (1927) points out in detail an interesting adaptation, insuring cross fertilization by the hummingbird, in the flower of *Macranthera lecontei*. He says: "Of all the forms that I have studied this is the most exclusively Hummingbird flower, and I recall seeing no other honey-gatherers in its vicinity."

Voice.—The notes that come from the hummingbird's tiny throat are high pitched and have a petulant quality, reflecting the bird's irritable nature. Sometimes the notes are angry-sounding, mouselike squeals; sometimes they are run into a nervous, fretful chattering, always very sharp and clear, though by no means loud, and delivered in a jerky, excited manner.

A lone hummingbird is usually silent, except for the buzzing of its wings, but when several birds are together they often become very voluble and quarrelsome and jerk out their notes, now arranged in emphatic phrases, squealing and chattering back and forth as if they were carrying on an animated controversy in a jabbering language.

Sometimes a single bird approaches another one poised before a flower and disputes its right to the place. Both then express their mutual hostility by beginning to jabber, and after a dart at each other and a fight, or at least a whirling about in the air, the winner of the encounter returns quietly to the flower. Thus when we stand close to a company of hummingbirds we hear the sound of their voices rising and falling in irregular waves—anger or resentment mounting up again and again and, in between, a short truce, marked by the peace of humming wings.

The pitch of the notes is invariably high, but it varies a good deal. Sometimes a note rises almost to a piercing whistle, and often the tone suggests the steely voice of the chimney swift.

In the phrases the notes are arranged in many ways; usually both squeals and short *chips* are combined, but either may be given alone, and the pitch of either one may run upward or downward. The short notes, when uttered alone are generally in series, repeated without change over and over, coming in twos, threes, or more again and again, the last note of each series commonly accented sharply. When the squeals and chattering are interspersed they often fall into a very pleasing rhythm. For example, a form often given when one bird joins another is a single sharp note followed by a long, descending chatter.

The chief characteristics of the hummingbird's voice are the sharply cut, emphatic enunciation and the attenuated quality.

Mary Pierson Allen (1908), speaking of a fledgling hummingbird that she fed with sweetened water, says: "He had his mother's *zip-zip*, which meant flowers or happiness, and a plaintive baby *peet*, *peet*, when he wanted food."

Field marks.—Audubon (1842) states: "If comparison might enable you, kind reader, to form some tolerably accurate idea of their peculiar mode of flight, and their appearance when on wing, I would say, that were both objects of the same colour, a large sphinx or moth, when moving from one flower to another, and in a direct line, comes nearer the Humming-bird in aspect than any other object with which I am acquainted."

It is true that the ruby-throated hummingbird bears not the slightest resemblance to any other bird occurring in the Eastern and Middle United States. It is sometimes mistaken, however, for the hawk moths, which hover about flowers in the manner of a hummingbird.

The adult male differs from the female and the immature bird in possessing a highly colored throat, which gleams in the sunlight like a glowing coal, oftentimes nearer coppery brass than true ruby. The male's tail is plainly forked and is not marked by the white spots that distinguish the rounded tail of the female and the young bird.

Enemies.—In addition to the dangers of migration, notably the occurrence of frost when the hummingbird overruns the advance of spring, there are other hazards, chiefly of an accidental nature, imperiling the life of the bird.

Ralph E. Danforth (1921) speaks of a bird caught in "a pendulous mass of cobweb" from which he freed it with some difficulty, and Bradford Torrey (1903) relates what he calls "a pretty story" told to him by an observer whom he describes as "a seeing man." The man, hearing "the familiar, squeaking notes of a hummer, and thinking that their persistency must be occasioned by some unusual trouble, went out to investigate. Sure enough, there hung the bird in a spider's web attached to a rosebush, while the owner of the web, a big yellow-and-brown, pot-bellied, bloodthirsty rascal, was turning its victim over and over, winding the web about it. Wings and legs were already fast, so that all the bird could do was to cry for help. And help had come. The man at once killed the spider, and then, little by little, for it was an operation of no small delicacy, unwound the mesh in which the bird was entangled."

Joseph Janiec sends the following story to Mr. Bent: "While I was wandering through a large hollow one June afternoon, my attention was attracted to the unusual waving of a pasture thistle. No air was stirring, and my curiosity prompted me to ascertain the cause of the movements. As I approached the thistle I noticed what I at first supposed to be a large dragonfly impaled on the prickly purple flower; closer examination, however, revealed a male ruby-throated hummingbird stuck to the flower, his wings not being involved in the contact but his stomach feathers adhering to the prickly, pointed stamens. Cutting off the flower, I carried it and the bird home and carefully removed the bird. Although it lost a few feathers in the operation, the little bird flew away unharmed."

There is a surprising record from California telling of the capture of an unidentified species of hummingbird by a fish. Mary E. Lockwood (1922) says, quoting from a letter: "We were seated by the lotus-pool when a hummingbird flew and hovered over the pool. Suddenly a bass jumped from the water and swallowed the hummingbird."

George H. Lowery, Jr. (1938), reports the following apparently unique record:

I shot a female Eastern Pigeon Hawk (*Falco columbarius columbarius*) on April 16, 1937, at Grand Isle, off the coast of Jefferson Parish, Louisiana. Upon examination of its stomach contents, I was surprised to find the identifiable remains of a Ruby-throated Hummingbird (*Archilochus colubris*). Later, on a visit to Washington, D. C., I discussed the matter with Mr. Clarence Cottam, Director of the Food Habits Division of the Bureau of Biological Survey. With his permission and the assistance of Mr. Robert McClanahan of the Food Habits offices, I went through the extensive records of that division and found that no species of hummingbird had ever heretofore been recorded from any bird stomach.

L. T. S. Norris-Elye writes to Mr. Bent: "During the summer of 1934, James Ashdown, Jr., and his mother were walking in the woods at Kenora, Ontario, and heard a continuous rattling. Investigation showed it to be a male ruby-throated hummingbird on the ground, with a huge dragonfly on the bird's back; it had seized the bird by the neck. They drove the dragonfly away, picked up the bird, and held it in the palm of the hand for several minutes, after which it flew away.

"We have had instances of frogs capturing and swallowing ruby-throats, one at Gull Harbor and one at Gimli, Lake Winnipeg. The Gimli case was observed by my friend Hugh Moncrieff, who captured the frog (leopard) and had some boys cut it open and recover the bird, while he took some good motion pictures of the operation."

Fall.—Taverner and Swales (1907) describe vividly a great concourse of migrating hummingbirds on Point Pelee, Ontario, Canada:

The first three days of September in 1906 were notable for the vast numbers of Hummers present. In certain low slashings in the open woods were luxuriant growths of Jewel Weed (*Impatiens* sp.?) standing nearly shoulder high and so dense that to enter it one had to force his way through. It was simply spangled with blossoms, and all about and over it hovered and darted hundreds of Hummingbirds. From some little distance, as we approached such clumps, we were aware of innumerable little twitterings that followed each other so rapidly as to scarce be separable, one from another, and so fine, sharp, and high in pitch that it took a little effort to realize that it was real sound and not imagination or a ringing in the ears. Underlying this was a low hum that arose from the vibrations of many little wings. Approaching closer, the pugnacious little mites were all about us, chasing each other over the smooth rounded surface of the jewel weed or darting angrily at us from this side or that, with furious chatterings that made one instinctively cover the eyes, or involuntarily flinch at the expected impact of their sharp, rapier-like, little bills. * * * All these birds were juveniles. * * *

Keays noted that in 1901 the Hummingbird was the only species that did not turn back when, in migrating out the Point, it reached the end. We verified this many times. The final end of the Point stretches out for a couple of hundred rods, in the form of a long, low, more or less winding and attenuated sand spit. Stationed about half way out on this, it was most amusing to watch the little mites come buzzing over the last half of the red-cedar bushes and then drop down towards the ground and, without pause or hesitation, follow every winding of the ever-changing sand to its extreme end, and then, with a sudden and resolute turn, square away for Pelee Island, just visible on the horizon. Dr. Jones was stationed on the opposite islands from August 26 to September 2. 1905, and makes the following statement as to the movements of the species over the waters of the lake: "Hummingbirds were passing during the daylight, and all those noted were flying very low. In fact they dropped down between the waves for protection from the wind, which was quartering, or at right angles to their line of flight and seemed to disturb them. I noticed that in the strong westerly wind, all birds headed southwest, but always drifted south."

I remember seeing, in Lexington, Mass., on two or three occasions in September, a single hummingbird, a dozen feet from the ground, bounding past me through open country, undulating in long, low waves as it held a rapid course toward the southwest—the line of migration in autumn through eastern Massachusetts. And again in May I once saw a lone bird steering due north, or a little east of north, flying, straight as an arrow, not 2 feet above the grass blades.

DISTRIBUTION

Range.—Eastern North America and Central America.

Breeding range.—The ruby-throated hummingbird breeds **north** to rarely southern Alberta (Camrose); southern Saskatchewan (Indian Head and Fish Lake); southern Manitoba (Aweme, Shoal Lake, and Big Island Lake); northeastern Minnesota (Rice Lake and Isle Royal); southern Ontario (Goulais Bay, Algonquin Park, Cobden, and Ottawa); southern Quebec (Montreal, Quebec City, Kamouraska, and Godbout); New Brunswick (Chatham); Prince Edward Island (Malpeaque Bay); and Nova Scotia (Pictou). From this northeastern point, the range extends southward along the Atlantic coast of the United States to Florida (St. Augustine, Daytona Beach, New Smyrna, and Princeton). **South** to Florida (Princeton, Fort Myers, St. Marks, and Pensacola); southern Louisiana (Thibodaux and New Iberia); and southern Texas (Houston, Victoria, and San Antonio). **West** to eastern Texas (San Antonio and Waco); Oklahoma (Norman, Oklahoma City, and Tulsa); Kansas (Clearwater, Wichita, and Hays); South Dakota (Vermillion, Arlington, and Faulkton); eastern North Dakota (Wahpeton, Fargo, and Argusville); and rarely Alberta (Camrose).

Winter range.—The normal winter range extends **north** to southern Sinaloa (Escuinapa); probably rarely southeastern Texas (Port Arthur); probably rarely southern Alabama (Fairhope); and Florida (Pensacola, Tallahassee, and Jacksonville). **East** to Florida (Jacksonville, St. Lucie, Miami, Royal Palm Hammock and Key

West) ; Quintana Roo (Cozumel Island) ; Honduras (Tela and Lancetilla) ; Nicaragua (Ometepe Island) ; Costa Rica (San Jose) ; and Panama (Volcano de Chiriqui). **South** to Panama (Volcano de Chiriqui) ; El Salvador (La Libertad) ; and Guatemala (San Lucas). **West** to Guatemala (San Lucas) ; Chiapas (Comitan) ; Oaxaca (Santa Efigenia, and Tonguia) ; Guerrero (Chilpancingo) ; western Jalisco (Volcano de Colima) ; and southern Sinaloa (Escuinapa).

Spring migration.—Early dates of spring arrival are: Alabama— Autaugaville, March 29; Long Island, April 13. Georgia—Savannah, March 15; Atlanta, April 3. North Carolina—Raleigh, April 11; Weaverville, April 17. Virginia—Variety Mills, April 10. District of Columbia—Washington, April 16. Maryland—Mardela Springs, April 20. Pennsylvania—Philadelphia, April 16. New York—Ballston Spa, April 20; Buffalo, May 2. Connecticut—Jewett City, May 5. Massachusetts—Pittsfield, May 6; Boston, May 8. Vermont—Wells River, April 24; St. Johnsbury, May 8. New Hampshire—Hanover, May 10. Maine—Portland, May 9. Nova Scotia— Pictou, May 7; Wolfville, May 15. New Brunswick—St. John, May 17; Chatham, May 20. Quebec—Quebec City, April 25; Montreal, May 9. Mississippi—Biloxi, March 3. Louisiana—New Orleans, March 7. Arkansas—Helena, March 24; Delight, April 4. Tennessee—Chattanooga, April 5. Kentucky—Eubank, April 13. Missouri—St. Louis, April 5. Illinois—Odin, April 27; Chicago, May 7. Indiana— Fort Wayne, April 14. Ohio—Oberlin, April 12; Youngstown, May 6. Michigan—Detroit, April 28; Sault Ste. Marie, May 21. Ontario—Toronto, April 12; Ottawa, May 5. Iowa—National, May 7; Sioux City, May 17. Wisconsin—Madison, May 4. Minnesota— Minneapolis, May 1; Lanesboro, May 9. Texas—Brownsville, March 18; Gainesville, April 5. Kansas—Onaga, May 15. North Dakota— Fargo, May 16. Manitoba—Pilot Mound, May 16; Aweme, May 17. Saskatchewan—Indian Head, May 24.

Fall migration.—Late dates of fall departure are: Manitoba— Aweme, September 12. Minnesota—Minneapolis, September 24; Lanesboro, October 8. Wisconsin—Madison, September 20. Iowa— National, October 4; Keokuk, October 23. Missouri—Concordia, October 12; St. Louis, October 25. Ontario—Toronto, September 29; Ottawa, October 16. Michigan—Detroit, October 7. Ohio—Youngstown, September 24; Oberlin, September 29. Indiana—Fort Wayne, October 9. Illinois—Rantoul, October 6; Chicago, October 13. Kentucky—Eubank, October 1. Tennessee—Athens, October 28. Arkansas—Helena, October 8; Delight, October 15. Louisiana—New Orleans, November 1. Texas—Bonham, October 18; Brownsville, November 5. Quebec—Montreal, September 17. Prince Edward Island—North River, September 5. New Brunswick—St. John, September 17. Maine—Phillips, September 16; Portland, September 24.

New Hampshire—Durham, September 25. Vermont, Wells River,
September 16; St. Johnsbury, September 30. Massachusetts—Am-
herst, September 16; Boston, September 21. Connecticut—Hartford,
September 27. New York—New York City, September 26; Rochester, October 1. New Jersey—Morristown, September 29. Pennsylvania—Philadelphia, October 12. Renovo, October 15. District of
Columbia—Washington, October 20. North Carolina—Raleigh, October 7; Weaverville, October 15. Georgia—Atlanta, October 18.

Although the Biological Survey does not advocate the banding of
hummingbirds, several have been successfully marked and a few have
been recaptured at banding stations in Maine and Massachusetts in
subsequent seasons.

Casual records.—Among the records of occurrence of the ruby-
throated hummingbird outside its normal range, the following may
be cited: A male was obtained at Casa Blanca, near Habana, Cuba,
on April 4, 1937, and it is probable the species occurs in the western
part of this island with fair regularity. To the north it was recorded
on August 15, 1901, at Ellis Bay and on July 18, 1898, at English
Bay, Anticosti Island; it was reported as seen at Grande Greve on
July 6, 1919, and at Gaspé Basin, Quebec, on August 21, 1924; a
specimen was obtained at Davis Inlet, Labrador, on July 17, 1882;
one was seen at Red Deer River, Manitoba, on August 16, 1881; the
Hudson's Bay agent at Lac La Ronge, Saskatchewan, has reported
the species as of casual occurrence in his flower garden; and the
United States National Museum has a mummified specimen picked
up by a native on the beach at Klukatauck, near St. Michael, Alaska,
probably during 1925.

Egg dates.—Florida: 23 records, March 25 to June 15; 12 records,
May 10 to 20, indicating the height of the season.

Michigan: 8 records, June 1 to July 17.

New York: 30 records, May 23 to July 4; 15 records, June 13 to 26.

North Carolina: 25 records, May 2 to June 20; 13 seconds, May 11
to June 4.

ARCHILOCHUS ALEXANDRI (Bourcier and Mulsant)

BLACK-CHINNED HUMMINGBIRD

PLATE 58

PLATE 58

This active little hummer is accredited with a rather wide breeding range, from southern British Columbia and western Montana to
northern Mexico and western Texas, but it is comparatively rare over
much of this range. It is most abundant in the southern portions of
the range, especially in southern California, southern Utah, Arizona,

and portions of New Mexico. In the dry foothills and canyons of the Upper Austral Zone in this general region, it is one of the commonest of the hummingbirds. Dr. Joseph Grinnell (1898) says that in Los Angeles County it is a "summer resident from the lowlands to the summit of the mountains, but most abundant in the foothill regions, where it breeds in the cañons in some years by the thousands. * * * By the first of July, when the vegetation of the foothills becomes dry, and flowers cease to bloom, the Hummingbirds are found in countless thousands at higher elevations (6000 to 8500 feet) where summer is just dawning."

He says elsewhere (1914), referring to the Colorado Valley: "At Ehrenberg the last week of March and opposite Cibola the first week in April, the species was abundant in the desert washes, feeding about the profusely blossoming palo verdes. * * *

"The males were more seldom seen, and the females became closely restricted to the willow strip along the river, in which association we were convinced that this was the only species of hummingbird breeding. The males were not seen in the willows, but only in the mesquite association and up the desert washes. The females foraged everywhere except on the desert mesa, but nested exclusively in the willows."

In southern Arizona we found the black-chinned hummingbird to be the most abundant species of the family; its favorite haunts seemed to be about the mouths of the canyons, where a line of sycamores followed the underground course of a mountain stream out onto the plains; it was also commonly found in the small patches of willows along the dry washes, where water had formerly flowed, or where, probably, an underground supply still kept the trees and shrubs alive. It was not seen in the mountains above 6,000 feet.

Courtship.—The courtship flight of the black-chinned hummingbird is much like that of the closely related eastern ruby-throated hummer, consisting mainly of the long, swinging, pendulumlike swoops, with some variations. Laurence M. Huey (1924) describes it very well as follows:

The female was perched on a dead, horizontal limb about five feet from the ground and the male took flight from a position approximately twenty feet above her on the twig of a cottonwood, against the trunk of which I was quietly resting. With a bold sweep and a whizzing noise made by flight, which resembled that of the Costa Hummer except that the tone was not so intense, he passed very close to her and headed up to a point about fifteen feet above. There, while the upward motion died until a complete stop was reached, he seemed to pat his wings together underneath him, causing a sound much like that of a bathing bird flopping its wings in the water after they have become thoroughly saturated. After a second downward swing, with the whizzing noise, he rose to another point about fifteen feet up, where again the wing flopping performance was repeated. This U-shaped figure was repeated five different times, and, at each stop at the apex, the flopping of wings was indulged in, after which the bird again sought his perch on the cottonwood above his mate. I was close enough almost to hear his wing beats as he sped to and fro, and I watched the pair for three minutes, when they both flew off of their own will, without being disturbed. At no time during the minute and a half duration of the nuptial flight was there any vocal demonstration, though both birds were rather vociferous when perched.

Mrs. Bailey (1923) saw some "giving their aerial courtship dance from among the mesquites. One that I watched varied the usual triangulation by first flying back and forth horizontally across the face of a bush, then making narrow V's with the point at the bush, followed by wide-sweeping swings out over the mesquites as if from pure spirits."

Robert S. Woods (1927b) writes:

The shuttling of the Black-chinned Hummingbird, which follows a path like a narrow figure 8 lying on one side, has often been mentioned in accounts of the species. Its other form of nuptial flight most closely resembles that of the Rufous Hummingbird, just described [a swooping dive, punctuated at the bottom of its course by what might be described as a tremulant squeak or a rapid sucession of about four thin, vibrant notes], but the vocalization is more prolonged and of rather different character—a long-drawn, pulsating, plaintive, liquid note, probably the most pleasing utterance of any of our Hummingbirds. The heavy droning sound of its flight, so noticeable in the shuttling movement, is heard in this case only while momentum is first being gained on the downward swing. The shuttling flight, it may be noted, is practiced almost solely by those species in which the wings of the male are specially modified for noise-making purposes.

Nesting.—Major Bendire (1895) gives a rather comprehensive account of the nesting of black-chinned hummingbirds, and I cannot do better than to quote his remarks. He says:

Throughout the greater part of their range, it rarely begins laying before May 1, and the season is at its height through this month, while second or possibly third sets are found up to the latter part of July, and occasionally still later. The nest is readily distinguishable from that of the Ruby-throated Hummingbird by not being covered on the outside with lichens. It is composed of plant down, varying in color from white to buff; the latter is obtained from the under side of the young leaves of the sycamore, the former probably from willows, milkweed, or thistles. These materials are well worked together, and the outside of the nest is thickly coated with spider web. In an occasional specimen a small leaf or two, or a few flower blossoms of the oak are worked in the outer walls. In a specimen from Marfa, Texas, the outside is well covered with small flower spikes, the male aments of a species of oak, hiding the inner lining completely.

He mentions a beautiful nest that "is mainly composed of white willow down, mixed on the outside with a few small leaves and the scales from the willow buds."

These are firmly held in place by an abundance of spider web, with which it is also securely attached to the little fork in which it is saddled. The outer diameter of this nest is about 1⅝ inches by 1 inch in depth; the inner cup is 1 inch in diameter by five eighths of an inch deep; and while some specimens before me are a trifle larger, others are considerably smaller. Nests taken in the Sequoia National Park, in Tulare County, California, have perceptibly thicker walls than those from the warmer lowlands, and are also correspondingly larger. The nests are either saddled on a small, drooping branch or on a fork, one or two of the smaller twigs composing this usually being incorporated in the walls and holding it securely in place. Many of the nests resemble small, fine sponges, and are equally elastic, readily regaining their shape after being squeezed together. They are generally placed from 4 to 8 feet from the ground, mostly in the shrubbery found near small creeks or springs, and frequently their nests overhang the water or the dry creek bed. Alders, cottonwoods, oak, sycamore, laurel, and willows are most often selected for nesting sites, as well as young orchards, especially apple and orange trees, where they are available.

Frank Stephens wrote to Bendire that he "found a set of eggs of this species * * * laid in a nest of the House Finch, *Carpodacus mexicanus frontalis*. No lining had been added, or any other changes made; the bird evidently was in haste to lay, her nest, perhaps, having been suddenly destroyed."

Nests have also been found in a pear tree in an orchard, in a wild grape vine, in a tree-rose in a garden, and even on the stalks of various weeds; Dr. Grinnell (1914) mentions one that "was four feet above the ground on a slanting dead stalk of arrowweed beneath a large spreading willow." John McB. Robertson (1933) reports a nest in a most unusual location. It was built in the loop of a small rope that hung from a board in his garage. The nest rested on a knot at the bottom of the loop and was supported on opposite sides by the rope, to which it was securely tied with spider web; it was made of plant down and covered on the outside with stamens of eucalyptus blossoms. "Other objects to be seen in it are several tiny bits of eucalyptus bark, a scrap of dry leaf, several long human hairs, a small feather that is probably from a Linnet, a pair of bracts from a plant that furnished down, and a seed of alfilaria."

The nest of the black-chinned hummingbird is an exquisite structure, semiglobular in shape, or little more than half of a sphere, as if less than the upper half of the globe had been removed; it is deeply hollowed, and the rim is curved inward at the top, a wise provision of the builder to prevent the eggs or small young from falling out, as the supporting twig or weed stalk is swayed by the wind. It is firmly felted with plant down of various colors, mainly in different shades of buff, from "cartridge buff" to "pale pinkish buff" or "cinnamon-buff"; an occasional nest, in some 40 that I have examined, is made of the buffy-white or pure white down of the willow. The elastic, spongy structure is well reinforced and firmly bound to the supporting twigs with spider web, giving it much greater strength than it appears to have. Its durability is remarkable for such a frail-looking nest, as frequently a new nest is built on the well-preserved remains of a nest of the previous season.

The nest seems hardly large enough at first to contain even the small young, but, as the young increase in size, the elastic top expands, as Bayard H. Christy (1932) so gracefully portrays it: "As the young continue to grow a beautiful contrivance comes into play; the surrounding wall of the nest becomes as it were a living integument about the chicks; it expands with their growth; its rim yields to their little strugglings; its sphere opens like a flower-bud; until the little birds, all but ready to take flight, remain resting upon the full-blown corolla."

Mrs. Bailey (1896) gives the following account of the nest building: "The peculiar feature of the building was the quivering motion of the bird in moulding. When the material was placed she moulded the nest like a potter, twirling tremulously around against the sides, sometimes pressing so hard she ruffled up the feathers of her breast. She shaped the cup as if it were a piece of clay. To round the outside she would sit on the rim and lean over, smoothing the sides with her bill, often with the same tremulous motion. When she wanted to turn around in the nest she lifted herself by whirring her wings."

In southern Texas this hummingbird sometimes builds its nest at greater heights above the ground than mentioned above; Van Tyne and Sutton (1937) report two such nests found in Brewster County; one was "about twenty feet from the ground on a slender willow branch," and the other was "fully thirty feet from the ground in a gigantic cottonwood."

James B. Dixon writes to me from Escondido, Calif.: "Like most of the hummingbirds they are sometimes found nesting in very unexpected locations, such as on a porch where doors were swinging open at all hours of the day or night, on a steel rod poked into the roof of a blacksmith shop where men were busy at an anvil, and on an old piece of haywire stuck into a chink in the wall of a barn. Two locations seem to be preferred in the wilder places, the most popular being a long, meandering canyon filled with scrawny sycamores in the bottom and located where the surrounding hillsides are covered with flowering sage; the other location is in the dense willow thickets, locally known as willow montes, which border running streams or lakes. Here the black-chinned hummingbird is found breeding in large numbers, and it is not unusual to find a nest on the average of every hundred feet in such locations. I have found as high as three-storied nests of his bird, where apparently the bird had returned to the same nest for three successive seasons and built a new nest on the foundations of the previous year's home."

The nest shown on plate 58 illustrates the durability of the apparently fragile material used in its construction; it was composed exclusively of plant down firmly bound with cobwebs, and had served for the rearing of two young, meanwhile experiencing three 11-hour overhead irrigations.

Roy W. Quillin writes to me from Bexar County, Tex.: "All the nests I have seen were made of plant down of various colors and plastered on the outside with tiny lichens, very much like the nest of the rubythroat. They are totally different from nests of this species that I have examined from California. The fact that the nest of the blackchin, in this locality, is much like that of the rubythroat and the fact that the latter species is in migration here when the blackchin is nesting have caused records of the nesting of the rubythroat to be printed for Bexar County. I do not think it nests here."

Eggs.—The black-chinned hummingbird lays ordinarily two eggs, but several sets of three have been found, and occasionally a single egg is incubated. The eggs are much like those of the ruby-throated hummingbird but average a trifle smaller; they are about elliptical-oval, pure white, and without gloss. Often two and sometimes three broods are raised in a season. The measurements of 52 eggs average 12.51 by 8.30 millimeters; the eggs showing the four extremes measure 13.72 by 8.64, 13.21 by 8.89, 11.68 by 8.13, and 12.19 by 7.87 millimeters.

Young.—The period of incubation, performed by the female only, is said to be about 13 days. Mary Beal (1933) writes of the young:

At feeding-time they looked like pale yellow-brown caterpillars with widely gaping mouths, stretching up hungrily. Mother Hummer left the nest every fifteen minutes, and each alternate time on her return she fed the babies, thrusting her long bill down their throats until I held my breath lest she'd punch a hole through them, and every time I breathed a sigh of relief when it was safely over.

They grew amazingly fast. In a week they made quite a respectable appearance, and at the end of two weeks they were beautiful, shapely birdlings, completely filling the nest. * * *

On the nineteenth day, the babies perched on the edge of the nest and tried their wings with a quick humming motion just like Mother's, but they made no attempt to lift themselves into the air. They were still fed as regularly as clockwork, every half hour.

The day they were three weeks old, they left the nest, flying about with a smart little air of importance, giving thin squeaks of excitement.

The care and feeding of the young seem to depend entirely on the female, as well as the building of the nest. The male is seldom seen even in the vicinity of the nest.

Plumages.—The naked young soon begin to acquire a nestling, or juvenal, plumage and are fully fledged before they leave the nest at the age of about three weeks. The nestling has a much shorter bill than the adult; the crown is a mixture of grayish buff and dusky;

the back shows a mixture of dusky and glossy green, the latter feathers tipped with buffy; the throat and abdomen are dull white; the flanks are light drab; and the remiges, except the middle pair, are tipped with dull white. This plumage, which is much like that of the adult female, is apparently worn through most of or all the summer; I have seen it in its purity as late as August 24; but I have seen young males that were beginning to acquire a few violet feathers in the gorget as early as July 20. Progress toward maturity is rather slow and is prolonged through the winter; I have seen young males with imperfect gorgets in February and as late as May 15. As the ruby-throated hummingbird is said to have a complete molt in spring, this may also be the case with the black-chinned, which is so closely related; if this is so, the fully adult plumage must be acquired at this molt. Ridgway (1911) says that the young male is "similar to the adult female, but feathers of upper parts margined terminally with pale grayish buffy, under parts more or less strongly tinged or suffused with pale buffy brownish, and throat always (?) streaked or spotted with dusky"; and that the young female is "similar to the young male, but throat usually immaculate or with the dusky spots or streaks smaller and less distinct."

Adult females are considerably larger than adult males, the wing averaging nearly 10 percent longer. This seems to be more or less true of all the species of *Archilochus* and *Selasphorus*.

Food.—The black-chinned, like other hummingbirds, feeds on insects and sweets, mostly obtained from various flowers. It does not seem to be very particular in its choice of flowers in which to forage, though I was greatly impressed in California with the popularity of the "tree tobacco" (*Nicotiana glauca*) as a feeding ground for this and other hummingbirds. This is a small tree or large shrub that grows from 12 to 20 feet high and bears numerous clusters of slender, yellow, tubular flowers. The hummers frequent these little trees in large numbers; Major Bendire (1895) says that R. H. Lawrence saw some 70 or 80 hummingbirds in a patch of wild tobacco in less than two hours. The same observer noted that this and Anna's and Costa's hummingbirds "were attracted by a bright red flower (*Delphinium cardinalis*) growing on a clean, slender, juicy stalk, from 2 to 6 feet high."

In the Santa Rita Mountains, Arizona, Mrs. Bailey (1923) took one "feeding from the orange-colored tubes of honeysuckle (*Anisocanthus thurberi*)"; its throat was full of nectar; others were seen about the red terminal blossoms of ocotillo. In the Colorado Valley, Dr. Grinnell (1914) found it feeding about the flowering bushes of *Lycium andersoni*, about the profusely blossoming palo verdes, and about the lavender flowers of ironwoods. George Finlay Simmons (1925) says that, in Texas, it "hovers and feeds about the laterally-clustered pink flowers of the Texas buckeye, the pink flowers of the Texas redbud, and the rich purple and overpoweringly-perfumed flowers of the Texas mountain laurel on slopes and flattened valleys in the hills, largely on minute insects but also on nectar, pollen, and dew." Robert S. Woods (1927), at a time of unprecedented drought in southern Arizona, noted that "aside from a very few scattered mescals, there was an entire lack of flowers, in lieu of which the hummingbirds were systematically probing the clusters of leaves at the ends of the live oak twigs." The black-chinned hummingbird, like its eastern relative, has been known to feed on syrup made of sugar or honey and placed in artificial containers.

This hummer also poses as a flycatcher, as noted by several observers. Milton P. Skinner writes to me: "I saw one perched on a bush, 12 feet above ground on the edge of an open space. It was watching for insects. When one came within reach the humming-bird darted after it, sometimes going as much as 40 feet. It perched quietly and was quite hump-backed, but its head turned constantly from side to side. Generally its prey was not high up, but once the bird shot up into the air at least 50 feet. After watching it for half an hour I left it still looking for insects as at first. Later another one was seen buzzing about the bases of some willows. This one caught its insects as it came to them, but it did not perch and watch for them."

Behavior.—The flight of the black-chinned hummingbird when traveling from one place to another is swift and direct. While hovering about its feeding stations it has perfect control of its movements; it can remain stationary in the air, rise or fall at will, and even move backward with a downward thrust of its broad tail. The little wings vibrate with astonishing rapidity, as described more fully under the ruby-throated hummingbird; no ordinary camera shutter is quick enough to stop the motion. Mr. Skinner says in his notes: "Early in the morning these birds are rather quiet, but by 9 o'clock they become livelier and are really quite nervous. About 9 a. m. one was seen to fly to a small creek and have a good splatter bath in a shallow pool; then it flew up on a 12-foot willow to sun itself and preen. When they perch on willows and small limbs they alight both crosswise and lengthwise of the perch. As a rule they seem bold and unafraid of people."

W. L. Dawson (1923) relates the following:

Once, a hummer, finding itself entrapped in a porch by a wall of "chicken-wire" netting with meshes only an inch and a half in diameter, first passed slowly before the face of the screen, searching whether there might be any exception in his favor. Finding none, he made up his mind and darted through. So swiftly was the passage effected that the eye could detect no change in the position of the bird's wings. Only the ear noted an infinitesimal pause in their rhythm. Yet to accomplish this, the bird had been obliged to suspend the propeller motion of its winds, to furl them, to halve their normal spread, and to resume again upon the other side of the screen.

Voice.—Mr. Simmons (1925) tersely describes the vocal efforts of this bird as follows: "Song, by male, a sweet and low, though very high-pitched warble, like the sound produced as a result of whistling through the teeth; on still air, can be heard for 25 or 30 feet. Chase note, similar to song, but louder and chippering, like a light and rapid smacking of the lips together, uttered as one bird rapidly chases another hither and thither."

Mr. Woods (1927b) describes a courtship note as "a long-drawn, pulsating, plaintive, liquid note, probably the most pleasing utterance of any four Hummingbirds."

Field marks.—The male black-chinned hummingbird is easily recognized by the black chin and sides of the head and by the conspicuous white collar separating the square-cut gorget from the rather dark under parts; the violet gorget, just below the black chin, is not easily seen unless the light happens to strike it just right; there is a white spot behind the eye, which can be seen at short range. The female is not so easily recognized; it is much like the female Anna's hummingbird and is often seen with it, but it is decidedly smaller; the female Costa's and female black-chinned are so much alike that they can be distinguished only by a close view of the tail. In Costa's, according to Ridgway (1911), the middle pair of rectrices are bronze-green, the next pair similar, but with terminal portion black; third pair tipped with dull white or pale brownish gray, extensively black subterminally and dull brownish gray basally, the gray and black separated (at least on outer web) by more or less of metallic bronze-green; fourth and outermost pairs with whitish tip broader, basal grayish more extended, and with little if any metallic greenish between the gray and black. In the black-chinned, the three outer rectrices on each side are broadly tipped with white, the subterminal portion extensively black, the basal half (more or less) metallic bronze-green (sometimes grayish basally). Thus, the comparative amount of green on the two outer pairs of tail feathers determines the species.

DISTRIBUTION

Range.—Western North America.

Breeding range.—The breeding range of the black-chinned hummingbird extends **north** to southwestern British Columbia (probably Brentwood, Chilliwack, probably Vaseaux Lake, and probably Edgewood); and probably northwestern Montana (Columbia Falls). East to probably western Montana (Columbia Falls, Flathead Lake, Missoula, and Stevensville); south-central Idaho (Blue Lake); western Colorado (Glenwood Springs, Grand Junction, and Paradox); New Mexico (Espanola, Roswell, and Carlsbad); and western Texas (San

Angelo, Kerrville, San Antonio, and Losoya Crossing). **South** to southern Texas (Losoya Crossing, Somerset, and Chisos Mountains); southern Chihuahua (Rio Sestin); southern Sonora (San Javier and Guaymas); northeastern Baja California (Cerro Prieto); and southern California (Palo Verde and San Diego). **West** to California (San Diego, Escondido, Santa Barbara, Gilroy, Marysville, and Dales); Oregon (Prospect and Eugene); Washington (Prescott and Yakima); and southwestern British Columbia (probably Brentwood).

Winter range.—During the winter season this species is apparently concentrated in the region from extreme southern California (Palm Springs and San Diego); south to Guerrero (Venta de Zopilote and Chilpancingo); and the Federal District of Mexico (Mexico City).

One was seen at Marysville, Calif., on December 23, 1910, while another was noted at Fresno on January 8 and again on January 18, 1937.

Spring migration.—Early dates of spring arrival are: Texas— Kerrville, March 11; San Antonio, March 27. New Mexico—Rodeo, April 9. Colorado—Ouray, May 10; Fort Lewis, May 12; Grand Junction, May 20. Montana—Columbia Falls, May 17; Cornwallis, May 29. Arizona—Phoenix, February 10; Paradise, April 1; Tombstone, April 21. California—Santa Barbara, March 27; Los Angeles, April 3. Oregon—Prospect, April 10; Corvallis, April 15; Portland, April 22. Washington—Yakima, May 13; Pullman, May 28. British Columbia—Victoria, May 4; Agassiz, May 13.

Fall migration.—Very little information is available concerning the fall movement, but late dates of departure are: Washington— Yakima, September 18. Oregon—Coos Bay, August 10. California— Los Angeles, September 3. Texas—Somerset, November 4.

Casual records.—A specimen was collected at Kearney, Nebr., in August 1903.

Egg dates.—California: 105 records, April 3 to September 3; 53 records, May 8 to June 6, indicating the height of the season.

Texas: 20 records, April 4 to June 12; 10 records, April 12 to 21.

CALYPTE COSTAE (Bourcier)

COSTA'S HUMMINGBIRD

PLATES 59–61

HABITS

This little feathered gem is, to my mind, the prettiest of all the North American hummingbirds. The gorgeous, glowing colors of its brilliant helmet adorn, in the male, the top of the head, the throat, and the elongated feathers on the sides of the gorget; the burnished metallic violet of these feathers changes in certain lights to royal purple, magenta, blue, or even green, a beautiful display of colors at various angles.

Its breeding range in the United States is in the Lower Austral Zone in southern California, southwestern Utah, Arizona, and southern New Mexico; and it extends southward throughout the whole of Baja California. It winters mainly in southern Baja California and northwestern Mexico but has been seen casually in southern California in winter.

It is less dependent on the presence of water than some other hummers and seems to prefer the more arid regions in the deserts, the chaparral, the sagebrush plains, and the desert washes. Ralph Hoffmann (1927) describes these washes very well, as follows: "In the foothills of southern California the dark green belt of orange orchards is here and there interrupted by wide tongues of stones and gravel poured out by the canyon streams. These stony plains are overgrown by cactus, sumach, and occasional junipers, but in May and June are gay with scarlet larkspur, tall white yuccas and other humbler bloom. If one stands for a moment in the midst of this bee paradise, the tiny figure of a Hummingbird shoots past or stops to probe the tall spikes of the white ball-sage. After feeding, the little creature perches perhaps on a dead twig, and, protruding its long needle-like tongue, wipes off the last bit of honey against its slender bill."

Spring.—Costa's hummingbird is a summer resident in the United States, arriving during the latter half of March or early in April and making a rather short stay. Robert S. Woods, who has had considerable experience with this and other hummingbirds, says (1924a) that "the males arrive about the last of March, or later, according to the season, and leave early in June, females or young being seen for some time thereafter." He says elsewhere (1927b) that these hummingbirds, when they first arrive, "are almost constantly in a state of activity, so that it is often difficult to obtain more than a fleeting glimpse of them as they chase one another about. At these times there appears to be a great preponderance of males, which is partly accounted for, no doubt, by the quieter and more retiring habits of the females." Again (1922), he writes:

"In no case have I seen a male hummingbird in the vicinity of the nest or in any way showing interest in the matter. In fact, all the males had apparently started on their southward migration by the middle of June, 1922, or soon after the eggs had been laid in the last nest and while the young in the second nest were no more than half grown. None was seen earlier than May, probably on account of the lateness of the season, so their stay was very short this year. By July 1 the females and young were also noticeably scarcer. If the owner of the third nest had remained to hatch out and rear her young she would probably have been detained beyond the usual time for migrating."

Courtship.—The courtship performance of Costa's hummingbird follows the same general pattern of that of other hummingbirds, consisting of spectacular swoops, dives, and loops in the vicinity of its observing mate. James B. Dixon (1912) says that for a short time prior to the nesting season "they are quite noisy, chasing each other up, down and around through the surrounding bushes and trees." He continues:

Their note consists of a few sharp squeaks, given out more often when in very rapid flight than otherwise. During the breeding season the male has a very peculiar way of disporting himself before the female. When he locates his mate sitting on a tree, or more often on a low bush, he will ascend to an elevation of about one hundred feet and to one side of the female and will then turn and swoop down at a fearful speed, passing perhaps within a few inches of the watching female and ascending in the air to complete a half circle. This he keeps up until the female becomes impatient and endeavors to escape; then perhaps all that one will see is a streak, and a sharp squeak or two is heard as they flash up the hillside. The noise that the male makes in doing his fancy dive is easily heard at some distance and quite often heard when the bird himself is not visible on account of the extreme speed at which he travels on his downward plunge.

Mr. Woods (1927b), in comparing the performance of this hummer with that of the Anna's hummingbird, says: "The Costa's Hummingbird, instead of making a more or less abrupt turn, sweeps through a great arc to describe an immense letter **U**, then passes overhead to shoot downward again, either from the same direction or at a new angle. A continuous shrill whistle or miniature shriek accompanies most of the downward course and part of the upward—in other words, that part of the circuit in which the velocity is highest. This Hummingbird often ends his series of loops by darting away at high speed in an erratic, zigzagging flight."

W. L. Dawson (1923) says that the sound made by the male hummer in this flight is, he believes, "the very shrillest in the bird world, and one which is fairly terrifying in its intensity. This sound is generically like that produced by the Anna Hummer, but it is much more prolonged and more dramatic, more, in fact, like the shriek of a glancing bullet, or a bit of shrapnel."

Nesting.—Dr. T. S. Palmer (1918) has published an interesting paper on the early history of Costa's hummingbird, in which he makes the rather surprising statement, with the supporting facts, that "the first specimen, the first eggs, and the earliest nest of the season were all found in the southern part of Lower California at localities only a few miles apart. Twenty years elapsed after the species was first discovered before it was actually collected in California and nearly fifty years intervened before the eggs were found in the state."

Costa's hummingbird builds its nest in a great variety of situations and in many different kinds of trees, shrubs, and weedy plants. Among the trees recorded are various oaks, alders, bays, walnuts, willows, gums, sumacs, cypress, sycamore, hollyberry, hackberry, orange, lemon, olive, avocado, and Paraguay guava (*Feijoa sellowiana*). It has also been found nesting in sage and various other bushes, in dead yuccas, in *Opuntia echinocarpa*, *O. ramosissima*, and other branching cacti, and in various weeds, as well as in a hammock hook and a wire loop under a porch.

James B. Dixon writes to me: "Its range is in the more arid regions and the nesting locations are often a long way from known water. They often nest close by water also, and in favored locations are prone to colonize. I have found as many as six pairs nesting within a 100-foot radius in a dead cocklebur thicket near the edge of open water. One of their favorite nesting locations is the dead yucca stalks, where the nest is placed in the hard, dead framework of the last year's dead stalk, and usually some 4 or 5 feet from the ground. I have noted nest locations in dead trees, on top of thistle leaves, on clinging vines on cliff faces, and in citrus trees in open orchards, but not near houses. It does not seek nesting sites near habitations and seems to like the wild isolated areas the best."

Major Bendire (1895) says that "in the desert regions of southeastern California various cacti, the different species of sage (*Artemisia*) and greasewood bushes (*Larrea*), while in the canyons ash, sycamore, scrub oak, palo verde, cottonwoods, and willows, furnish their favorite nesting sites."

In the Thayer collection in Cambridge, there are 24 nests of this hummingbird, all of which I have examined. One of these was located in a sage over a stream, another in a weed over a road, and another over a stream in a white-alder bush, as well as many others in more usual locations. One nest was built on the top of an old nest of the previous season, the buffy color of the new nest contrasting with the dull, faded gray of the old one. The nests in this series show great variation in size and shape and in the material used in their construction. Most of them are rather shallow. The nests are not handsome or even neat in appearance, being rather loosely made, as a rule, of a great variety of materials, plant down of different colors giving a mottled appearance, shredded material from the sage, bits of gray lichens, scales of buds or flowers, thistledown, vegetable fibers, thin strips of bark, willow or yucca down, the whole tightly bound together with cobwebs or fine plant fibers. Many nests are more or less profusely lined with small, soft feathers of different colors, and some are decorated with these on the outside. Some nests are almost as simple as those of the black-chinned hummer, but even these show some mixture of some of the above materials. The outside diameter of the nests varies from 1¼ to nearly 2 inches, the average being about 1½; the height varies from about 1¼ to about 1½ inches.

Mr. Dixon says in his notes sent to me: "The nest of the Costa is very distinctive as to structure and material used, and I find this is true with all of the hummingbirds, it being easier to tell the nests apart than the female birds. The Costa uses dead weed leaves and cobwebs in building the outside of the nest and soft plant down and other soft materials for the lining. The general structure is of a grayish tone and very distinctive in this respect." This grayish tone of the nest helps to conceal it when it is built on a dead branch, a dead yucca stalk, a gray-toned cactus, or, especially, in a sagebush where the shreds of sage leaves with which it is decorated blend perfectly with its surroundings.

Griffing Bancroft (1930) says that in Baja California "they nest in the immediate proximity of surface water, sometimes snuggled into grapevine leaves, sometimes near the tips of fig branches, but most often on the leaf stems of the date palm. The birds obviously seek and usually obtain the protection of living foilage. The sites selected average, in height above the ground, at least twice that of northern breeders; roughly eight feet against three."

Mr. Woods (1927b) says: "At Azusa, California, the nests have been found at heights ranging from two to nine feet, but most commonly in the neighborhood of four feet. When a bush or small tree is selected, as is frequently the case, the nest is almost invariably located at a height of approximately one-half of the total height of the tree, but near the outside rather than the center, and in a position from which a reasonably clear outlook may be obtained. On this account trees of dense, leafy growth, such as an orange tree in thrifty condition, are not favored. * * * If in a large tree, the nest is usually on a small twig near the end of a projecting lower limb."

Major Bendire (1895) says: "They are usually placed in low situations, from 1 to 6 feet from the ground, rarely higher, although Mr. W. E. D. Scott records one taken on May 5, 1882, near Riverside, in southern Arizona, from the extremity of a cottonwood branch 35 feet from the ground."

Mr. Woods (1922) writes:

On June 2, 1922, I found another Costa Hummingbird building a nest near the end of a long horizontal limb of a good-sized avocado tree, at a height of about five feet from the ground. Her method was first to alight in the nest, then place the material under her and compact it by treading with the feet and turning about. Material for the outside of the nest was placed while hovering or while perched on a branch. On one occasion after leaving the nest the bird flew up to a twig a few feet above, whereupon I was surprised to see another hummer alight in the nest and rearrange some of the material, afterwards sitting there for some time until the presumably rightful owner presently darted at the intruder and drove her away. The nest was composed largely of small achenes bearing soft pappus. Other items noticed were fibers, minute leaves, feathers and a short piece of string, the whole bound securely to the branch with cobwebs.

Eggs.—Costa's hummingbird lays almost invariably two eggs. Sidney B. Peyton has a set of three eggs, taken in Ventura County, Calif.; a third egg was laid to complete a set of two, now in the Thayer collection, after one egg had fallen from the nest. I have no record of a complete set of one. The eggs are like other hummingbirds' eggs, dead white, without gloss, and elliptical-oval with an occasional tendency toward elliptical-ovate. The measurements of 51 eggs average 12.4 by 8.2 millimeters; the eggs showing the four extremes measure **14.0** by 7.8, 12.7 by **9.4, 11.4** by 7.8, and 11.6 by **7.6** millimeters.

Young.—There seems to be considerable difference of opinion as to the period of incubation, which is performed by the female alone. Mr. Woods (1927b) writes:

An interval of about two days separates the laying of the eggs. Incubation, in every case that I have observed, has begun with the laying of the first egg, and the young are usually hatched out a day or more apart. If we are to accept the widely differing periods reported—from nine to eighteen days—the time of incubation must be regarded as extremely variable. On account of absences I have not succeeded in collecting as full information on this subject as could be desired, but data of varying accuracy obtained during five successive years indicate that the normal incubation period for Costa's Hummingbird in the San Gabriel Valley is about sixteen days, lengthening in certain instances to as much as eighteen days, but never falling below fifteen days. * * *

The growing period of the young is even more markedly prolonged than is the incubation. Some eight broods for which the time was determined with fair accuracy remained in the nest from twenty to twenty-three days after hatching, with all but two approximating the higher figure. * * *

Even more pronounced than in most other altricial birds is the contrast between the newly hatched Hummingbird and its parents. The minute grub-like creature is black above and brownish below, with the body entirely bare except for a row of yellowish filaments along each side of the median line of the back. The bill is yellow and triangular, its length being but slightly greater than its width at the base. The eye sockets project beyond the base of the bill. Until about the sixth day, when the pin-feathers begin to appear, the most notable change, aside from the increase in size, is the gradual lengthening and darkening of the bill. The first part of the young Hummingbirds' lives is spent stretched out on the bottom of the nest, but after a time they become longer than the interior of the nest, so that they are gradually forced to raise their heads against its sides until at one stage of their growth their bills are pointing directly upward. After this their development is more rapid, and when they begin habitually to hold up their heads and assume an alert appearance, they are nearly ready to fly. The last few days before leaving the nest, the young birds frequently exercise their wings, sometimes perching on the edge of the nest for freer action. Finally a time is reached when, contrary to their former indifference, they are likely to leave on very slight provocation. A person may be quietly standing and watching them when as with one impulse both spring from the nest and fly in different directions. It sometimes so happens that the younger of the two is thus induced to venture forth before its wings are capable of sustained flight or of enabling it to obtain a foothold in a tree. On two such occasions I found that the bird might readily be picked up and when restored to its nest gladly settled itself to await more adequate strength.

The young Hummingbirds are fed by regurgitation, of necessity, at intervals of about half an hour. The feeding requires perhaps half a minute in all and is accomplished by a violent pumping process, with the bill thrust deep into the open mouth of the young bird. One would not judge that the slow growth of the Hummingbird was due to inability to supply sufficient food, since the mother, though bearing the entire care of her offspring, does not seem overworked, but has plenty of time to rest, preen her plumage and engage in skirmishes with other Hummers. Her care of the young continues for some time after they have left the nest. Then their call for food may be heard at intervals, a shrill cheep resembling the cries of other young birds rather than the voice of the adult Hummingbird. After the young have attained their full growth in other respects, they may still be recognized by the comparative shortness and straight, subulate form of the bill.

Major Bendire (1895) quotes R. H. Lawrence, regarding the feeding of the young, as follows:

She fed the young by touching the point of her bill to the tips and sides of the bills of her youngsters, as if to urge or invite them to stir and open their mouths, not inserting her bill over one-fifth or one-fourth of its length. Once she thrust it down half its length into the throat of one nestling, who then clung to it to the very last moment of its withdrawal, apparently reluctant to let the very smallest particle of the regurgitated food miss its way or remain on the parent's bill. The performance was rather ludicrous, as both old and young, especially the youngsters, went through many wriggling and squirming motions. * * * Once, upon her return, settling down to brood the youngsters, she kept up for some moments a kind of paddling motion, as if she were giving them a little massage treatment. Her respiration was very rapid after this exertion. Life with these atoms of sensitiveness must be at a white heat always. The young were lying side by side, but headed in opposite directions. Both had voided excrement in one case, but the parent did not remove either deposit while I was there. Except for this and a piece of eggshell, the nest appeared clean.

Plumages.—The young Costa's hummingbird is hatched blind and nearly naked; at first there is only a narrow line of pale, yellovish down along each side of the back; this spreads within a few days to cover the back, wings, and top of the head, through which the juvenal plumage later appears; and at the end of twelve days, they are fairly well feathered (Wheelock, 1904).

In full juvenal plumage, the young male is much like the adult female, but the feathers of the upper parts are more or less margined with grayish buff; the tail is double rounded, instead of wholly rounded; the throat is spotted with dusky, most heavily on the sides; and there are usually some, often many, violet-purple feathers on the throat; in a considerable series of young males that I have examined, I have not seen any that did not have at least a few of these violet feathers on the throat; one had a little bunch of them in the elongated lateral extension of the gorget only. Later in the season these metallic feathers appear in the crown, but there is not very much progress toward the fully adult plumage until the complete prenuptial molt takes place late in winter or early in spring, when young birds become indistinguishable from adults.

The young female is similar to the adult female, except for the buffy margins on the feathers of the upper parts. Young females can be distinguished from young males by having immaculate, instead of spotted, throats. I have seen young females, probably very young birds, that were strongly washed with pinkish buff on the flanks, and more faintly tinged with buff on the throat; the feathers of the head and back in these birds were broadly tipped with grayish buff; probably the buff soon fades and the tips wear away.

Both adults and young apparently have a complete molt late in fall and early in winter; I have detected it in February.

Food.—The usual hummingbird food nourishes this species; probably it consists mainly of small Diptera, Hymenoptera, and other minute insects, sweetened with nectar or honey from various flowers; the amount of the latter is difficult to determine, as it is not easily detected in the stomach, where it is so soon digested. As to the flowers from which the food is obtained, Bendire (1895) says that "in Inyo County, California, Costa's Hummer seems to be very commonly found about the flowers of the squaw cabbage, a species of *Stanleya*, also about wild rose, plum, or cherry bushes (*Prunus*) growing in the canyons, as well as about other shrubs and plants found in these desert regions."

Mr. Woods (1927b) says: "During the nesting season it has seemed to me that the female Costa's Hummingbird visits the flowers much less than does the male. At such times the female may often be seen buzzing about inside non-flowering trees and shrubs. While the search may be primarily for cobwebs or other nesting material, numerous minute insects and spiders might incidentally be obtained. * * * Costa's Hummingbird, for some reason, seems less partial to the Tree Tobacco than do the larger species."

Dr. Grinnell (1914) says that, in the Colorado Valley, "they were feeding about the spiny bushes of *Lycium andersoni* which were at this time profusely laden with flowers. A tall-stalked milkweed (*Asclepias subulata*) growing high among the precipitous peaks was also an attraction; so, too, a sage (*Hyptis emoryi*)."

In probing into the flowers in search of food this and other hummingbirds serve a useful purpose for the plants in pollination, as do the bees, by helping to transfer the pollen from stamens to pistil; the bills and heads of hummingbirds are often smeared with pollen.

Behavior.—Quoting Mr. Woods (1924a) again:

As the male Hummingbird takes no part or interest in the nest-building or the rearing of the young, and a brief visit to any convenient flowers serves to satisfy his appetite, he has considerable spare time at his disposal. Most of this he spends on certain favorite observation posts, one of which is shown in the photograph, whence he sallies forth occasionally in pursuit of a trespassing Hummer or bird of some other sort. Even the Cliff Swallow is not immune from his attacks and seems quite unable to avoid his onslaughts. The Hummingbird frequently mounts vertically into the air until almost out of sight, then descends like a bullet directly at the object of his attention. If the other bird flies, the Hummingbird follows; if not, he passes within a few inches, sweeping through an arc which carries him upward again to repeat the process until tired. The downward swoop is accompanied by a long shrill whistle which is characteristic of the species and is often the first indication of its arrival in the spring.

Elsewhere (1927b) he writes: "There is a remarkable difference in the shyness of the various individuals when on the nest. Some will leave as soon as a person comes into sight, perhaps forty feet away; others will permit one to reach within a few inches, or possibly, with care, even to touch them, without leaving the nest. The shyer ones, however, are inclined to hold to the nest more closely as the incubation advances, and especially around the time of hatching. Most of them, though easily frightened from the nest, will soon return if one stands quietly a few feet away, a decided reversal of the tendencies of the majority of nesting birds."

A case of tameness, or curiosity, is reported by F. C. Lincoln (1917): "Mr. Figgins had an interesting experience with one of these birds while sketching under his umbrella. The bird, a female, was fearlessly curious and repeatedly came under the umbrella and perched on the ribs, or the canvas, once flying so close to his face that he (Mr. F.) forgetting the protection afforded by his glasses, shut his eyes for fear the bird would strike at them."

Hummingbirds seem to have few enemies. Perhaps they are too small to attract birds of prey, or too active to be easily caught. But accidents will happen occasionally. Mr. Woods (1934) reports finding a bird of this species hopelessly entangled in a coarse, heavy spider's web; it was released with some difficulty and was at first unable to fly away, but it finally recovered.

Voice.—Mr. Woods (1927b) remarks that "the presence of a Costa's Hummingbird is frequently announced by the two-or-three-syllabled whistling call with which he greets passing members of the tribe from his perch or salutes his mate as he hovers before her. The young males begin practicing on these whistling notes, which are doubtless among the highest-pitched sounds audible to the human ear, before they have yet attained their brilliant gorgets, with results that sometimes rather resemble the song of the Anna's Hummingbird, though much fainter and less sustained."

Field marks.—With the exception of the calliope, Costa's hummingbird is the smallest of the common North American species. The adult male should be easily recognized by its full helmet, crown, gorget, and elongated sides of the gorget, of brilliant amethyst, purple-violet, though these colors appear black in certain lights. The young male is like the female but usually shows some violet feathers about the head. The adult female is almost impossible to distinguish from the female black-chinned in the field; for the characters that distinguish these two females the reader is referred to the field marks of the black-chinned hummingbird.

DISTRIBUTION

Range.—Southwestern United States and Mexico; only slightly migratory.

Breeding range.—Costa's hummingbird breeds **north** to southern California (Fresno and Owens Valley); southern Nevada (Cave Spring and Bitter Springs); and probably southwestern Utah (Beaverdam Mountains). **East** to probably southwestern Utah (Beaverdam Mountains); east-central Arizona (Salt River Reservation); and rarely southwestern New Mexico (Cliff). **South** to rarely southwestern New Mexico (Cliff); southeastern Arizona (Tombstone and Huachuca Mountains), and southern Baja California (La Paz and Santa Margarita Island). **West** to Baja California (Margarita Island, Magdalena Bay, Cerros Island, San Benito Island, Todos Santos Island, and Los Coronados Islands); and California (El Cajon, Escondido, Santa Barbara Island, Glendale, and Fresno).

Winter range.—In the winter season this species is found **north** to southern California (Azusa, Riverside, Palm Springs, and rarely Amboy); and southwestern Arizona (Camp 117, Phoenix, and Tinaches). **East** to southern Arizona (Tinaches and Tucson); Sonora (Tiburon Island and Tesia); and southeastern Baja California (La Paz). **South** to southern Baja California (La Paz and Santa Margarita Island). **West** to Baja California (Santa Margarita Island, Magdalena Bay, Cerros Island, and Rosarito); and southwestern California (San Diego and Azusa).

Migration.—The only data available are applicable to the spring migration. The following are early dates of arrival: Arizona—Tombstone, March 5. California—Los Angeles, March 21.

Casual records.—A specimen was taken at Oakland, Calif., on May 8, 1890, well north of the normal range.

Egg dates.—California: 100 records, March 11 to June 29; 50 records, May 12 to June 10, indicating the height of the season.

Baja California: 14 records, February 24 to June 5; 7 records, May 26 to 30.

CALYPTE ANNA (Lesson)

ANNA'S HUMMINGBIRD

PLATE 62

HABITS

CONTRIBUTED BY ROBERT S. WOODS

In two respects Anna's hummingbird occupies a unique place among our hummingbirds. It is the only species the greater part of whose general range is included within a single State of the Union, and the only one that winters mainly within the United States. It is also the species most familiar to residents of California, since its territory includes all the more populous districts of the State, where it is a constant and by no means shy visitor to city parks and gardens. Anna's hummingbird seems to be in some degree nomadic in its habits, and it probably shifts slightly southward during the colder months, but it performs no true migration, thereby differing from all our other species except that portion or race of Allen's hummingbird resident on the Channel Islands of southern California.

Courtship.—In April, in the blooming orange groves of southern California, at least five of the six species of hummingbirds regularly occurring in that region may sometimes be seen together, in considerable numbers and feverish activity. No small part of that activity consists in the practicing of highly specialized forms of courtship flight. While the males of all California hummingbirds can easily be recognized when clearly seen, identification is more difficult when the bird persists in manifesting itself as a vague streak rather than a definite object. Under these circumstances a knowledge of the specific distinctions in "nuptial flight," and particularly of the peculiar and entirely characteristic utterances accompanying such flight, is often of great assistance in determining species.

The most elaborate of these nuptial flights is that of Anna's hummingbird, in which the bird mounts upward until almost lost to sight, then shoots vertically downward at tremendous speed, finally altering his course to describe an arc of a vertical circle, which carries him as closely as possible past the object of his attention as she sits quietly in some bush or tree. At the lowest point of the circuit he gives utterance to a loud, explosive chirp, which so nearly resembles the "bark" of a California ground squirrel (*Citellus beecheyi*) that one who is familiar with that sound may easily be deceived. From this point he continues along the arc until he arrives at a point directly above his mate, where he hovers for a few seconds with body horizontal and bill directed downward, rendering his squeaky "song." Then, without change of attitude, he begins to rise rapidly and vertically, repeating the entire maneuver until he tires or the other bird departs, with himself in hot pursuit.

Presumably this practice originated strictly as a courtship display, but it now has a much broader application, frequently being directed at other species or at birds of wholly different kinds. Young males begin performing the flight as early as September of their first year, and it is continued through at least the greater part of the year. Anna's hummingbird is not addicted to the shuttling flight so much used by those species in which the wings of the males are modified in such a way as to produce a metallic rattling sound. The actual mating, which is not often witnessed, has been described by Leroy W. Arnold (1930): "When first observed, the birds were playfully chasing each other about and suddenly swooped down to within about eighteen inches of the ground where the leading bird, which proved to be the female, stopped and faced about. The male approached and the mating was consummated in the air, the birds breast to breast and with the male somewhat under the female. The male then settled down to the ground for a few moments, fanning out his tail and pointing his beak upward, while the female flew to a nearby perch. After a short rest, the male rose and flew after the female who returned to her former position and mating again took place as before."

Nesting.—With reference to the nesting habits of hummingbirds, few distinctions can be drawn between the various species even under quite different ecological conditions, except in the matters of season, locale, type of site, and nest materials. The nesting of Rieffer's hummingbird (*Amazilia tzacatl tzacatl*) in Central America has been carefully observed by Alexander F. Skutch (1931), and the agreement in procedure between this species of the humid Tropics and those of the semiarid Temperate Zone is most striking. The principal specific variations in this connection among North American hummingbirds concern the selection of materials for the nest, but there is also considerable individual latitude that tends to bridge the gaps.

Although Anna's hummingbird is generally distributed west of the Sierra Nevada and the Colorado Desert, it is rather definitely classified as a breeder in the Upper Sonoran Zone and is less partial to arid localities than is Costa's hummingbird. The nesting season begins before the arrival of any of the migrants, sets of eggs having been found by various persons as early as December. The nesting prob-

ably continues normally through late winter and spring and sporadi-
cally throughout summer, with some evidence of its extending even
into the fall. With the breeding season so greatly prolonged, it is of
course difficult to determine exactly how many broods are raised each
year, but it may be inferred that two is the usual number, as in the
cases of the black-chinned and Allen's hummingbirds. During one
season throughout which I was able to follow the activities of one
pair separately, by the aid of artificial feeding, the movements of the
female indicated—though the nest was not found—that the first incubation period began late in January, the second just two months
later. Incidentally, it is hard to explain satisfactorily why these
species, which quite certainly raise two broods yearly, do not gain in
numbers relatively to the Costa's, rufous, and calliope hummingbirds,
which usually do not remain on their breeding grounds long enough
to permit more than one.

Nests of Anna's hummingbirds have been described or photographed on almost every kind of site to which it would be possible
to attach the structure, except on the ground or any extensive horizontal surface. It is usually, without doubt, birds of this species that
now and then achieve newspaper publicity by nesting in some unexpected spot in the business district of Los Angeles. The distance
from the ground at which the nests are placed is also extremely variable. Of 52 nests found by W. Lee Chambers (1903) between January 1 and February 18, 1903, the heights ranged from 17 inches to
30 feet. James B. Dixon, of Escondido, Calif., writes (MS.) concerning nests and their sites: "The female seems to select the nesting site and
so far as I have ever observed did all of the nest building. The nest
location may be in a wide variety of locations, as I have seen nests in
the following locations: On insulated electric-light wires under the
crossarm of a service pole 30 feet from the ground; on a climbing
vine on a granite cliff face within a few feet of an occupied nest of
the golden eagle; in citrus trees, both oranges and lemons; in brush
far removed from any wooded areas; and in dense oak groves in
narrow wooded canyons. The last-mentioned place is by far the
most favored as to nest location and I should say was typical of this
area. The nests are large and well made and are usually devoid of
camouflage when first built but are decorated with lichens during the
incubation period and by the time the young are hatched are very
beautiful structures and in my estimation are the most beautiful of
all the hummingbird nests. The nests are made of plant down put
together with cobwebs and are often lined with fine bird feathers
and plant down. Often eggs are laid in the nest when it is a mere
platform and the remaining part of the nest is built up around the
eggs and the finishing touches of lichens and plant seed put on last.

Two eggs are usually laid, although I have seen nests with one and three eggs, which I feel sure were sets. The female is usually very tame after brooding a short time and is very curious if disturbed and will fly right into your face to look you over and try to scare you away from the nest. I have never seen the male bird feed the young or help build the nests. Anna's hummingbird does not colonize like some of the others and seems to prefer an area to itself."

W. Leon Dawson (1923) states that "nests of the Anna Hummer vary in construction perhaps more widely than those of any other local species. Some are massive and as heavily adorned with lichens as those of the eastern Ruby-throat." According to all available data, however, they can probably be regarded as essentially similar to those of Costa's hummingbird except for their slightly larger size; fibers and stemmy materials usually being used in the walls, and ornamentation on the exterior, while feathers are frequent in the lining. An interesting account of the nesting activities has been given by A. W. Anthony (1897):

Sometime about April 1, an Anna's Hummingbird began her nest in a cypress in front of my residence in San Diego. I could not be sure as to the exact date of beginning, but on the 6th, when I first noticed the bird at work, there was nothing but a little platform the size of a silver twenty-five cent piece, fastened to the upper side of a twig which nearly overhung the front walk, and was but just high enough to escape being struck by anyone passing below.

From an upper window I could look down upon the growth of the downy cup, and watch the diminutive builder from a distance of but a few feet, as she brought almost imperceptible quantities of cotton and tucked them into the sides and rim of the prospective nest. In working the material into the structure she always used her body as a form around which to build, tucking the cottony substance into the side and pushing it with her breast, frequently turning about to see if it were the right size all around.

On April 12, when the nest was apparently but half finished, and little better than a platform with a raised rim, I was surprised to see an egg, which the mother carefully guarded as she buzzed about, still bringing nesting material.

The following morning the second egg was added, and on one or two occasions the male made his appearance, and tried, seemingly, to coax the female to leave the nest, even making several attempts to push her from the eggs when other means failed. He soon became discouraged, however, and departed for parts unknown, leaving his demure little spouse to care for the eggs and complete the half finished nest.

For several days incubation progressed just about two minutes at a time. The Hummer, after arriving with material and building it into the slowly rising rim, would incubate for two minutes, seldom more than a few seconds more or less, before leaving for another consignment.

Her periods of absence were of almost exactly the same duration. It was not until incubation was more than half complete that the nest was finally finished, but unadorned by the usual bits of lichen. These were added from day to day until May 1, when the first egg hatched, either eighteen or nineteen days after incubation began. Owing to the unsettled actions of the bird on the 12th and 13th of April I could not satisfy myself as to when incubation really began.

The second egg never hatched, and after the nest was abandoned the broken shell was found buried in the bottom of the nest.

Eggs.—[AUTHOR'S NOTE: The usual two eggs of Anna's hummingbird are indistinguishable from the eggs of other hummingbirds of similar size. The measurements of 50 eggs average 13.31 by 8.65 millimeters; the eggs showing the four extremes measure **14.3** by **9.0**, **12.7** by **9.4**, and **11.3** by **7.7** millimeters.]

Young.—It will be noted from Mr. Anthony's account that the incubation period is considerably longer than that of most common passerine birds, despite the smaller size of the eggs. This is confirmed in the following description by J. H. Bowles (1910) of the nesting of an Anna's hummingbird at Santa Barbara:

The first egg was laid January 3, but during the following night a heavy frost left ice more than a quarter of an inch in thickness on the puddles. * * *

I think the icy weather must have been too severe for the first egg, for, whatever the cause, only one egg hatched. This took place on January 22, showing the period of incubation to be just seventeen days. It may be interesting to note here that I have found thirteen days to be the period of incubation for eggs of the Black-chinned Hummer (*Archilochus alexandri*). This great difference I think may be attributed in part to the consistency of the albumen, which in eggs of *C. anna* is thick and almost gummy, while in *A. alexandri* it is thin as in eggs of other small birds.

In spite of the very cold, rainy weather my young hummer grew very rapidly; but it was not until he was thirteen days old that his eyes opened. * * *

On February 13, when he was just three weeks old, the young bird left the nest.

I believe, however, that the difference in incubating time between Anna's hummingbird and other species cannot be so great as assumed by Mr. Bowles, as I have found the period for both black-chinned and Costa's to be about 16 days, while, on the other hand, Donald R. Dickey (1915) gives an even shorter time for Anna's hummingbird, as observed in the Ojai Valley of Ventura County:

Finally, on the fourteenth day of incubation—a long period for so small a bird—the young hatched into black, grubby caterpillars, with smoky fuzz in two lines down the back, and squat, yellowish mouths that gave no hint of the future awl-like bills. Now the mother's care was redoubled, and on the fifth day their eyes opened. Two days later respectable pin feathers transformed them from loathsome black worms into tiny porcupines.

Now we saw more and more often the grewsome-seeming spectacle of their feeding. The female's foraged burden of small insect life, culled from the flowers' corollas, and doubtless nectar-sweetened, is transferred to the young by regurgitation, and to avoid waste the mother's needle bill is driven to its hilt down the hungry youngster's throat. It suggests, as someone has said, a "major surgical operation," but the young so obviously enjoy and thrive upon it that we outsiders slowly lost our fear for them. At last the feathers broke their sheaths and the wee mites took on the semblance of real hummers. And then one night the worst happened—a prowling cat found the nest and exacted nature's price of death!

The disagreement in the figures of Bowles and Dickey as to the age at which the eyes are opened is probably due to the fact that the eyes are habitually kept closed for a good while after they are capable of being opened. Despite the great number of nests described or recorded, there seem to be few published figures on the length of time the young Anna's hummingbird remains in the nest. The single occupant of the nest watched by Mr. Anthony left after 18 days, undoubtedly a shorter than average time, since the period of three weeks recorded by Mr. Bowles corresponds very closely with my determinations for Costa's and the black-chinned, which range from 20 to 23 days for each species. This period in the case of the hummingbirds is more uniform than it is with most species of passerine birds and averages at least 50 percent longer.

Plumages.—The molting of the body plumage, as indicated by a slightly unkempt appearance, seems to take place in July and August. The luminous feathers of the crown and gorget are not replaced at that time, however, but begin to be shed in October, the ruff being completely lost and the throat and head becoming decidedly ragged, the former showing streaks of gray. The entire process to the completion of the new gorget requires perhaps a month. During this time the remainder of the plumage shows no sign of molting. The practice of the "nuptial flight," in so far as I have observed, seems to be discontinued during this period.

The outline of the gorget becomes visible on the throat of the young male soon after it has left the nest. The area gradually becomes sooty black, with glints of red, and slowly grows redder, the throat feathers lengthening into a ruff. Even in fall, however, when this first gorget is apparently complete, it still is lacking something in brilliancy and form; but it is almost immediately shed, to be replaced by the full perfection of the adult.

In the male Anna's and Costa's hummingbirds, alone among the species occurring in the United States, the crown is like the throat in color, but the two differ from each other not only in the color of the gorget but in its shape. As viewed from the front, that of Anna's is deeper and its lower border forms nearly a straight line, while the lower outline of the Costa's gorget is decidedly concave and its ruff is narrower and more prolonged. In both, the area of the crown is separated from that of the throat by a light streak running backward and downward from the eye, but in the Anna's only a very narrow gray line divides the luminous area behind the eye from that of the crown.

Among hummingbirds, and especially in the present species, individual variations seem more pronounced than among most birds. The color of the back ranges from slightly bluish metallic green to decidedly bronzy green in different individuals; the rose-red of the crown and gorget changes to purple as a secondary color in some instances, while in others gold and greenish lights are frequently seen. Ridgway (1892) refers to this as "perhaps the most beautiful of North American Humming Birds" and quotes Gould's Monograph of the Trochilidae as follows:

When studying the diversified forms and coloring of the Trochilidae, I have frequently been struck with the fact that those districts or countries having a metalliferous character are tenanted by species of Humming Birds which are more than ordinarily brilliant and glittering. This is especially the case with the species inhabiting Mexico and California: in illustration of this assertion, I may cite the three California species, *Selasphorus rufus*, *Calypte costae*, and the present bird, *C. annae*, all of which are unequaled for the rich metallic brilliancy of certain parts of their plumage, by any other members of the family. The two latter, *C. costae* and *C. annae*, have not only the throat, but the entire head as glitteringly resplendent as if they had been dipped in molten metal.

Food.—The food of the hummingbird is divided quite definitely into two classes: Carbohydrates, consisting of the nectar of flowers and more rarely of fruit juices and the sap of trees; and proteins, as furnished by the minute insects and spiders obtained either in conjunction with the other food or as the product of separate hunting activities. In late afternoon or on a cloudy day a hummingbird may frequently be seen perched upon some exposed twig or wire, from which it sallies forth at intervals to engage in strange aerial evolutions that might well mystify a stranger, since the flying insects it pursues are too small to be discerned at any distance. A specific instance of this sort is thus described by Frank F. Gander (1927): "On the morning of Thanksgiving Day, November 25, 1926, in Balboa Park, San Diego, California, I watched three male Anna Hummingbirds (*Calypte anna*) catching insects on the wing. A rain the night before had cleared the air and I could easily see the sun glistening on the gossamer wings of a host of tiny midges flying all about me in the air. The male hummers would hang on rapidly vibrating wings for a second and then dart suddenly a short distance and one of the glistening insects would disappear. This was repeated time and time again, and the birds seldom missed; on the rare occasions when they did miss they relentlessly pursued their chosen prey until it was captured."

Many observers have mentioned the hummingbirds' habit of searching the trunks and branches of trees for animal food and of extracting from spiders' webs small entangled insects or even the proprietors themselves. In their account of Anna's hummingbird in the Yosemite Valley, Grinnell and Storer (1924) have described some of its lesser-known feeding habits:

During November and December of 1914 we saw individuals almost daily at El Portal. At this time of the year there were no flowers of any sort to be found in the vicinity, but the Anna Hummingbirds seemed to find enough good forage on the foliage of the golden oaks, about which they were seen almost exclusively. The minute insects which live on the leaves of the golden oak probably afforded sufficient forage of one sort, but the hummingbirds had another source of food supply.

It was noted that one or more Anna Hummingbirds were to be found regularly about a certain golden oak, but the reason for their attraction to this particular tree was not discerned for several days. Then, on December 11, one of these birds was seen hovering before, and drinking from, some punctures made by a Red-breasted Sapsucker in the bark of the oak tree. The hummer visited puncture after puncture just as it would the individual blossoms in a spike of flowers, and evidently partook of both the sap and the smaller of the insects which had been attracted by the sap.

It is rather contrary to the traditional conception of hummingbirds that they should deliberately frequent the higher altitudes devoid of flowers, but there are undoubtedly times, following especially severe frosts, when members of this species in many parts of California must be compelled to obtain their living in other than the usual way. Mr. Dawson (1923) also mentions the use of sap: "Anna's Hummer is fond of the sap of our common willows (*Salix laevigata* and *S. lasiolepis*). It will also follow the Red-breasted Sapsucker (*Sphyrapicus ruber*) into the orchards and glean eagerly from its deserted borings. A catalogue of Anna's favorite flowers would be nearly equivalent to a botany of southern California. But if one had to choose *the* favorite it would probably be *Ribes speciosum*, our handsome red flowering gooseberry, for it is upon the abundance of this flower that Anna relies for her early nesting."

Naturalists in the eastern and northern parts of the country have found that hummingbirds are more attracted to red flowers than to those of any other color. The early-flowering gooseberry above mentioned and the paintbrush growing along a creek, which M. P. Skinner, in his notes, tells of seeing an Anna's hummingbird visit to the exclusion of other flowers, are both red; but in all these cases the flowers are probably seen against a green background, and since red is the complementary color of green, the greater visibility of that color may be more of a factor than any preference which the birds might feel. At any rate, there seems to be no such favoritism in the more arid parts of the Southwest, where the backgrounds are often grayish or tawny. Bits of red and blue cloth seemed to attract equal attention, though green was ignored.

Like most young animals, immature hummingbirds are filled with curiosity and are quick to investigate any brightly colored object; a bunch of carrots will attract them as readily as a flower. Through this process of trial they presently learn to discriminate among the flowers and often to choose those of inconspicuous appearance over the more brilliant kinds. As experience thus supplants curiosity, they cease to show much interest in unfamiliar brightly colored objects, unless it may be in times of food shortage, or when invading new territory where exploration must be carried on to locate its floral resources. Among familiar surroundings, memory for location undoubtedly guides the hummingbird to a large degree in its feeding.

As a general rule, hummingbirds prefer flowers of tubular form and are comparatively indifferent to composites and double flowers, such as roses. Within certain limits, size seems to be of little moment. One of the most valuable plants to Anna's hummingbird, especially, is a naturalized introduction from South America, the tree tobacco (*Nicotiana glauca*). This tall, sparse-foliaged, drought-resistant shrub bears a profusion of narrowly tubular blossoms practically throughout the year. Somewhat sensitive to cold, it is found only in the warmer parts of California. As an example of the hummingbirds' frequent disregard of bright coloring, they will probe the greenish-yellow newly opened flowers of this plant in preference to the purer yellow mature blossoms, which evidently contain less nectar. The greatest concentration of hummingbirds is seen about the tall, treelike flower stalks that culminate the life cycle of the common "century plant" (*Agave americana*), abundantly grown in California. The numerous greenish-yellow blossoms are dull-colored, but evidently they offer a rich store of nectar. Various species of eucalyptus, some of which bloom in winter, also attract large numbers of hummingbirds. The State of California must now be capable of supporting a much larger population of these birds than would have been possible under primitive conditions.

At times when their natural food is scarce, hummingbirds will gladly avail themselves of offerings of saturated sugar solution, which seems to be preferred to commercial honey. When flowers are plentiful and hummingbirds not too numerous they pay less attention to the artificial food than do the orioles and house finches, which are equally fond of sweets and not so well fitted to extract them from the flowers. It is during the latter half of the year that the hummingbirds will make most frequent use of sugar syrup in order to compensate for the comparative scarcity of flowers, though when the habit is once formed it may be continued even through spring. Visits are made at intervals during the day, perhaps only half-hourly when the temperature is high, but with increasing frequency toward evening, the height of this activity occurring between sunset and ten minutes after, when feeding ceases for the day. The use of clear glass vials affords an opportunity to observe the hummingbird's manner of drinking. When the liquid is out of reach of the bill, it is lapped up by rapid movements of the tongue, which can be extended an additional distance equal to the length of the bill. Should the vessel be filled nearly to the top, the syrup is either sipped with the end of the bill submerged or lapped with the tip of the bill held just at the surface and the tongue protruded only slightly. An Anna's hummingbird ordinarily consumes about two teaspoonfuls of saturated solution daily, only a few drops being taken at a time.

Various means may be used for the artificial feeding of the hummingbirds, ranging from small vials tied to the branches of trees to large and elaborate self-feeding devices, with provisions for discouraging the visits of ants, bees, and larger birds. Syrup in ordinary small brown bottles is often discovered by the birds without any kind of lure, but in more complex arrangements it is usually necessary to first guide them by inserting a flower in the opening. A change in the design of the container will cause much confusion and uncertainty for a time. Of other liquids than sugar solution, maple syrup and strained honey are acceptable, though the latter sometimes seemed to cause inconvenience because of its viscosity. Milk was not taken, and preserved fruit juices, though heavy with sugar, were apparently not palatable.

Naturally the proportion of liquid food in the ordinary diet of the hummingbird cannot be determined by an examination of stomachs, but Junius Henderson (1927) lists the identified contents of a large number of stomachs, as reported by Beal and McAtee in Farmers' Bulletin 506 (1912), as follows: Anna hummingbird (*Calypte anna*), 111 stomachs—vegetable matter, only a trace of fruit pulp; Diptera (gnats and small flies, largely neutral), 45.23 percent; Hymenoptera, mostly useful, 35.03 percent; Hemiptera, 17.30 percent; spiders, 2 percent.

F. C. Clark (1902) found that one stomach examined contained 32 treehoppers, 1 spider, 1 fly, and other insect remains. Fruit juices doubtless form only an inconsiderable part of the hummingbird's diet, but occasionally in fall an Anna's hummingbird may be seen sipping the juice of a persimmon that has been pecked by other birds and has softened on the tree, or the juice of a partially eaten tuna or pricklypear (*Opuntia*).

That the females in the nesting season require some additional mineral constituents in their diet was made clear to me upon seeing a female Anna's hummingbird upon several occasions visit a spot where particles of mortar were scattered. Hovering close to the ground, she appeared to be picking up the small grains and at other times would repeatedly plunge her bill into the loose sandy soil near by. Mr. Arnold (1930) tells of seeing Anna's hummingbirds alight on patches of ground where sand and plaster were strewn and seem to be picking up something, which he did not identify.

The changing seasons of the flowers have made expedient for the hummingbirds a somewhat nomadic existence, aside from true migrations. Perhaps this instinct for change has become so strong in the nonmigratory Anna's hummingbirds that they are unable to remain in one locality permanently. The sugar syrup containers maintained for their use have been visited by a constantly changing succession of individuals, some remaining only a few days, a few for a period of months, but all have eventually felt some urge more potent than the desire for a sure and easy living.

Behavior.—The flight of the hummingbird resembles that of no other bird, but rather that of certain insects, such as dragonflies or hawk moths, though stronger and swifter. Some of the earlier ornithologists expressed doubt of any bird's ability actually to fly backward, suggesting that the hummingbird's withdrawal from the depths of a tubular flower was accomplished by a forward flirt of the tail. A little careful observation would soon remove any skepticism as to its ability to easily fly backward, sidewise or in any other direction. While the tail is rhythmically vibrated forward and backward as the bird probes the flowers, it can be seen that its movements are not at all related to the backward flight, and that it is, in fact, seldom widely opened.

A hummingbird's wings are in almost uninterrupted motion while it is in the air; occasionally it will glide for an instant while in rapid flight. The amplitude of the wing beat is variable, but it often describes an arc of nearly 180° when the bird poises in the air. Sometimes the wings seem not to rise above the level of the back, but when the bird hovers over a cluster of upturned blossoms they may travel through the upper portion only of the complete arc. The confidence and sureness with which a hummingbird threads its way through a maze of twigs without injury while apparently devoting all its attention to the flowers cause one to admire, but its instant coordination of perception and movement can perhaps best be appreciated by noting the ease and certainty with which it thrusts its bill into a small tubular flower blown by a gusty wind.

That the flight of the hummingbird is by no means effortless, however, may be realized on a hot day, when one of them, returning to its shaded perch after an extended sortie, will sit for a minute or two with wide-open bill, panting with a violence that shakes its entire body. Though an immense amount of unnecessary flying is done, apparently in sport, the obtaining of food is evidently listed under the heading of work, and a hummingbird will seldom overlook an opportunity to perch, even to the extent of hanging almost upside down while reaching into a flower. The only sound produced by the normal flight of either sex of Anna's hummingbird is a low hum, which rises in volume and pitch when the speed is accelerated and has a slight suggestion of the rustling of silk. In wet weather, however, one may often hear from a flying hummingbird a sort of clapping noise of short duration, as if it were striking its wings together to rid them of moisture.

The sense of hearing, like that of sight, is keen, and a slight crunching of fallen leaves will evoke an attitude of alert apprehension, just as it does in many other wild creatures. The reaction to a sharp noise, though, is likely to be merely a nervous start, instead of the immediate flight, which is precipitated by any abrupt visible movement. This latter response is so invariable that it may well be regarded as a reflex rather than a volitional action. There seems to be no convincing evidence that the sense of smell plays any part in the discovery of food. A perfumed green-wrapped vial of sugar syrup attracted no attention, though a nearby unperfumed red-wrapped vial was quickly investigated. Some of the most heavily scented flowers, such as the jasmine and the large white blossom of the cactus *Trichocereus spachianus*, are comparatively neglected. Sense of location is very well developed, and when a bottle of syrup that has been regularly visited by a hummingbird is moved with its support to a different part of the grounds, the bird upon returning will hover in the exact spot from which the bottle was removed, often making several trips before finally becoming convinced.

Most writers have credited hummingbirds with extreme quarrelsomeness among themselves and a tyrannical disposition toward other birds. Careful observation has convinced me that their pugnacity has been greatly exaggerated, especially with reference to birds of other kinds. I believe that a hummingbird pursues other birds for exactly the same reason that a small dog will run after any passing vehicle, but immediately lose interest in it when it stops. Even the smallest passerine birds show no fear of the hummingbirds, nor are they molested if they fail to enter into the spirit of the game. Furthermore, I have often seen Anna's hummingbirds forced away from their sugar syrup by house finches or Audubon's warblers without the slightest show of resentment. Of course, a hummingbird that has preempted a certain territory resents any trespassing by other hummingbirds, who usually seem to recognize his rights and seldom dispute them; it is when an interloper resists eviction that the most earnest hostilities occur. Among the migrants in spring and among the immature birds late in summer, however, the constant chases and skirmishes appear to be carried on in a spirit of sport much more than of spite.

Probably because of their constant association among the flowers, hummingbirds show little fear of bees. I have sometimes seen an Anna's hummingbird, in order to reach a supply of sugar syrup, thrust its bill through a struggling mass of the insects. In contrast to this, a few small ants walking around the mouth of the bottle will often keep the bird away entirely. Whether this fear is an instinct founded on the occasional destruction of nestlings by ants is, of course, merely a matter of conjecture. Although the humming-birds ordinarily treat the bees with indifference, I have watched one attack bees flying around an agave stalk, darting at one after another with open bill as if trying to bite them.

When a male hummingbird preempts a certain territory, he chooses one or more elevated exposed perches from which he can survey his domain and quickly detect trespassers. Sometimes he will use the same perch almost constantly through a whole season, seeking a more sheltered place only in very hot or windy weather; other individuals will alternate between two or more favorite perches, or select new ones at intervals without apparent reason. Acknowledging no family responsibilities, the males spend a large proportion of their daylight hours on these perches; but even the females who are caring for the young unaided seem to have an abundance of leisure in which to rest, preen their plumage, and engage in skirmishes.

Hummingbirds are fond of bathing, especially during the cooler part of the year. Often they seem afraid to enter water of any appreciable depth, but they enjoy bathing in a thin film of water flowing over a flat rock. Most of their bathing is done on dew-covered foliage in the early morning and, when available, in the fine spray of a lawn sprinkler. They revel in misty or drizzly rain and are particularly active under such conditions. Carroll Dewilton Scott, of Pacific Beach, Calif., writes (MS.) : "Anna's hummingbirds have a strong attraction for moving water. They will hover over irrigation ditches, evidently fascinated by the running water. I have never seen one drink anywhere or take a bath in still water. But the spray of a hose or a fountain is irresistible for a shower bath, even in January. Whenever I spray the garden a hummer is sure to appear." Unusual actions of a bathing hummingbird are described by F. N. Bassett (1924):

On August 17, 1924, while watering my lawn in Alameda, California, I placed the sprinkler in position and had just turned on the water when an adult male Anna Hummingbird (*Calypte anna*) flew into and poised in the dense spray. After glancing about for a moment he gradually assumed a vertical position and spreading his tail, then slowly settled to the ground, meanwhile drawing the tail back until it nearly reached the horizontal plane, when he actually "sat" on the grass, the body erect and the tail spread out fanwise behind him. The wings continued to vibrate while in this position, but the strokes were much less frequent than when flying, being just sufficient to maintain a vertical balance. In a few seconds he began increasing the wing strokes and slowly ascended about a foot above the ground where he poised a moment and then repeated the entire performance several times, after which he flew to a wire overhead.

Sun-bathing is less frequent and appears to be an individual rather than a general custom. Shortly after noon on a hot July day I saw an immature male Anna's hummingbird alight on a bare patch of ground and, heading directly away from the sun, stretch out flat on the soil with wings fully extended and the feathers of the back erected. Again, about two months later, at about the same time of day, the identical action was repeated on the lawn by the same individual. In both instances he remained on the ground less than a minute.

As to the intelligence of hummingbirds, I find no evidence to support W. H. Hudson's contention that they resemble insects more than birds in their mental processes. Their tameness cannot reasonably be attributed to mere stupidity, but rather to justified confidence in their own agility and swiftness, and perhaps also in human good will, since their power of discrimination is shown by their noticeable wariness toward cats. In their disposition and temperament hummingbirds are hardly comparable to any other birds but remind one most strongly of chipmunks.

Voice.—Of the seven species of hummingbirds found in the State of California, Anna's is the only one that may be said to possess a song. The "song" can hardly be called melodious, being a thin, squeaky warble suggestive of filing a saw. Nevertheless, it is delivered with fervor and remarkable persistence, with little regard for season. This song, which in addition to its use in courtship seems to serve the purpose of a general greeting or challenge, or sometimes merely a form of self-amusement, is peculiar to the males, who begin practicing it almost before their gorgets have started to develop. During the rendition, which often lasts for a rather long time, the bird leans forward on his perch, extends his neck, and holds his bill tightly closed, as far as can be detected at a distance of several feet. The clear, high-pitched, 2- or 3-syllabled whistling call of the male Costa's hummingbird, though less persistently used, appears to be entirely analogous to the Anna's song.

The ordinary notes common to both sexes are similar to those of other species. They consist of the feeding note, a mechanical "tick" or a more liquid chirp uttered at measured intervals as the bird goes from flower to flower; a similar note repeated more rapidly and animatedly while perching and often accompanied by a wagging of the head from side to side, expressing excitement or warning to trespassers; and the shrill twittering, which indicates a chase or skirmish. The begging call of the newly fledged young is much like that of other young birds.

Field marks.—Anna's hummingbird is the largest species found within its ordinary range, but there is integradation in measurements with all but the calliope hummingbird, whose small size is usually sufficient to distinguish it from Anna's at any time. Both sexes of Anna's can be separated from the rufous, Allen's, and broad-tailed hummingbirds by the entire absence of rufous or brownish coloring in the plumage. The male differs from the black-chinned and Costa's in the color of its throat and crown and in the fact that the gorget is bordered below by gray instead of white. The adult female usually has a central patch or scattered spots of luminous red on the throat; otherwise it can generally be distinguished from Costa's by its larger size and darker underparts, and from the black-chinned by its stouter form. In size and general appearance, including the color of the throat, Anna's is probably most like the broad-tailed, but the normal ranges of the two species are entirely separate.

Enemies.—The hummingbird is one of the most notable exceptions to the rule that smaller animals must be more prolific than larger ones in order to compensate for an inherently higher mortality rate. Nevertheless, the eggs and young of hummingbirds seem to be subject to more than ordinary vicissitudes. The small size and fragility of the nest, together with its usually exposed situation, make it liable to destruction by storms or accidents, while the long period between the laying of the eggs and the fledging of the young increases the possibility of loss. The eggs are said to be often taken by the California jay (*Aphelocoma californica*), and quite possibly they may be eaten by the banded racer (*Bascanion laterale*) and the alligator lizard (*Gerrhonotus scincicauda*), as these reptiles are frequently seen climbing through the foliage of shrubs and trees. In some cases, also, one of the eggs will fail to hatch, even though not disturbed. In their earlier stages, the young are probably threatened by the same enemies previously mentioned, while the spotted skunk (*Spilogale phenax*) is always a definite peril if the nest is within its reach. Another source of danger to the young birds is mentioned by Mr. Anthony (1923):

The ornithologist visiting San Diego is usually impressed with the surprising scarcity of nesting birds in Balboa Park, though the surroundings seem to be ideal. It was not until I had been at the San Diego Museum of Natural History a year, that the possible explanation was presented. A swarm of bees that had been installed as an exhibit in the museum was destroyed in a few days by an insignificant ant. This ant, I was told, had in all probability reached our shores with some of the trees or shrubs brought in from South America. It was known as the Argentine Ant. * * *

If bees were killed by ants, why not young birds? Several nests of the Anna Hummingbird (*Calypte anna*) were located and kept under observation and in every case the young were killed and eaten within two or three days of the time they hatched.

Dependence upon one parent alone would also theoretically increase the chances of failure. All in all, it would seem that the number of young fledged could not represent a very large proportion of the eggs laid. Once the young bird is able to fly, however, the situation is wholly changed, and the fledgling may look forward to the expectancy of a long life. If this were not true, the members of this family could not have maintained their present abundance with their small annual increase. The adult hummingbird seems to have no enemies of importance; certainly no predatory bird could capture it except by accident. On rare occasions a cat will catch one, in all probability an immature individual that has not yet learned caution, as seems to be generally the case among other birds. There are a few accounts of disaster through the agency of an unintentional enemy, such as the following from the manuscript notes of Carroll Dewilton Scott: "On one occasion I rescued a female Anna from impending death. A giant black spider had hung an enormous orb web among pendant eucalyptus limbs about 8 feet from the ground. One spring morning after a foggy night I noticed a female Anna fluttering on the edge of the web. The spider was nowhere to be seen and had not herself entangled the bird who had been snared, possibly, while gathering webs for binding her nest. But she was hopelessly caught by both wings in the tough, elastic, wet, sticky strands of the spider. After I pulled the webs from her wings she flew to an adjoining tree and sat quite still for several minutes."

That these incidents happen so seldom is a tribute to the hummingbird's alertness and quick perception, since the opportunities for such mishaps are very numerous, and the webs of these large orb-weaving spiders have been proved capable of holding considerably larger birds. Mr. Scott also mentions finding a dead Anna's hummingbird at the base of a window, presumably killed by striking the glass. Eric C. Kinsey states, however, that hummingbirds kept in glass-sided cages soon become accustomed to the glass and do not injure themselves by flying against it.

Of Anna's hummingbird, specifically, it would appear that the most destructive enemy is the exceptional period of cold weather that comes once in a cycle of years and, with native plants and animals alike, may overcome the powers of resistance built up to withstand ordinary winters. In this connection Mr. Dawson (1923) says:

Hummingbirds, one sees, even though they be so frail, possess an amazing vitality or recuperative power. But it is not too rare an experience to find one stranded, or numbed with the cold; and, to cite the extreme instance, the big freeze of January 2nd, 1913, undoubtedly cut down the resident hummer population of southern California (all Annas) one-half. It is quite worth while upon finding such a waif to try various methods of first-aid. The first expedient is, of course, heat—that of the closed hand may suffice. Or, it may be that the little engine only lacks "gas". Sweetened water, of a pretty strong solution, offered in a pipette, or medicine dropper (pressed upon attention, or flooding the bill until the tongue gets the flavor), will sometimes resuscitate a fallen hummer like a magic potion.

Nevertheless, the hardiness of Anna's hummingbird is greater than might be expected of so small a bird, belonging to a family predominantly tropical. In January 1937, during the most prolonged period of freezing weather in the history of southern California, when the temperature repeatedly fell to 24° F. at my home in the San Gabriel Valley, when ice remained on pools and birdbaths throughout the days and the sky was dark with soot from orchard heaters, half a dozen or more hummingbirds buzzed and twittered about a tall blooming eucalyptus tree and seemed not in the least distressed.

DISTRIBUTION

Range.—Chiefly California and Baja California; east casually in winter to Arizona and the mainland of Mexico; apparently not regularly migratory.

The breeding range extends **north** to northern California (Yreka and Mount Shasta. **East** in this State to Mount Shasta, Pyramid Peak, Big Creek, and the San Bernardino Mountains; and Baja California (San Pedro Martir Mountains). **South** to northern Baja California (San Pedro Martir Mountains, San Quintin, and San Telmo). The western boundary of the breeding range extends north from this point along the coast of Baja California and California to Red Bluff and Yreka.

During the winter season there is only a slight withdrawal from the northern parts of the summer range, as the species has been recorded at this time north in California to Ferndale and Red Bluff. The most southerly record at this season is Cerros Island, Baja California, about 200 miles south of known breeding areas. During the winter the species also is sometimes common in the southern part of Arizona (Roosevelt Lake and probably Salt River Reservation).

Casual records.—This species has been reported from the following other localities in Arizona: Camp Grant (September), Santa Catalina Mountains (October), and the Huachuca Mountains (October). A specimen was taken on February 21, 1934, at Punta Penascosa, Sonora.

Egg dates.—California: 86 records, December 21 to August 17; 43 records, February 22 to May 18, indicating the height of the season.

SELASPHORUS PLATYCERCUS PLATYCERCUS (Swainson)

BROAD-TAILED HUMMINGBIRD

PLATES 63, 64

HABITS

The broad-tailed hummingbird is *the* hummingbird of the Rocky Mountain region, ranging from southern Idaho, Montana, and Wyoming to the Valley of Mexico, and it is essentially a mountain bird.

It has been recorded from extreme eastern California, Inyo Mountains, and eastward as far as western Nebraska and western Texas. M. P. Skinner says, in his notes from Yellowstone National Park: "I have seen this little bird at all altitudes from the lowest up to 8,000 feet above sea level. I have seen it in the open, in lodge-pole pine forest, and in alder thickets." Mr. Ridgway (1892) says: "In the Rocky Mountain district proper, as in Colorado, for example, it breeds at an elevation of from 4,000 to 11,000 feet, and I found it having about the same vertical range in the East Humboldt Mountains." Dr. Jean M. Linsdale (1938) found that "the broad-tailed hummingbird made up almost the entire hummingbird population of the Toyabe Mountains," in Nevada, where "observations indicated that the normal habitat for this species is close to mountain streams." We found it in the Huachuca Mountains, Ariz., mainly along the swift mountain streams, at altitudes of from about 5,000 to 7,000 feet. Mr. Swarth (1904) says: "It is possible that this species remains in the Huachucas through the winter as I saw a male bird near the base of the mountains on February 28, 1903; and though not at all common, I saw and heard them a number of times through the month of March. It was the middle of April before they began to appear in any numbers, and from then on they became more and more abundant. At this time they were seen at a low altitude and along the canyons; but after the summer rains began and the grass and flowers sprung up, I found them mostly in the highest parts of the range. * * * They breed in the highest parts of the mountains, often in the pines and at a considerable distance from the ground."

Dr. Mearns (1890) writes: "This beautiful hummingbird is an inhabitant of the highest land of Arizona, being rarely encountered until one is well within the spruce belt, when it suddenly becomes extremely plentiful. About springs and willow-edged water-courses swarms of these gay birds congregate. * * * It ranges to the very summit of San Francisco Mountain, being abundant in the highest timber." And Mrs. Bailey (1928) says:

The Broad-tailed Hummingbird, with the deep rose gorget and green crown, is one of the most abundant birds of the New Mexico mountain region. Its characteristic machine-like clicking, suggestive of the buzz of the cicada, made, Mr. Henshaw explains, by the "attenuation of the outer primaries," was heard by us at all levels from the foot of the Sangre de Cristo Mountains at 7,400 feet up to 12,700 feet at the highest terrace on the side of Wheeler Peak where there was water; for during the season it follows the successively blooming flowers up the mountain sides. * * *

The Broad-tails are seen not only in the uninhabited mountains but occasionally in towns. On the campus of the Santa Fe Indian School Mr. Jensen found two pairs nesting in 1921 and 1922; and in front of a hotel in Rincon in 1920 Mr. Ligon saw one playing in the spray of a lawn sprinkler.

Major Bendire (1895) writes: "On the first arrival of this species in the spring it is comparatively common in the lower foothills and valleys, and unquestionably breeds here. By the time the young are large enough to leave the nest the majority of the flowers have ceased blooming, and as the country begins to dry up more and more these Hummingbirds retire to higher altitudes in the mountain parks, where everything is now as green and bright looking as it was in the lower valleys two or three months earlier. Here they raise their second broods under nearly similar conditions as the first; the former are by this time well able to take care of themselves and can be seen frolicking about everywhere."

Courtship.—Dr. Linsdale (1938) watched two hummers of this species on June 5, 1932, "that were definitely distinguished as a male and female which were going through mating antics. At first both were in flight together. Then the male flew up into the air about 30 feet and made a U-shaped dive. Next, both birds flew up in the air for about 90 feet, one lower than the other by 4 or 5 feet, and they came down at the same time. One flew off to the side but returned immediately. Both flew up and repeated the dive. Then the male hovered for half a minute, over birches and cottonwoods along the stream, until the female disappeared. No noise was made by the male bird while hovering."

Alexander F. Skutch sends me the following note on the courtship of the Guatemalan race of this species: "It was during the brightest, warmest hours of the day that I saw the broad-tailed hummingbirds rising and falling above the brushy growth on the sunny mountainside where the salvias bloomed. One morning I watched a female as she perched within 2 feet of the ground in a little thicket where there was an abundance of flowers. Presently a male of her kind appeared; and she rose a few inches into the air and hovered with her bill pointed toward him, while he poised motionless on beating wings in front of and a little above her, displaying his brilliant red gorget before her eyes. Then of a sudden he rose almost vertically 30 or 40 feet into the air, whence he dropped straight downward and shot through the edge of the thicket directly in front of the female, who meanwhile had resumed her perch. Once past her, he inclined his course slightly upward and darted away over the mountainside."

Nesting.—Major Bendire (1895) makes the following general statement about the nests of the broad-tailed hummingbird:

Nests from different localities vary considerably in make-up as well as in size. Nests saddled on good-sized limbs, like those found in the mountains of Colorado, are occasionally almost as large again as others placed on small twigs. One now before me, from the Ralph collection, taken by Mr. William G. Smith, at Pinewood, Colorado, on June 23, 1892, measures 2 inches in outer diameter by 1⅜ inches in depth, while one taken by Mr. Ridgway, in Parley's Park, Utah, on July 23, 1869, measures only 1⅝ by 1 inch outside measurement. The difference in size of the inner cups of these two nests is even more noticeable, the former measuring 1 inch by three-fourths of an inch, the latter three-fourths by one-half of an inch. While the walls of both of these nests are mainly composed of willow or cottonwood down, their outer covering is entirely dissimilar. The outside of the larger one is profusely covered with small bits of lichens, like the nest of the Ruby-throat; the smaller one is decorated with shreds of bark, fine leaves, and dry plant fibers, resembling more the nests of Costa's Hummingbird in this respect. * * * The inner lining appears to be composed entirely of willow or cottonwood down, and none of the specimens before me contain even a single feather. The outer covering or thatching is firmly secured to the walls of the nest with spider webs or silk from cocoons. The majority of the nests of the Broad-tailed Hummingbird are placed on low, horizontal branches of willows, alders, cottonwoods, etc., at no great heights from the ground, or overhanging small mountain streams, while others are saddled on boughs or limbs of pine, fir, spruce, or aspens, from 4 to 15 feet from the ground, rarely higher. Occasionally a nest may be placed on a curled-up piece of bark or on a splinter of a broken limb.

Robert B. Rockwell tells me that "the broad-tailed hummingbird seems to be the only really common species about Colorado Springs. I have seen it as late as September 18, 1911. In 1923 one built a nest on a small branch of an elm tree overhanging a porch outside of our dining room. The nest was about 7 feet above the porch." He tells in his notes of another nest in a yellow pine tree, 8 feet above ground, and of another that was saddled on a dead limb of a small cottonwood, about 5 feet from the ground. He says (1908), in his paper on the birds of Mesa County, Colo., that it "frequents the timber along the streams from 6000 feet up and raises two broods in a season and possibly three. I found them breeding abundantly on Buzzard Creek at about 8000 and found nests containing fresh eggs, freshly hatched young and fledglings just ready to leave the nest on the same day and within a radius of half a mile. * * * One nest found was built on a root protruding from a bank directly over and within 2 feet of the swift running water of Buzzard Creek." Aiken and Warren (1914) say that "one confiding bird built its nest on the electric light fixture directly before the front door of a house, on a porch where people were continually going and coming, and raised two young."

R. C. Tate (1926) says that Oklahoma nests that he has examined were made of "rock-moss, lint from cottonwoods and willows, fine willows, fine shreds of thin inner bark from cottonwoods, and fine rootlets of blue-stem and gama grass."

Frank C. Willard's notes contain the records of six nests in the mountains of southern Arizona, at altitudes ranging from 4,900 to 6,000 feet. One nest was 8 feet up in a scrub oak, three were in sycamores 3 to 20 feet above ground, and two were in pines 20 and 30 feet from the ground.

The six nests of the broad-tailed hummingbird in the Thayer collection in Cambridge show about the same range of variation in size, shape, and make-up as those described by Bendire above. One nest, however, is decidedly smaller, measuring only 1¼ inches in diameter and 1 inch in height externally; the walls are very thin and the cup is very shallow; it is made of the usual materials, mixed with the winged seeds of milkweed or thistle. Another nest is worthy of mention, as illustrating camouflage to match its surroundings; it was built on a sycamore branch, composed of sycamore or willow cotton, and was decorated on the outside, almost completely covered, with pale gray and buff lichens, producing a soft, buffy effect to harmonize with the branch that held it.

Eggs.—The broad-tailed hummingbird lays almost invariably two eggs; I have no record of more or fewer. These are like those of other hummingbirds, pure white, without gloss, and about elliptical-oval in shape. The measurements of 62 eggs average 13 by 8.8 millimeters; the eggs showing the four extremes measure **14.5** by 9.9, 13.8 by **10.0, 11.9** by 8.4, and 12.2 by **7.9** millimeters.

Young.—The period of incubation is probably about 14 days, as with other related species. Incubation is performed wholly by the female, and she takes full care of the young; she is a brave and devoted mother. The young are fed at first on regurgitated, semi-digested food, but as they grow older they are given an increasing amount of minute insects; they are fed at more or less irregular intervals. Dr. Linsdale (1938) says of a nest that he watched: "At 10 o'clock I saw the female go to the nest and feed 5 times, the last for only a short period, and then brood. The first thrust was deep down the gullet of the young, and then the bill was withdrawn gradually. At 10:12 the female was off the nest. At 10:19 it returned and fed 4 times and brooded. Each feeding required between 5 and 10 seconds. It was not more than a minute from the time of arrival to time of settling on the nest. The bird faced at least 3 directions while brooding but always stood on the north rim to feed. When it left at 10:27, there were clouds and a cold wind. At 10:31 it returned directly to the nest and began to brood."

Plumages.—I have no data on the development of the juvenal plumage in the nestling broad-tailed hummingbird, but it probably does not differ materially from that of the rufous hummingbird, described under that species.

Ridgway (1911) describes the young male, in juvenal plumage, as "similar to the adult female but feathers of upper parts (especially rump and upper tail-coverts) indistinctly margined terminally with pale brownish buff or cinnamon, and lateral rectrices with much less of cinnamomeous on basal portion." The young female, he says, is "similar to the young male but rectrices as in adult female."

Young males begin to acquire some red in the throat before the end of July and assume the fully adult plumage late in the following winter, or early in the spring, at the complete annual molt.

Food.—Mrs. Bailey (1928) gives, as the food of the broad-tailed hummingbird in New Mexico, "insects found in flowers, as pentstemon, larkspur, agave, gilia, gooseberry, and on willow catkins." Elsewhere (1904), she says that "the throat of one shot was full of honey and long-tailed, wasp-like insects." Bendire (1895) mentions the flowers of *Scrophularia* and *Ocotilla* as favorite feeding places. Mr. Rockwell says in his notes: "August 3, 1902, at some willows on a ranch near Crested Butte, I saw four hummingbirds. They seemed to be interested with something in the willows, and I found many perforations in the bark made by sapsuckers; many ants and other insects were about these perforations; whether it was the sap or the insects that attracted the birds I could not tell."

Dr. Linsdale (1938) writes: "On June 18, 1930, at 7,000 feet on Kingston Creek, a female broad-tailed hummingbird was watched which apparently was feeding upon flying insects caught in the air. It was in a small clearing near the creek. After a poise the bird would dart 3 feet after an insect, then poise and go after another. This was repeated half a dozen times, the bird being about 10 feet above the ground."

Apparently this, like other hummingbirds, lives to a large extent on small spiders and minute insects of the orders Diptera, Hymenoptera, Hemiptera, Coleoptera, etc., which it finds in the flowers; nectar, honey, or sap may not be what at first attracted the birds, but they have proved to be very acceptable foods, just as the eastern rubythroat has learned to feed freely from glass containers filled with syrup. Sugar is a very nourishing and strengthening food.

Behavior.—Robert Ridgway (1877) writes thus attractively of the behavior of the broad-tailed hummingbird:

The flight of this Humming-bird is unusually rapid, and that of the male is accompanied by a curious screeching buzz, while it is followed through an undulating course. Long before the author of this curious sound was detected its source was a mystery to us. This shrill screeching note is heard only when the bird is passing rapidly through the air, for when hovering among the flowers its flight is accompanied by only the usual muffled hum common to all the species of the family. During the nesting-season the male is of an exceedingly quarrelsome disposition, and intrepid, probably beyond any other bird, the Flycatchers not excepted. All birds that approach the vicinity of his nest, whether they be his own species or of the size of hawks, are immediately assaulted with great force and pertinacity by this seemingly insignificant little creature, the vigor of whose attacks, accompanied as they are by the shrill piercing noise we have mentioned, invariably puts to flight any bird assaulted. We have thus seen the Western Kingbird (*Tyrannus verticalis*), the Black-headed Grosbeak (*Hedymeles melanocephalus*), and the Sharp-shinned Hawk (*Nisus fuscus*) beat a hasty retreat before the persevering assaults of this Humming-bird. When thus teasing an intruder the little champion ascends almost perpendicularly to a considerable height, and then descends with the quickness of a flash at the object he would annoy, which is probably more frightened by the accompanying noise than by the mere attack itself. As we chanced, while hunting on the mountains, to pass through the haunts of this Hummer, it frequently happened that one of the little creatures, prompted apparently by curiosity, would approach close to us and remain poised in one spot, its wings vibrating so rapidly as to appear as a mere haze around the body; now and then it would shift from one side to another, its little black eyes sparkling as it eyed us intently. So close would it finally approach that to strike it with a hat or a stick seemed to be quite an easy matter, but upon the slightest motion on our part the little thing would vanish so quickly that its direction could scarcely be traced.

Mr. Swarth (1904) testifies on the swiftness of the flight of this bird, as follows: "The shrill buzz of its wings, that is of the male bird, is frequently heard; and time and again as the sound approached, passed, and died away in the distance, I watched, but in vain, to catch sight of the author of it. Several times I have seen one leave its perch on a twig and dart off in pursuit of another of the same species, and even then was unable to follow him with my eye; and though presently the sound of wings announced his return, I was seldom able to see the bird before he dropped onto his perch. * * * The flight of the female is not accompanied by the buzzing noise made by the male bird, and from their habits they are more inconspicuous and less frequently seen than their mates."

Curiosity is shown in various ways, beside the case cited above. Mr. Rockwell tells, in his notes, of one that flew against the window of a laboratory where he was sitting; another "hovered before a mirror that was hanging to a tent pole outside" of his camp, but "it made no attempt to fight its image"; again it, or another, alighted "on a guy rope, then hovered before the tent, and finally flew over to the car, and in front of every window, apparently attracted by its image." Dr. Mearns (1890) writes: "Its boldness is without parallel; it knows no fear. A member of our party on San Francisco Mountain wore a scarlet cap, but he found these audacious birds so troublesome from their constant attacks upon it that he was glad to pocket it in order to be rid of the irate little furies."

All hummingbirds are fond of bathing, and this species is no exception. On May 15, 1922, while climbing to the summit in the Huachuca Mountains, and following the course of a little mountain stream that flowed swiftly over its stony bed, we stopped to watch a pair of broad-tailed hummingbirds that were bathing in the brook. They chose a spot where the water barely covered a flat stone, settled down in the shallow water, which barely covered their little bodies, and fluttered their wings as they faced upstream; after a few seconds in the cold water, they flew off to a nearby branch to shake themselves and preen their plumage. Dr. Merriam (1890) says that, on San Francisco Mountain—

They wake up very early in the morning and go to water at daylight no matter how cold the weather is. During the month of August, and particularly the first half of the month, when the mornings were often quite frosty, hundreds of them came to the spring to drink and bathe at break of day. They were like a swarm of bees, buzzing about one's head and darting to and fro in every direction. The air was full of them. They would drop down to the water, dip their feet and bellies, and rise and shoot away as if propelled by an unseen power. They would often dart at the face of an intruder as if bent on piercing the eye with their needle-like bill, and then poise for a moment almost within reach before turning, when they were again lost in the busy throng.

Voice.—The loud, screeching sound, referred to by several observers, is probably mechanical, made by the rushing of the air through the flight feathers. Mrs. Bailey (1928) says that "besides their squeaky little song they gave some small staccato notes." And Robert S. Woods (1927b) says: "A rather faint, muffled staccato note is uttered twice in quick succession at the lowest point of its vertically diving nuptial flight."

Field marks.—The broad-tailed hummingbird suggests the ruby-throated in general appearance, but the rufous edgings in the tail will mark the former, and the ranges of the two hardly come together. Mr. Woods (1927b) writes:

The appearance of the Broad-tailed Hummingbird is not especially distinctive in any way. The color of the gorget, aside from its somewhat inferior brilliancy, is very similar to that of Anna's Hummingbird, though showing at some angles a more purplish cast. A convenient recognition mark of the male is the rufous edging of certain of the tail feathers, in conjunction with the solid green color of the back and upper tail-coverts. It may be safely said that the Broad-tailed Hummingbird is much more readily identified by ear than by eye. The loud metallic noise produced by the flight of the male is an agreeable, almost musical sound, clearer in tone than that made by the Rufous, Allen's or Black-chinned Hummingbirds, while the notes of the female seem more liquid than those of other species.

The rose-pink gorget and the green crown distinguish the broad-tailed from the males of other western hummers. But the females are not so easily recognized; the female broadtail has less rufous in the tail than the rufous or calliope, only the three outer tail feathers being basally rufous; the calliope is considerably smaller; the female broadtail may be distinguished from the female black-chinned by the presence of some rufous in the flanks of the former.

Fall.—Mr. Henshaw (1886) found the broad-tailed hummingbirds "extremely numerous" late in summer in the mountains of New Mexico. He says:

Young birds were noticed August 1, and by the 10th they became common. By August 1 the males of this species began to get less numerous, and by the 10th there were none; in fact, I saw very few after that date. * * *

In this locality at least there is an evident reason for this. Just about this date the *Scrophularia*, which is the favorite food plant of the Hummers, begins to lose its blossoms, and in a comparatively short time the flowers give place to the seed pods. Though there are other flowers which are resorted to by the Hummers, particularly several species of *Pentstemon*, they by no means afford the luxurious living the former plant does. It seems evident therefore, that the moment its progeny is on the wing, and its home ties severed, warned of the approach of fall alike by the frosty nights and the decreasing supply of food, off go the males to their inviting winter haunts, to be followed not long after by the females and young. The latter—probably because they have less strength—linger last, and may be seen even after every adult bird has departed.

DISTRIBUTION

Range.—Western United States and Central America.

Breeding range.—The breeding range of the broad-tailed hummingbird extends **north** to central Nevada (White Mountains, Toquima Mountains, Monitor Mountains, and the Snake Mountains) ; northern Utah (Brighton, Salt Lake City, and Parleys Park) ; and northern Wyoming (Yellowstone National Park and Midwest). **East** to eastern Wyoming (Midwest, Douglas, Wheatland, and Laramie) ; eastern Colorado (Greeley, Denver, Colorado Springs, and Beulah) ; New Mexico (Culebra Mountains, Pecos, and the Sacramento Mountains) ; and southwestern Texas (Chisos Mountains). **South** to southwestern Texas (Chisos Mountains) ; northeastern Sonora (Oposura) ; southern Arizona (Huachuca Mountains and Santa Rita Mountains) ; southern Nevada (Charleston Mountains) ; and east-central California (Inyo Mountains). **West** to eastern California (Inyo Mountains and Cottonwood Creek) ; and western Nevada (Davis Creek, Chiatovich Creek, and White Mountains). It has been stated that this species breeds south to the "Valley of Mexico," but the evidence is unconvincing, particularly in view of the absence of breeding data through the mountainous regions of northern Mexico. A closely related subspecies is found in the highlands of Guatemala.

Winter range.—During the winter season the broad-tailed hummingbirds appear to be concentrated in west-central Mexico, as in the States of Zacatecas (Bolanos), Jalisco (Volcano de Colima), Mexico (Eslava), and Guerrero (Taxco).

Spring migration.—Early dates of spring arrival are: Arizona—Tucson, March 25; Tombstone, April 4. New Mexico—Apache, April 9; Chloride, April 13. Colorado—Beulah, April 23; Durango, April 26; Boulder, May 4. Wyoming—Laramie, May 20. Utah—Salt Lake City, May 3.

Fall migration.—Late dates of fall departure as: Wyoming—Fort Sanders, September 3; Laramie, September 16. Colorado—Durango,

September 12; Colorado Springs, September 21. New Mexico—
Apache, October 5.

Casual records.—A specimen was collected at Mount Vernon, Oreg.,
on June 30, 1915, and another was seen at Enterprise on July 27,
1921; one was taken at Big Butte, Idaho, on July 19, 1890, and one
was seen at Spencer on July 9, 1916; in Montana one was obtained at
Chico in 1902, while two have been taken in Glacier National Park,
one on May 23 and the other on June 17, 1895; a pair were reported
as seen daily between August 18 and 22, 1906, at Glen, Nebr., and one
was collected at Kearney on July 22, 1914.

Egg dates.—Arizona: 20 records, May 8 to July 30; 10 records,
June 11 to July 16, indicating the height of the season.

Colorado: 18 records, May 22 to July 17; 9 records, June 13 to 26.

Utah: 10 records, June 6 to July 23.

SELASPHORUS RUFUS (Gmelin)

RUFOUS HUMMINGBIRD

PLATES 65–67

HABITS

Although I have always considered Costa's hummingbird to be the
most beautiful of our North American hummingbirds, on account of
the charming colors reflected in its crown and gorget, it must yield
the palm for brilliancy to the rufous hummingbird and its near
relative, Allen's. The brilliant scarlet of the rufous hummer's gorget,
which often glows like burnished gold, puts it in the front rank
as a gleaming gem, a feathered ball of fire. It is not only fiery
in appearance, but it has a fiery temper and makes things lively for
any rivals near its feeding stations or its nest.

It ranges farther north than any of our other hummingbirds,
breeding from about latitude 61° N. in Alaska and southern Yukon
southward to Oregon and southwestern Montana. It is exceedingly abundant from the Rocky Mountains westward on its migrations to and from its winter home in southern Mexico. And it
may yet be found breeding at high elevations in some of the mountain ranges south of its present known breeding range. Henshaw
(1886) was perhaps mistaken in assuming that this hummer was
breeding in the region of the upper Pecos River in New Mexico,
though he states that it was abundant at altitudes of from 8,000 to
9,000 feet "during the entire summer"; but he found only one nest,
"and this after it was deserted." Mrs. Bailey (1928) says: "There
seems to be no known instance of the Rufous Hummingbird nesting
in Arizona, Colorado, or New Mexico, though the species has been
included in the breeding lists of these States for the last thirty

years." Mr. Ridgway (1911) includes these States, as well as some mountains in California, in the breeding range. The fact that early migrants appear in these regions in July may have led to the assumption that the species was breeding in the vicinity, but no occupied nest seems to have been reported.

Spring.—The rufous hummingbird apparently makes its northward migration in spring mainly to the westward of the Rocky Mountains; according to Mrs. Bailey (1928) "it is unknown in spring in both New Mexico and Colorado"; and Mr. Swarth (1904) did not see it in the Huachuca Mountains at any time in the spring and considers it of comparatively rare occurrence in Arizona at this season. In southern California, and probably throughout the State, it is a very common spring migrant, especially through the valleys and foothills of the Pacific slope. Referring to Los Angeles County, Robert S. Woods (1927b) says that, after the arrival of Anna's hummingbird, "the Rufous Hummingbird is the next of the migrants to appear, usually arriving early in March and leaving late in April. During part of this time it is the commonest species. My earliest record for the Rufous is February 17 (1926) and the latest for the spring migration May 1 (1924)."

Leslie L. Haskin writes to me from Oregon: "In the Willamette Valley the rufous hummingbird is the first of the family to arrive. It appears normally about the first of March, although an occasional earlier individual may often be seen. The males precede the females by a considerable time. My observation is that, while the males are very abundant throughout March, few females will be seen before the last week of that month. The main body of the rufous hummingbird migration arrives just as the crimson-flowered currant (*Ribes sanguineum*) is bursting into bloom, and of the flowers of this shrub the hummingbirds are especially fond. At that time every bush is alive with the darting hummers, and it is one of the most brilliant bird and flower spectacles of the West. The glittering, coppery sheen of the birds and the crimson flowers, borne in profuse drooping panicles, make a brilliant combination."

Courtship.—A very good account of this bird's courtship is given by G. D. Sprot (1927) as follows:

In the displays I have witnessed, which have been many, a careful survey of the ground beneath the performer invariably revealed the female sitting motionless on some twig of the low-growing underbrush, and as the aerial acrobat reached the limit of his upward flight she was seen to turn her head slightly and glance admiringly aloft. The male ascended usually with his back towards his mate, then turning, faced her, and with gorget fully expanded descended swiftly until within an inch or two of her, when spreading both wings and tail he checked himself and soared aloft again to repeat the performance, or else settled on some near-by bush. As he so checked his flight the whining note was produced, undoubtedly by the rush of air through the outspread feathers.

On two occasions, in May, 1925, and May, 1926, I witnessed in connection with the above performance what I believe to be the actual mating of the birds. After one or two towering flights by the male, the female rose from her perch and the male immediately closed with her. Then over a distance of some ten or twelve feet, and horizontally, they swung together backwards and forwards through the air, just as one often sees insects so doing. The regular swinging hum of the wings is hard to describe but is just what one might expect. So fast is this swinging flight, and so close was I, not over four or five feet away in one instance, that I was totally unable to see the birds except as a blurred streak of color. As the flight ceased I saw them separate, and in one instance the female was seen to fall to the ground, but later to regain her perch, while the male continued his towering flights.

Mr. Haskin says in his notes: "Besides the diving act it has another modified performance. In this act the male 'teeters' in the air above the female who is hidden in the grass below. It is like the dive, but the arc is much shorter and flatter—a shallow curve of only 6 or 8 inches. The male in this stunt shoots forward with the tail spread and much elevated, followed by a quick backward dart, tail lowered, and twittering and buzzing to his utmost. This is repeated again and again."

Nesting.—A. Dawes DuBois has sent me some very elaborate notes on the nesting habits and home life of the rufous hummingbird in the vicinity of Belton, Mont., subsequently published by him (1938). The nest that he studied "was five feet from the ground, in a small balsam fir, among the branches of a close-standing birch. It was situated at the bottom of the slope of a foothill. The foothills were wooded chiefly with larch, spruce, hemlock, fir and cedar, and on this particular slope was a growth of birch. It was constructed of soft, cottony, plant materials felted together and thickly covered exteriorly with lichens held in place by cob-webs." He gives the dimensions of the nest as diameter at the rim 1 inch, diameter at the bulge 1⅞, inside depth ⅞, and outside depth 1¼ inches.

D. E. Brown has sent me the following notes: "The rufous hummingbird returns to western Washington by the middle of March and commences nest building a month later. They colonize to a certain extent in favorable localities, and I have seen as many as 10 nests in a small patch of gorse. The nest is near the ground as a rule, but sometimes it is placed higher up in either conifers or deciduous trees. The drooping branches of conifers are favorite sites, the nest often being placed on the lowest branch; and a branch that has a sharp downward bend is so well liked that the bird often returns to the same place the next year, and even the third year. A nest built on such a branch is fastened to it from the bottom to the very top, which is built out to level things up. The next year's nest is placed on the old one but securely tied to the stem, and the third nest is built the same way. Double nests are not at all uncommon, and I have seen three where the third nest had been added."

J. H. Bowles (Dawson and Bowles, 1909) writes:

There is scarcely a conceivable situation, except directly on the ground, that these birds will not select for a nesting site. Such odd places have been chosen as a knot in a large rope that hung from the rafters of woodshed; and again, amongst the wires of an electric light globe that was suspended in the front porch of a city residence. It may be found fifty feet up in some huge fir in the depths of the forest, or on the stem of some blackberry bush growing in a city lot.

Very often they form colonies during the nesting season, as many as twenty nests being built in a small area. Some large fir grove is generally chosen for the colony, but a most interesting one was located on a tiny island in Puget Sound. This island has had most of its large timber cut away, and is heavily overgrown with huckleberry, blackberry, and small alders. In the center is the colony, the nests placed only a few yards apart on any vine or bush that will serve the purpose. Huckleberry bushes seem the favorites, but many nests are built in the alders and on the blackberry vines.

A. W. Anthony wrote to Major Bendire (1895): "I found the Rufous Hummingbird very abundant at Beaverton, Oregon. Here they nested in oaks, blackberry vines, and on dry roots projecting from upturned trees. One nest hung from the end of a tall fern, while others, drooping over it from above, hid the beautiful structure from all but accidental discovery. Their favorite sites, however, seemed to be the long, trailing vines overhanging embankments and upturned trees. A number were found in railroad cuts; frequently several nests were situated within a few feet of each other, a slight preference being shown for embankments having a southern exposure."

What few nests of the rufous hummingbird I have seen are rather large, well made, and handsome structures; the body of the nest, including the lining, is made up mainly of pale buff cottony substances, apparently from willow blossoms; but this is mixed with and profusely covered externally with bright-green moss, so that the nest appears to be made largely of this moss; it is often more or less decorated on the outside with leaf or bud scales, shreds of inner bark, lichens, and various other plant fibres, all of which are securely bound on with spider web, making a firm compact structure. Bendire (1895) says that "an average nest measures 1½ inches in outer diameter by 1¼ inches in depth; the inner cup is about seven-eighths of an inch in width by one-half inch deep." One that I measured was 1¾ inches in outside diameter. The favorite nesting trees seem to be firs, spruces, and other conifers, but nests have also been found in willows, cypresses, ashes, apple trees, various oaks, and probably other trees, as well as numerous bushes, such as wild currant, salmonberry, hazel, etc. The nests are usually artfully decorated to match their surroundings. Dawson and Bowles (1909) say that "the nesting season is greatly protracted, for fresh eggs may be found from April till July. This makes it seem probable that each pair raises at least two broods during the spring and summer."

Eggs.—Two eggs almost invariably make up the full set for the rufous hummer, but Major Bendire (1895) records a set of three, taken by Clyde L. Kellar, of Salem, Oreg. D. E. Brown tells me that often there is only one, and he has "seen one nest that contained four, evidently contributed by two females." The eggs are like other hummingbirds' eggs, dead pure white and varying from oval to elliptical-oval in shape. The measurements of 53 eggs average 13.1 by 8.8 millimeters; the eggs showing the four extremes measure 14.0 by 8.7, 13.1 by 10.0, 11.4 by 8.9, and 13.0 by 7.7 millimeters.

Young.—The period of incubation is said to be 12 days (Burns, 1921), but probably it is nearer 13 or 14 days, as with some other hummingbirds. This duty and the care of the young are performed entirely by the female; the male seldom, if ever, comes near the nest after the eggs are laid. William L. Finley (1905) writes:

As soon as the cottony cup was finished and the mother had cradled her twin white eggs, the father disappeared. He merely dropped out of existence, as Bradford Torrey says, leaving a widow with twins on her hands. This generally seems to be the case, for at the different nests where I have watched, I never but once saw a male hummer near the nest after the young were hatched. I was lying in the shade of the bushes a few feet from the nest one afternoon. For two whole days, I had been watching and photographing and no other hummer had been near. Suddenly a male darted up the canyon and lit on a dead twig opposite the nest. He hadn't settled before the mother hurtled at him. I jumped up to watch. They shot up and down the hillside like winged bullets, through trees and over stumps, the mother, with tail spread and all the while squeaking like mad. It looked like the chase of two meteors, that were likely to disappear in a shower of sparks, had they struck anything. If it was the father, he didn't get a squint at the bantlings. If it was a bachelor a-wooing, he got a hot reception.

On the other hand, Alfred M. Bailey (1927) saw, in southeastern Alaska, an adult male incubating on a set of eggs nearly ready to hatch, of which he says: "I was walking along the base of a precipitous cliff when I noticed the handsome little male hovering over my head, about twenty feet up, and was then surprised to see him climb into a nest, in the terminal branches of a drooping spruce. When incubating, the little male squatted far down in the nest, with tail and beak pointed almost vertically, and he proved so tame that I believe I could have touched him."

The following statements are based on, and the quotations are taken from, some elaborate notes sent to me by A. Dawes DuBois, who made an intensive study of a nest of the rufous hummingbird near Belton, Mont. In order to be able to study the parent and the single young bird at close range, he concealed himself in a "balsam cloak," which was "prepared by sewing balsam boughs all over the outside of an old brown bathrobe. An old felt hat was covered with boughs, which hung down all around to hide the observer's head and face while permitting observation through the interstices of the foliage." Under this disguise, he could stand, motionless as a tree, with his eyes within 10 or 12 inches of the nest and slightly above it.

Before the eggs hatched the female incubated almost constantly with absences of only a few minutes; one day, while the sun was shining on the nest most of the time, she was gone for more than an hour; during two hours of watching, on the day before the one egg hatched, the bird left the nest five times, for intervals varying from 5 to 19 minutes. One of the two eggs did not hatch, and, as the bird did not remove the remnants, Mr. DuBois did so.

After the one young bird hatched the female brooded it with frequent intervals of absence, much like those taken during incubation, up to the time that it was seven days old; from that time on, she "was absent much of the time during the mornings. In the afternoons she had to shelter the nestling from the sun."

When the nestling was two days old, it was fed only three times between 8:45 a. m. and 6 p. m., but the observer was absent from 12 m. to 1:33 p. m. and from 3:30 to 3:45 p. m. "When four days old, the average of seven known intervals was about 44 minutes. When six days old, the average of 11 known intervals was 32 minutes. The frequency of feeding increased in the latter portion of the day."

The number of regurgitations for each feeding varied from two to five; the total time occupied for five pumpings and subsequent examination and tidying of the nest was somewhat less than one minute. On July 20, when the nestling was two days old, "at 10:30, there was no pushing up and down; the parent seemed to pump the fluid by the slightest visible motion of her own throat. At 5:35 the same day she poked rather vigorously while regurgitating; and two days later, the poking was extremely vigorous. As observed on the 24th, the young bird's head moved up and down with the mother's bill. During one of the feedings, as I stood close to the nest with my head covered, I could see the liquid welling up in the young bird's mouth. At the age of 5½ days, the young one responded very vigorously and took the whole length of the parent's bill into his throat.

"The alvine discharges of the young hummingbird were forcibly ejected in a manner to render nest cleaning unnecessary. Very close observation from the balsam cloak, on July 22, indicated that the parent did not take excrement from the young or nest; nor did the young emit excrement after being fed. On the 23d, while the parent was absent, I observed the method employed by the nestling, then five days old. Following a slight shaking of the nest, it struggled to reach the top of the high nest wall. The great depth of the nest made this very difficult, but the young bird accomplished it, standing literally on its head, braced against the wall of the nest. The discharge was projected to a distance of several inches beyond the nest."

Mr. DuBois could not mention in his notes the length of time that his young bird remained in the nest, as it died prematurely, but Gladys Hammersley (1928) observed that the altricial period is about 20 days; she writes:

As the young hummers grew bigger they gradually tramped the nest out of shape, so that when they flew away on June 23rd it was no longer a dainty little cup, but an almost shapeless platform in comparison. There were no flying lessons; the little hummers buzzed fearlessly out into the world as though they had been accustomed to flying every day of their lives. They were not so expert with their feet, however, making several ineffectual attempts before securing a safe landing. I never found any young return to the nest having once left it, but they will return regularly to a chosen perch day after day, even when disturbed several times during the day, generally returning to precisely the same spot on the same twig each time.

Plumages.—Mr. DuBois says that the young rufous hummingbird, when first hatched, is about as large as a honey bee, nearly black and quite naked, except for two slight tracts of grayish natal down extending longitudinally along the back. It is blind at first, but when six days old a slit begins to show in the membrane covering the eye, and by the twelfth day the eyes are well opened. The natal down grows longer day by day, and pinfeathers begin to show on the sixth and seventh days. From that time on the juvenal plumage continues to grow.

When fully fledged in fresh juvenal plumage the young male is similar to the adult female, the back largely green, but the upper tail coverts are "cinnamon-rufous" with terminal spots of metallic bronze-green; the throat is dull white, spotted with dark bronzy; the chest is dull white, and the sides and flanks are heavily washed with "cinnamon-rufous." Usually in August, but sometimes as early as the middle of July, some metallic red feathers begin to appear in the throat, increasing more or less during fall and winter; but I have seen one young male, taken as late as March 17, that still shows no red in the throat, though the back and rump are practically all rufous. The juvenal tail, with terminal white spots on the three outer rectrices somewhat smaller than those of the female, is worn all through fall and winter, until the complete annual molt, late in winter and early in spring, produces the adult plumage; I have seen one young male, taken on April 15, that was just completing this molt. Young females are like young males but have more green on the back. Adults apparently molt at the same time as young birds, late in winter and early in spring.

Food.—The rufous hummingbird finds its nectar and probably its insect food in a great variety of flowers and in the blossoms of trees and shrubs, showing a decided preference for red flowers. Mr. Haskin, writing from Oregon, tells me that "early in spring the crimson-flowered currant is their favorite flower, next to that they resort in great numbers to another red flower, the columbine. Of white flowers, their favorite is the blossom of the madrona tree (*Arbutus menziesii*), whose flowers are perfect honey pots. A tree of the madrona in full bloom attracts them literally by the hundreds." Frank L. Farley writes to me that in Alberta in July and August "its favorite flower appears to be the bright-colored nasturtium."

M. P. Skinner says, in his notes from California, that it feeds on red columbine and "paint brush." Of its insect hunting, he says: "Another individual alighted on some willow twigs beside a river and watched for the insects that flew by at frequent intervals. Twice it rose 5 or 6 feet for one and then dropped back to its perch. Twice it caught an insect 40 feet above its perch, showing what keen eyes it had. Then it made a dizzying swift dart down among the willows. After that this bird came back at intervals all through the morning to do the same kind of insect hunting over the willows and over the river waters."

Mrs. Bailey (1902) writes:

On the birds' breeding ground the flowers they feed on, as far as I have observed, are mainly red, as the hummer's coloration might suggest. On San Francisco Mountain, Arizona, they were especially fond of the scarlet pentstemons. On Mount Shasta they fed from the painted-cups, tiger lilies, and columbines. Any spot of red would attract them as it does other hummers, and they investigated it fearlessly even when it adorned the person of a collector.

One of the birds actually crossed a wide meadow of green brakes straight to a single columbine standing most inconspicuously near the woods. But the painted-cups were their especial delight on Shasta, and a meadow full of the flowers was fairly alive with them.

William H. Kobbé (1900) says that, in Washington, about Cape Disappointment, "they are particularly abundant about the flowering salmon-berry bushes and also the thimble-berry, but they seemed to be fonder of the honeysuckle blossoms than of either of the others." Dr. A. M. Woodbury (1938) saw a rufous hummingbird feeding at the working of a red-naped sapsucker on some willows; they were apparently eating the sap that exuded, but may have been obtaining some of the insects that were attracted to the workings.

Harry S. Swarth (1922) relates the following story: "For a hummingbird to appear as a menace to a farm crop was a new rôle for a member of that family, but we heard of one such complaint of damage done. Mr. W. E. Parrott, of Sergief Island, had a large strawberry patch, the fruit of which he marketed in the nearby town of Wrangell. Time and again, so he told us, he had seen a hummingbird dash at one of the bright red berries, apparently under the impression that it was a flower, and the bird's bill would be thrust through the fruit, which, of course, was ruined. He had found a number of berries pierced in this way, and was puzzled to account for the damage until he saw a hummingbird in the act."

Mr. DuBois says, in his notes, that the bird he was watching paid no attention to a red-clover blossom that he dipped in diluted honey and hung on a branch near the nest. He saw one "feeding in a novel manner over the small garden in the clearing. The bird was about 30 feet in the air, now poised on vibrating wings, now darting here and there like a dragonfly, apparently catching small insects on the wing. One day (July 22) I saw her drinking at the spring. She hovered above the pool, as she would above a flower, dipping her bill into the water several times. On the 27th, I again saw her getting water at the spring, but in a different manner. She stood, for a second or two at a time, in the film of water that flowed over a board, and dipped her bill into it several times."

Behavior.—All observers seem to agree that jealous courage and pugnacity are among the chief attributes of the rufous hummingbird; it seems to be the dominant species in the vicinity of its nest and about its feeding places, driving away, not only other hummingbirds, but other species of larger birds and animals; it seems to love to fight and often appears to provoke a quarrel unnecessarily. Mr. DuBois has sent me the following note: "Once during the afternoon of July 17, while the hummingbird was incubating, an olive-backed thrush inadvertently came too close to the nest. The little bird darted after him so suddenly and violently that she made him squawk as he hurried away. Another intruder was a chipmunk. He was searching for huckleberries—running on the ground and climbing in the small bushes—and at length his occupation brought him almost beneath the hummer's nest. She darted after him; and the sudden onslaught evidently filled him with terror. He beat a hasty retreat, squealing lustily as he ran. It is not surprising that the sudden movements of the hummingbird and the ominous sound of her wings, at close quarters, are terrorizing to any trespasser. On another occasion she chased a good sized bird away from the neighborhood."

Mrs. Wheelock (1904) saw a male rufous hummer attack and drive away a Brewer's blackbird that had chanced to alight in the bush containing the hummer's nest. "This blackbird was nesting in a hollow post which stood in four feet of water fifty feet from the bush. His usual course in leaving his nest was over the hummer's bush, and the male seldom failed to dart out at him from his watch tower near by."

Mr. Kobbé (1900) writes:

The pugnacity of these birds is the most prominent characteristic of the species and when they are not fighting among themselves they make war upon other birds. The males are nearly always the participants and seem to take great delight in fighting each other with their utmost strength. It is a very common sight to see a male Hummer perched upon a telegraph wire or exposed twig watching for others of his own sex with which to do battle. Although they sometimes fall over and over toward the ground like two huge bees, they seldom disable one another, since their bills are very weak. The greatest efforts on the part of one of the Hummers only succeed in pulling out a few feathers of his adversary, who is finally driven away in a rather bedraggled condition. * * * On several occasions I have seen male Hummers fight and drive off Swallows from the vicinity of their nest, particularly when it contained eggs. During the nesting season the males frequently, but not always, sit near the tree in which their home is placed and attempt to drive all birds from the vicinity of the nest. They pay great attention to their duty and seldom fail to dart after other Hummers, even if they are simply passing the tree in which the nest is placed. I have good reasons to believe that they do this more from a love of fighting than from parental instinct or devotion, since the male birds rarely appear upon the scene when their nest is being taken.

Henshaw (1886) writes of behavior on their feeding grounds in New Mexico:

Males and females all flock to the common feeding ground, and as the Hummers, especially of the Rufous-backed species, are pugnacious and hot tempered in the extreme, the field becomes a constant battle-ground whereon favorite flowers and favorite perching grounds are contested for with all the ardor that attaches to more important conquests. The fiery red throat of the Rufous-backed Hummer is an index of its impetuous, aggressive disposition, and when brought into conflict with the other species it invariably asserts its supremacy and drives its rival in utter rout from the fields. Nor do the males of this species confine their warfare to their own sex. Gallantry has no place apparently in their breasts, and when conquest has put them in possession of a perch near a clump of flowers they wage war on all comers, females as well as males. * * *

When the attack is urged against the males of the Broad-tailed species the contest is less fierce, the latter species usually abandoning the ground in hot haste. The latter result always follows the assault of a male upon the females who, if less valiant in battle, are scarcely less backward when it comes to the assertion of their rights against intruders of their own sex. The rivalry the females display is not less marked if the battles it prompts are less fierce than when the males are engaged; occasionally the females will fight with all the ardor displayed by the males.

The elaborate notes that Mr. DuBois has sent me on his intensive study of the home life of this species well illustrate its tameness, its devotion to its young, and its lack of fear after it had learned to trust him. He was able to approach cautiously, without any concealment, to within about 18 inches of the nest and to take numerous photographs at short range, without causing the bird much concern. On the second day the camera was placed on the tripod close to the nest; she examined it thoroughly several times and from all sides but did not seem much afraid of it; and on the following day she sat with her tail toward the instrument, thus showing her indifference to it. For a close study of the care of the young, he disguised himself as a balsam tree, being well covered with balsam boughs and twigs; the bird paid almost no attention to him with this disguise, and he was able to watch proceedings for long periods with his face within about a foot of the nest. At first she was suspicious and would not go to the nest but buzzed all around him, chirping and examining his make-up very minutely, and when she came within an inch or two of his ear, he found the boom of her wings a formidable sound; she repeated this examination twice more before she settled on the nest for any length of time.

It is a well-known fact that hummingbirds are attracted to investigate any red object that might suggest a flower. Dr. Grinnell (1909) records that, on Admiralty Island, Alaska, a brilliant male rufous hummer "buzzed about some bright red tomato cans that had been thrown out. Stephens records that at the same place, May 2, a male came around camp investigating everything that was red, such as a red-bordered towel, the red places on the end of a fruit box, an empty salmon can, and particularly a red bandana handkerchief hanging on a bush; this the bird went to three times."

Voice.—During the courtship performance a twittering note is heard from the male, as well as a whining sound, which is probably caused by the rush of air through the wings. Ralph C. Tate (1928) heard "a peculiar sound, somewhere between a buzz and a grunt," from a male that was feeding at the flowers of a trumpetvine on his porch. Dr. Wetmore (1921) says that "in flying their wings made a subdued humming and the birds called *chewp chewp* in a low tone."

G. Hammersley (1928) writes from Crofton, British Columbia:

When the fruit trees came into blossom, Mr. Hummer was in the orchard every day. One does not have to see him in order to know that he is there, as he has his own peculiar song or "drumming." It is uttered as he swoops past one or shoots swiftly overhead and might be written *ch-ch-ch chut-churrr* or *tut-ut-ut-ut-turrre*. Immediately after making this sound he darts straight upwards until reaching the desired height when he comes to a sudden and complete full stop, remaining stationary in the air like a glittering ruby set in the blue sky. Whilst in this position he will repeat the ordinary call note of *tchik* which is common to both the sexes, then dropping suddenly he flies back to his "watch-tower". I think that the drumming sound is probably produced by the tail feathers. The male hummer has the monopoly of another and quite different sound also. This sound is produced continually as long as the bird is on the wing, and only varies by increasing in volume each time the bird moves from its position in the air. The sound is difficult to describe, but might be likened to tiny beads vibrating regularly in a thin metal box. Although, as far as my own observations go, the male rufous never flies without making this vibrating sound, the female never at any time produces it.

Mr. DuBois says in his notes: "Usually the mother bird was silent; but when the nestling was two days old I once heard the mother chirping for a moment, from among the branches of a fallen tree, before she came to settle in the nest." When agitated she chirped while on the nest.

Field marks.—The male rufous hummingbird can be easily recognized by the large amount of rufous on the upper parts, including the posterior portion of the crown, the back, and most of the tail; the brilliant metallic scarlet gorget is very conspicuous and shines like burnished gold in some lights; the chest is white, but otherwise the underparts are pale rufous. The only species that closely resembles it is Allen's hummingbird, which has a green back.

The female can hardly be distinguished in the field from the female of Allen's, as both have much light rufous on the underparts, and their tails are largely rufous basally, the three outer rectrices being broadly tipped with white. A close inspection of the tails will show slight differences between the two species. The outer tail feathers of the rufous are broader at the black space, about 0.15, as against about 0.10 of an inch in Allen's. Ridgway (1911) says that in the rufous "middle pair of rectrices metallic bronze-green (usually more dusky terminally), both webs broadly edged basally with cinnamon-rufous (sometimes with whole basal half or more of this color); next pair with more than basal half cinnamon-rufous, then metallic bronze-green, the terminal portion purplish black." And, of Allen's, he says: "Middle pair of rectrices with basal half (laterally, at least) cinnamon-rufous, the terminal half (more or less) metallic bronze-green; next pair similar, but terminal portion (extensively) black, the tip of inner web sometimes with a small spot of white."

Enemies.—Mr. Sprot (1927) tells of a male rufous hummer that tried its towering flight once too often, "when he staged a drop on a Black Pigeon Hawk, and got caught." Probably other hawks, and perhaps owls, have taken their toll. Mr. Skinner says in his notes: "One was seen resting on a willow twig in the sun until an irascible Audubon's warbler made a dive at it and drove it away, but in a moment the hummer was back again. After its return, it seemed very nervous, as if the rowdy Audubon had ruffled its feelings. Another one was chased away by a lutescent warbler."

Mr. DuBois (1938) saw a large black and yellow fly attack the young hummer that he was watching and slightly wound it; it might have killed it, if he had not driven it away. The mother of this young bird disappeared mysteriously, and he suspected a weasel might have been the cause.

Fall.—The fall migration from its breeding grounds in Alaska starts early, and sometimes these hummers wander out over the ocean. S. F. Rathbun tells me that on July 20, 1914, while he was crossing the Gulf of Alaska and was just within sight of land, off Nespina Glacier, a male rufous hummingbird came aboard and alighted on one of the stays of the ship's stack. It showed no alarm, and after about 15 minutes it flew off toward the land.

After the breeding season the summer wanderings of this hummingbird extend well up into the mountains, even in Washington. On Mount Rainier, on August 6, Taylor and Shaw (1927) saw individuals flying over the glaciers at 6,000 and at 9,000 feet altitude. "We were now hung, as it were, between earth and heaven, 2,500 feet above timber line. The water supply froze shortly after 5 o'clock p. m., and the midsummer breeze was cold and cheerless. What was our surprise to find the hummers still with us. One whizzed past us as we were making camp, and two more were observed the following morning."

On the southward migration through the Rocky Mountain region, the rufous hummingbird is sometimes very abundant at high altitudes, wherever it can find flowers in bloom; it has been seen as high as 12,600 feet on Truchas Peak in the Upper Pecos region, N. Mex., according to Mrs. Bailey (1904). Henshaw (1886), writing of this same region, says:

The number of representatives of this and the preceding species that make their summer homes in these mountains is simply beyond calculation. No one whose experience is limited to the Eastern United States can form any adequate idea of their abundance. They occur from an altitude of about 7,500 feet far up on the mountain sides, as high up, in fact, as suitable flowers afford them the means of subsistence. They are most numerous at an altitude of from 8,000 to 9,000 feet. During the entire summer they frequent almost exclusively a species of *Scrophularia* which grows in clumps in the sunnier spots in the valleys. From early dawn till dusk the Hummingbirds throng around these plants intent in surfeiting themselves on honey and the minute insects that the honey attracts. The scene presented in one of these flowering areas is a most attractive one. * * *

Some idea of the number of Hummingbirds in this locality—and in this respect this whole mountain area is alike—may be gained from the statement that in a single clump of the *Scrophularia* I have counted eighteen Hummers, all within reach of an ordinary fishing rod. There was scarcely a moment in the day when upwards of fifty could not be counted within an area of a few yards in any of the patches of this common plant.

Mr. Swarth (1904) says of its appearance in the Huachuca Mountains, Arizona: "I have not seen this species at any time in the spring, but about the middle of July they begin to make their appearance; and throughout the month of August I found them very abundant, but frequenting the highest parts of the mountains, principally; more being seen between 8000 and 9000 feet than elsewhere.

"The flowering mescal stalks are a great attraction to them, and they seem to frequent them in preference to anything else. I have seen as many as twenty Rufous Hummingbirds around a single stalk, mostly immature birds, but with a fair sprinkling of adult males. No adult females were taken at any time."

Grinnell and Storer (1924) say of the migration in the Yosemite region, in California:

Most of the northbound movement probably takes place at low altitudes and in any event occurs too early in the spring to be observed by most visitors in the Yosemite section. But the migration initiated in late June or early July continues until the middle of September, and especially at the higher altitudes is much in evidence. * * *

The first representatives of the species to be seen in the southbound migration are males. Thus the bird seen near Yosemite Point on July 1 was a fully adult male, as it showed an all-rufous back. But later in the same month the females and their young began to pass through. Of the birds seen in Lyell Cañon on July 23 at least one was a female (immature). The southbound migration was evidently in full swing by that date as no less than 5 separate individuals were seen during two or three hours spent on the meadows and adjacent slopes.

A visit to Parsons Peak on September 6, 1915, showed that the migration was still in progress, and further, that the Rufous Hummingbirds were evidently using the crest of the Sierra Nevada as a fly-way. During the short time spent at the top of the peak, 12,120 feet, two of these dimunutive travelers were seen flying southward, laboring against the strong southerly breeze; both took advantage of the same gap in the rocks to gain a slight respite from the buffeting of the wind. Other observers have told us of similar incidents noted by them while visiting peaks elsewhere along the backbone of the Sierra Nevada.

Mr. Woods (1927) says of Los Angeles County lowlands: "The adult male is only an occasional visitant on the southward migration in late summer, though the females, or more probably immature birds of both sexes, are seen more frequently." The inference from all the foregoing observations is that the northward migration in spring is mainly through the lower levels and chiefly to the westward of the main mountain chains and that the southward migration in fall follows mainly the crests of the Rocky Mountains and the Sierra Nevada.

DISTRIBUTION

Range.—Western North America.

Breeding range.—The breeding range of the rufous hummingbird extends **north** to southeastern Alaska (Montague Island, probably Cordova, and Carcross). **East** to eastern Alaska (Carcross); British

Columbia (Telegraph Creek and Fort St. James); southwestern Alberta (Banff); and western Montana (Belton, Anaconda, and Red Lodge). **South** to southern Montana (Red Lodge); southern Idaho (Blue Lake); and east-central California (Silver Creek). **West to** California (Silver Creek and Mount Shasta); Oregon (Newport and Netarts); Washington (Gig Harbor, Lake Crescent, and Tatoosh Island); western British Columbia (Courtenay and Graham Island); and southeastern Alaska (Ketchikan, Sitka, Point Couverden, and Montague Island).

Winter range.—During the winter months this species is more or less concentrated in the Mexican States of Zacatecas (La Parada), Jalisco (Volcano de Colima), Mexico (Tlalpam), and Michoacan (Lake Patzcuaro).

Spring migration.—Early dates of spring arrival are: California—Haywards, February 11; Berkeley, February 12. Oregon—Newport, March 4; Corvallis, March 11. Washington—Tacoma, February 26; Ilwaco, March 9; North Yakima, March 12. British Columbia—Massett, April 2; Chilliwack, April 11. Idaho—Rathdrum, May 5. Montana—Missoula, April 30. Alaska—Ketchikan, April 10; Juneau, April 18.

Fall migration.—Late dates of fall departure are: Alaska—Craig, September 9; St. Lazaria Island, September 30. British Columbia—Arrow Lakes, September 22; Courtnay, October 4. Washington—Seattle, September 26; Clallam Bay, October 7. Oregon—Newport, October 18; Coos Bay, October 28. Montana—Fortine, September 13; Belton, September 14.

Casual records.—The rufous hummingbird has been detected outside its normal range on several occasions, some cases being notable records. It was reported as observed at Camrose, Alberta, on August 24, 1930, and there are at least two and probably three specimen records for the vicinity of Eastend, Saskatchewan, the dates being August 11, 1939, August 18, 1932, and July 31, 1933. The species was reported from Kenton, Okla., under date of August 10, 1927, and a specimen was collected at Brownsville, Tex., on January 19, 1892. One was found dead at Pensacola, Fla., on November 29, 1934, two others being seen in the same area until December 13, while it was again recorded from this point on December 8, 12, 14, and 17, 1935. A specimen was taken in Charleston, S. C., on December 18, 1909.

Egg dates.—British Columbia: 7 records, May 6 to July 6.

Oregon: 11 records, April 27 to June 29.

Washington: 12 records, April 22 to June 7; 6 records, May 3 to 30, indicating the height of the season.

SELASPHORUS ALLENI Henshaw

ALLEN'S HUMMINGBIRD

PLATES 68, 69

HABITS

This is another very brilliant hummingbird, which is closely related to the rufous hummingbird, and much like it in appearance and behavior. It seems to be confined, in the breeding season at least, to the coastal district of California, from Humboldt County to Ventura County and the Santa Barbara Islands. It may possibly be found breeding in Oregon, and there are two authentic records of its occurrence in Washington. There was formerly a specimen in the United States National Museum, which has since been destroyed, that was collected at Fort Steilacoom, on April 26, 1856, and was identified by both Henshaw and Ridgway. S. F. Rathbun collected an adult male near Seattle on May 27, 1894, which is apparently the only Washington specimen in existence; he tells me that this specimen is now in the State Museum, at the University of Washington, in Seattle. Dr. Tracy I. Storer (1921) has made a careful study of all other records north of California and reports that no others are authentic.

Courtship.—Robert S. Woods (1927b) says on this subject: "Allen's Hummingbird flies rather slowly back and forth along a path such as would be described by a giant pendulum, with a sort of lateral writhing movement of the body and extended tail and a vibratory metallic noise, but without vocal sound. Again it will poise itself close in front of another bird and rapidly shuttle to and fro sidewise through a space of perhaps a foot or two."

Frank N. Bassett (1921) gives a somewhat different and more elaborate account of it, as follows:

On the afternoon of April 16, 1920, I was walking through the hills back of the Claremont Club golf links when I was brought to a halt by a rather prolonged buzzing sound, very penetrating and metallic in quality, somewhat similar to the sound produced by drawing a fine-grained file over the edge of a piece of sheet steel with a sudden jerk. Looking in the direction of the sound I saw poised in the air about twenty feet from the ground, a male Allen Hummingbird (*Selasphorus alleni*), uttering his commonly heard mouse-like squeaks. Then followed the performance of the nuptial flight, similar to that of the Anna Hummingbird, though the path described in the air was somewhat different. He "rocked" back and forth over the female, which was perched on a twig of a low poison oak (*Rhus diversiloba*), describing a semi-circle about twenty-five feet in diameter. There was a pause at each end of the arc, and before the pause he spread his tail and shook his whole body so violently that I wondered how his feathers remained fast. During this time he continued uttering the characteristic squeaks. After several of these semi-circles were described he began his climb to a height of about seventy-five feet; and then came the "high dive." He swooped down with the speed of a comet, and on passing over the female gave the low-pitched but resonant buzzing sound which had first attracted my attention; then he curved upward and came to a pause about twenty-five feet in the air, where I had first seen him. The sound emitted on passing over the female was of a second or more in duration, and differed greatly from the instantaneous, metallic *clink* of the Anna Hummingbird.

Nesting.—Charles A. Allen, of Nicasio, Calif., who discovered this species, and for whom it was named, wrote to Major Bendire (1895) as follows:

Allen's Hummingbird arrives in the vicinity of Nicasio, California, about the middle of February, and commences to nest soon after arrival. The earliest date on which I found one was February 27, 1879; this was then about half finished, when a heavy storm set in which lasted about five days, and I did not visit the locality again until March 8, when the nest was completed and contained two fresh eggs. I have taken their nests as late as July 3, and am well convinced that two broods are raised in a season, at least by all of the earlier breeding birds. They select all sorts of situations and various kinds of trees and bushes to nest in. I have found their nests as low as 10 inches and again as high as 90 feet from the ground.

All the nests and eggs of this species [continues Bendire] in the United States National Museum were taken by Mr. Allen near Nicasio, California; one of these, now before me, is attached to the side of a small oak limb which turns abruptly at an angle of about 45° directly over the cup of the nest, protecting it above; another is likewise attached to the side of a small pendant oak twig, its base being supported by a bunch of moss. Some are securely saddled on small twigs of raspberry bushes, and several of these are usually incorporated in the walls of the nest. Occasionally they nest in hedges, on weed stalks, or on bushes overhanging water.

The nests are well and compactly built, the inside being lined with vegetable down, while the outer walls are composed of green tree mosses, and a few bits of lichens, securely fastened in place with a spider web. Nests built on trees seem to be generally somewhat larger than those found in bushes. The average measurements of one of the former is 1½ inches outer diameter and the same in depth; the inner cup is seven-eighths of an inch in width by three-fourths of an inch in depth. On the whole they resemble the nests of Anna's Hummingbird more than those of the Rufous, and appear to me to be better and more neatly built than either.

James B. Dixon has sent me the following note: "The only place where I have contacted this hummingbird in the breeding season was in San Luis Obispo County, in the dense willow montes where they were nesting in large numbers and were as common as the black-chinned hummingbirds are farther south. Here the nests were often found within 50 feet of each other. As with all the other hummingbirds, there seemed to be a wide variation in the breeding season, as nests with young half grown would be found close to nests with fresh eggs. The nests are larger and better built than those of most other hummingbirds. They have a habit of saddling the nests on a small limb growing away from the butt or main stem of a willow sapling, in much the same manner as the wood pewee; I have never found the other hummingbirds doing this. Nests are made of dried weed stems, weed seed, and plant down, bound together with cob-webs, and decorated outwardly with lichens; they do more toward decorating the outside with lichens as incubation advances."

Dr. Harold C. Bryant (1925) gives an interesting account of the colonial nesting habits of this species:

Heretofore I had believed along with others * * * that the favorite nesting place of the Allen Hummingbird (*Selasphorus alleni*) is the tangle of berry vines along a stream. But a recent experience in Golden Gate Park, San Francisco, has led me to alter my view. * * *

On April 19, a trip through a growth of cypress and Monterey pines netted eleven hummingbirds' nests, all, with the possible exception of one, being those of the Allen Hummingbird. Three of the nests found were in pine trees; all the rest of them were in Monterey cypress. The lowest one was about 5½ feet above the ground, the highest 15 feet. Measurement of the inside diameter of two nests showed them to be 1¼ to 1½ inches. Most of the nests contained eggs, but in one instance young birds ready to fly were found. In fact, one of the young birds launched out of the nest and had to be replaced. At least two nests were incomplete. One of these a week later was found to contain eggs.

In most instances the incubating female, frightened from the nest, helped in determining the location. On one area of less than an acre in extent, an unsystematic search disclosed five nests. In one instance nests were hardly 15 feet apart. Another casual search on April 26 disclosed three more nests on this same limited area, and undoubtedly several more nests could have been found had each tree been searched systematically. * * *

When we stop to think that the Rufous Hummingbird, a close relative, breeds commonly in coniferous forests of northwestern North America, it does not seem unreasonable that the Allen should chose a similar habitat in the humid coast belt of California. And evidently it was choice in this instance, for extensive tangles of berry vines near water were close at hand but were not chosen for nesting places.

Grinnell and Linsdale (1936) report two nests found in the Point Lobos Reserve, Monterey County, Calif.; one "found on April 18, was four and one-half feet up on a twig one-eighth inch in diameter, at the lower, outer end of a limb of live oak. * * * Another nest, found on May 18, was at least seventy feet above the ground on a small stub beneath a slender limb of pine in the woods."

Ernest D. Clabaugh (1936) tells of an Allen's hummingbird that built its nest on an ivy vine hanging down about 6 inches from the ceiling of a covered entrance to his house; one young was success-fully raised and left the nest on May 11; "the old nest was removed, and on June 4, another nest was built in the same spot." Joseph Mailliard (1913) records three nests built "inside of buildings more or less in use"; two of these were under the rafters of a wagon shed, one on a hanging pulley, and the other on the loop of a rope sling; the third was in a carriage house, on an iron hook that was used in cleaning harnesses, and about 5 feet from the ground; broods were raised in the first two, but the third was abandoned.

W. L. Dawson (1923) writes: "As for the Allen Hummer the black-berry tangles are her home, and all such other situations as assure a measure of protection from above. Thus, drooping vines falling over boulders offer ideal sites; for *alleni* is also fond of a swing. The most remarkable nest of our experience, a *five-story* one, was saddled upon the hook of a broken root, which was, in turn, caught upon a sprangle of roots above, unearthed by the under-cutting of the stream. This root could be lifted clear and replaced without injury; and its mistress added, in one season, stories No. 4 and No. 5, to our knowledge."

Two of the four nests of Allen's hummingbird in the Thayer collection in Cambridge are large handsome nests, suggesting the best types of nests of the rufous hummingbird. One of these was 8 feet from the ground and 20 feet out from the trunk on a branch of a spruce; it is composed of fine green moss, decorated with flakes of pale-gray lichens, bound on with spider web, and lined with willow cotton; it measures approximately 2 inches wide and 1 inch high externally; the inner cup is about 1 inch in diameter by five-eighths of an inch deep. The other large nest was built on a branch of a young live oak between upright twigs; it measures about 2 inches in diameter and 1½ inches in height externally; it appears to be made almost entirely, including all the rim, of the pale buff cottony down from willow blossoms; only the lower and external part of the nest is composed of green mosses and various brown fibers; it is a very pretty nest. The smallest nest in the lot was 2 feet from the ground in a shallow bend of a horizontal branch of a sagebrush; it measures 1¾ by 1¼ inches in external diameter, and is only three-quarters of an inch high, the inner cavity being very shallow; this is a very drab-looking nest, with no green moss in its composition; it is made of various gray and brown fibers and similar material, with very little cotton and a few small feathers in the lining; apparently it matched its surroundings in the gray sage.

Since the above was written Ernest I. Dyer (1939) has published a detailed account of the nesting of Allen's hummingbird, to which the reader is referred.

Eggs.—Allen's hummingbird lays almost invariably two eggs; I have no record of more or fewer. They are like other hummers' eggs, varying in shape from oval to elliptical-oval, and are pure white without gloss. The measurements of 55 eggs average 12.7 by 8.6 millimeters; the eggs showing the four extremes measure **14.0** by 8.9, 13.8 by **10.0**, and **11.7** by 7.6 millimeters.

Young.—The incubation period of this hummingbird is said to be 14 or 15 days, as is the case with several other hummingbirds. The female doubtless does all the incubating and assumes full care of the young. After describing so fully the home life of the preceding species, to which the present species is so closely related, it hardly seems necessary to enlarge here on the activities of the mother at the nest or on the development of the young. The rufous hummingbird and Allen's are much alike in appearance and behavior; their nesting habits are similar; and probably, although I have no notes on the subject, the care and development of the young follow along the same lines.

Since the above was written, Robert T. Orr (1939) has published a very full account of the incubation behavior and the care and development of the young, to which the reader is referred.

Plumages.—So far as I can learn from the literature and from the examination of specimens, the development of the juvenal plumage of Allen's hummingbird and its subsequent molts and plumages are the same as in the rufous hummingbird. The two species are almost exactly alike, except for the specific differences explained under the field marks of the two, the very narrow lateral rectrices and the greater amount of green in Allen's being the principal differences. Young male Allen's hummers begin to show red in the throat early in July. I have seen a young male, taken on June 1, that was molting into the adult plumage, some red coming in on the throat, and some of the outer rectrices still white-tipped, as in the juvenal tail, probably a belated molt.

Food.—I cannot find much in print about the food of Allen's hummingbird, which probably does not differ materially from that of other California hummers. Whatever brightly colored flowers happen to be in bloom are resorted to for honey and minute insects and spiders. That they are of service to the plants in cross fertilization is evident from the amount of pollen so often seen on their heads. The tree tobacco is popular with this hummingbird, as are the blossoms of *Ceanothus*, madroña, and the flowering stalks of the century plant; the scarlet sage, brightly colored mints, and various other flowers are attractive. Dr. Grinnell (1905b) says that, on Mount Pinos, in July, "masses of monkeyflowers (*Mimulus langsdorfi* and *cardinalis*), columbines (*Aquilegia* sp.?), and other plants (*Stachys albens, Castilleia grinnelli*, etc.) began to burst into bloom during the first week in July about the wet places in the cañon bottoms. And these flower masses were the scenes of many noisy revels among the Allen Hummers, sometimes as many as five of the birds taking part in what looked like a free-for-all fight."

Mr. Woods (1927) says that, on Santa Catalina Island, "towards evening, like other species, they make short sallies in Flycatcher fashion after passing insects too minute to be discerned by the human eye."

Behavior.—Henshaw (1877), with his original description of Allen's hummingbird, makes the following comparison of this species with the rufous hummingbird:

I am in possession of but few notes bearing upon the habits of this Hummer. Mr. Allen remarks incidentally in a letter that the Green-backs are much the livelier and more active of the two, keeping constantly in the open, and always perching upon the most prominent dead twigs they can find. Their extreme shyness, as contrasted with the unsuspicious nature of the Rufous-backed, is quite remarkable. They seem to possess a larger share than usual of the courage and pugnacity which is so constantly displayed in birds of this family. Not only do they always come off the victors when chance encounters take place between them and the Rufous-backs, but Mr. Allen has seen a pair attack and put to rout a Red-tailed Hawk; while, as he remarks, "Sparrow-Hawks have no chance at all with them." He has often seen the little fellows in hot chase after these latter birds, and their only care seemed to be to get out of the way as soon as possible of foes so determined.

Each male seems to claim a particular range, which he occupies for feeding and breeding purposes, and every other bird seen by him encroaching on his preserve is at once so determinedly set upon and harassed that he is only too glad to beat a hasty retreat. During their quarrels these birds keep up an incessant, sharp chirping, and a harsh, rasping buzzing with their wings, which sounds very different from the low, soft humming they make with these while feeding. Every action and motion at such times indicates that they are as mad as can be; the poor Anna Hummers have to get out of their way pretty quickly at any time, but especially when they encroach on their breeding grounds. The males very often have quarrels among themselves, and are then very noisy, while the females are more orderly and quiet; but even they have occasional little misunderstandings with each other, especially when a pair meet while feeding on the same bush; one generally vacates the premises very quickly, and as soon as she does all becomes quiet again.

Field marks.—The male Allen's hummingbird looks very much like the male rufous, but can be distinguished from it by the large amount of green in the back. Both sexes can be distinguished from other California hummingbirds, except migrating rufous, by the large amount of rufous in the plumage, especially in the tail. The female Allen's is practically indistinguishable, in the field, from the female rufous hummingbird; only a close comparison of the tails will distinguish the two species. The difference in the color patterns of the tails of the two females is described, as quoted from Ridgway (1911), under the field marks of the rufous hummingbird; but the difference seems to be very slight. The best distinguishing character, which might under favorable circumstances be seen in the field, is the width of the two outer tail feathers, as illustrated in Henshaw's cut (1877); in *S. rufus* the four lateral rectrices are "successively graduated in size, the outer the smallest"; and they are of normal hummingbird width; whereas in *S. alleni* the two outer feathers are "very narrow, linear, the outer nearly acicular," a well-marked difference.

Range.—Coastal regions of California and northwestern Mexico; casual in Washington, Oregon, and Arizona.

Breeding range.—Allen's hummingbird is found during the nesting season only in the narrow coastal district that extends nearly the full length of California from San Clemente and Santa Catalina Islands northward to San Francisco, Berkeley, and Eureka. Four specimens taken on July 10, 1905, in the San Pedro Martir Mountains, Baja California, may possibly indicate a more southern limit of the breeding range.

Winter range.—In winter the species is found **north** to southern California (Santa Cruz Island); and **south** to central Baja California (San Quintin and Santo Domingo). It also has been detected at Santa Barbara, Chihuahua, in the latter part of September.

Spring migration.—Early dates of spring arrival in California are: Berkeley, February 13; Haywards, February 16; Escondido, February 22.

Fall migration.—The species appears to retire from the northern parts of its range during August and September, late dates being: Palo Alto, August 24: Berkeley, September 29; Presidio of San Francisco, September 30.

Casual records.—Two specimens were collected at the mouth of the Pistol River, Curry County, Oreg., on June 23, 1929; and one was taken at Seattle, Wash., on May 27, 1894. In Arizona there are several records as follows: One was secured in the Santa Catalina Mountains, July 23, 1884; specimens were taken near Bisbee during August and September 1892 (?); and in the Huachuca Mountains in July 1896, in July 1902, and on July 10 and August 1, 1929.

Egg dates.—California: 100 records, February 2 to June 28; 50 records, March 21 to May 22, indicating the height of the season.

ATTHIS HELOISA HELOISA (De Lattre and Lesson)

HELOISE'S HUMMINGBIRD

HABITS

On July 2, 1896, two female hummingbirds were taken in Ramsay Canyon, in the Huachuca Mountains, Ariz., by H. G. Rising. These two specimens were sent to Mr. Ridgway, who described and named them (1898) as a new species, Morcom's hummingbird (*Atthis morcomi*), in honor of G. Frean Morcom. In his description he states that "the adult male of this species is unfortunately unknown. The adult female differs from that of *A. heloisa* in being pure bronze-green above instead of almost coppery bronze inclining to greenish only on upper tail-coverts and middle tail-feathers; in having the cinnamon-rufous on basal portion of the tail far more extensive, there being more on the middle rectrices in *A. heloisa*, while on the others it occupies very much less than the basal half, and is entirely hidden by the coverts; the sides and flanks are less deeply, and apparently less extensively, cinnamon-rufous, and the under tail-coverts are white or but very faintly buffy, instead of being deep cinnamon-buff."

In his "Birds of North and Middle America" (1911), Ridgway treats Morcom's hummingbird as a subspecies of *Atthis heloisa*, under the name *Atthis heloisa morcomi*, which he characterizes as "similar to *A. h. heloisa*, but smaller (except bill); adult female paler below, with bronzy spots on chin and throat much smaller, sides less extensively cinnamon-rufous, and under tail-coverts pure white."

According to our 1931 Check-list, *morcomi* is not accorded even subspecific rank and is regarded as identical with *A. h. heloisa*, to which race our Arizona specimens are now understood to belong. This is the race that is found in central and southern Mexico, from the States of Tamaulipas, Guanajuato, and San Luís Potosí to Guerrero and Tepic.

Nothing seems to be known about the habits of this subspecies and, so far as I know, the nest of the *species* has never been found. But Alexander F. Skutch has sent me the following notes on a closely related form, Elliot's hummingbird (*Atthis heloisa ellioti*), the Guatemalan race.

"Like so many of the Central American hummingbirds, the male Elliot's hummingbirds gather in definite assemblies to sing. Although I have found them in western Guatemala from 6,000 to 11,000 feet above sea level, they appear to be nowhere common. Yet where one finds a male singing persistently, day after day, from the same perch, there will generally be one or more others within hearing. About the middle of October 1933, I found an assembly of four males on a steep, bushy slope at an altitude of about 9,000 feet. Each bird had chosen as his singing perch the bare, exposed twig of a bush or the low branch of a tree. Their headquarters were separated from each other by 25 or 30 yards. They were stretched out in a line; and the birds in the middle could each hear two of their neighbors, but those in the end positions could hear only the one nearest to them—unless their ears were sharper than mine, which is certainly not improbable. These hummingbirds did not perch so close together by chance, for I found none other of the kind within a mile of this assembly.

"The assembly was established in a spot not far from the highway that crossed the mountain; and whenever I passed that way I would pause to listen, enchanted, to a song that amazed me, coming from so small a bird. The voice, although weak, was not squeaky. In its intensity, its variety of phrasing, and its rising and falling cadences the song reminded me not a little of the higher notes of a small finch and often suggested the impassioned conclusion of the lay of the little black-and-white Morellet's seedeater (*Sporophila morelletii*) of the lowlands. The hummingbird frequently sang without a pause for thirty or forty seconds. Were his song only a little more forceful, without any change of tune or phrasing, Elliot's hummingbird would be famous as a musician.

"As he poured forth his sweet, impassioned little lay, the hummingbird spread the stiff feathers of his gorget, which then appeared to form a scaly shield covering the throat, and turned his head from side to side. The feathers at the sides of the shield, longer than the rest, formed sharp points at the lower corners. When the bird faced directly toward me, the gorget reflected an intense magenta light; but as the head slowly turned away the color was gradually extinguished, and the shield, seen from the side, appeared velvety black. At certain angles, it sent a metallic-green reflection to my eye. At times the little singer vibrated his wings in his ecstasy, and either floated slowly to another perch or suspended himself in mid-air on invisible pinions, all without interrupting his song. At times he made a long, looping flight, returning again to the perch from which he started, and continued his singing during the entire journey."

Robert T. Moore found four species of hummingbirds feeding on the flowering tree in southeastern Sinaloa, referred to in his notes on the white-eared hummingbird. Among them was another race of this species, Margaret's hummingbird (*Atthis heloisa margarethae*), of which he says in his notes:

"Much the smallest of the four and one of the tiniest members of the family, this near relative of the so-called Morcom's hummingbird of Arizona flew into the tree at rare intervals. If the broad-tailed and Calliope hummers, of which there were always five or six, were feeding from the tree, *Atthis* would be permitted to probe the least attractive blooms. She experienced little difficulty in finding a few of the forty thousand flowerets, which had not already been deprived of their sweets. But when a single male white-ear blustered in among the busy gleaners, he would invariably launch an assault on the rare gem of the mountain and drive it away to the thicker growth of pines. For the time *Atthis* had to be content with a more frugal repast on the scarce blooms of *labiatae*, which starred the pine-needle floor of the forest with spikes of maroon-colored flowers. Margaret's hummingbird probably feeds from several kinds of flowers, but we actually observed it doing so from only three. In addition to the two mentioned, it sometimes prospected the exquisite tawny flowers of the huge Opuntias near our camp site, but the bird seemed to prefer those of the purple-bracted shrub, referred to above.

"No larger than a huge orange-marked bee, which was intoxicated by the same flowers, *Atthis heloisa margarethae* was not much larger than its name on this sheet. Slower in its movements than the other four hummingbirds, the revolution of its wings created only an infinitesimal murmur. As compared with the energetic nervous course of the white-ear, that of *Atthis* is slow and unwavering. It resembles more closely that of the calliope than either of the other two hummers. It is not nearly so swift as that of the broadtail.

"In northwestern Mexico Margaret's hummingbird seems to be confined to the Transition Zone, not descending very far below its lower margin, as all of our specimens have come from 5,700 feet to 7,500 feet. Occasionally occurring elsewhere at lower levels, a female was taken by Chester Lamb near the city of Tepic, Nayarit, at an altitude of 3,000 feet.

"I have no doubt that Margaret's hummingbird breeds in the lower margin of the Transition Zone in Sinaloa, but we have never found the nest."

DISTRIBUTION

Range.—Central Mexico south to Honduras; accidental in south-ern Arizona; not generally migratory.

The range of this species extends **north** to San Luis Potosi (Al-varez); and central Veracruz (Jalapa). **East** to Veracruz (Jalapa and Cordoba); and Honduras (San Juancito). **South** to Honduras (San Jauncito); Guatemala (Fuego Volcano and Atitlan); and Guerrero (Omilteme). **West** to Guerrero (Omilteme), Mexico (Santa Lucia); and southwestern San Luis Potosi (Alvarez).

Casual records.—The only records for the United States are for two specimens collected in Ramsay Canyon, in the Huachuca Moun-tains, Ariz., on July 2, 1896.

STELLULA CALLIOPE (Gould)

CALLIOPE HUMMINGBIRD

PLATE 70

HABITS

This tiny mite is the smallest member of the group containing the smallest North American birds. Grinnell and Storer (1924) state that "its average weight is only about 3 grams (one-tenth of an ounce) which is about half that of an Anna Hummingbird, or of a kinglet or bush-tit." The length of the male is about 2¾ inches and that of the female is less than 3 inches. But it is a hardy little midget and a long-distance traveler, migrating from northern British Columbia to Mexico City; it spends its summers in the Canadian zones at high altitudes in the mountains and at lower levels farther north.

Its generic name was well chosen, *Stellula*, little star, for the long, narrow, metallic purple feathers rise and spread, under excitement, above the snow-white background of the gorget, like a scintillating star. The choice of the specific name, *calliope*, was not so fortunate; Calliope was the muse of eloquence, and this is a very silent bird.

At least throughout the southern portion of its breeding range, and to some extent farther north, the calliope hummingbird is essentially a mountain species, though it breeds in the lower valleys and near sea level in some of the more northern portions of its range. Dawson (1923) says that in California—

it is essentially a mountain-loving species, and is, so far as we have been able to prove, the only breeding Hummer of the higher Sierran slopes. There is a 3000 foot record, by Stephens, of a nest in the San Bernardinos; but 4000 is the usual minimum, and 8000 a better average. In the Canadian zone, therefore, the bird knows no restrictions, save that it does not favor the densely timbered sections. In the Sierras it nests nearly up to timber line, 10,000 to 11,500 feet, and follows the advancing season to the limit of flowers. * * * A bit of heather on a northern peak, where we camped at an elevation of 8,000 feet, yielded thirty-two species of plants in conspicuous bloom within a stone's throw of the breakfast table.

Elsewhere (Dawson and Bowles, 1909) he says: "We have found it commonly in the northern and eastern portions of Washington at much lower altitudes, and have taken its nest in the Burning Gorge of the Columbia at an altitude of only six hundred feet."

James B. Dixon writes to me: "In the San Bernardino country it was a rare breeder at elevations from 6,000 to 8,500 feet above sea level, and there it nested along the stream beds where water ran all summer. In the Mono Basin they were found along running streams, generally in the aspen thickets, but sometimes out in the open forests high on the mountain sides and some distance from running water; they were much more common, however, in the aspen groves."

Ralph Hoffmann (1927) writes: "The flowering shrubs and vines about dwellings attract nearly all the different hummingbirds of the coast. One species, however, still keeps to the natural gardens on mountain slopes, where Indian paint-brush, mountain heather and columbine splotch the springy slopes with red, or wild currant forms extensive thickets. Here the little Calliope Hummer, the smallest and most delicately adorned of them all, flashes the lavender streaks on its gorget as it chases off some rival or pursues a female."

J. A. Munro (1919) says that in the Okanagan Valley, British Columbia, "a birch and maple draw is the favorite home of *Stellula calliope*, and one can often see six or eight, buzzing around a birch tree, which a Red-naped Sapsucker has girdled." Winton Weyde-meyer (1927), writing of its haunts in northwestern Montana, where it is a common breeder, says:

In Lincoln County the Calliope Hummingbird (*Stellula calliope*) nests along streams throughout most of the Canadian zone and downward into the upper borders of the Transition zone. During the nesting season and late summer it also frequents open mountains, ranging into the Hudsonian zone, and during May and August is commonly seen in the breeding areas of lower Transition zone species. Tree associations evidently have greater influence on its range than does elevation. In the eastern part of the country I have found the species to be common during the nesting season at 7,000 feet, although I have never chanced actually to see a nest above 4,800 feet. In the Kootenai Valley, near Libby, I have found it nesting abundantly at an elevation of less than 2,100 feet, and I have no doubt that it breeds below 1,900 feet a few miles distant, in the lower end of the valley, the only place in Montana where so low an elevation occurs.

Courtship.—The courtship performances of the hummingbirds all follow the same general pattern, with only slight variations, and this species is no exception to the rule. Grinnell, Dixon, and Linsdale (1930) describe it very well as follows:

An exhibition of courting flight that seemed fairly typical for this species was observed on May 16, 1924. A female was down in a blossoming currant (*Ribes cereum*) bush. A male started towering from her vicinity, slowly at first and with an audible buzz, then faster until he reached a height of fully twenty-two meters. Then he shot down in a broadly U-shaped course, passing the bush closely (barely missing it) and ascended to an equal height on the opposite tip of the "U." At the moment of passing the bush, within which the female was perched, he gave out a droll, flatted sound *bzt*—short, not loud, like a bee held down. After making three complete sky-dives, the male, on coming down the last time, perched six meters away at the tip of a stem of budding service-berry bush. The female began at once to feed at the currant flowers within the abundantly white-flowering bush.

The following variation in the antics was observed by L. E. Wyman (1920):

On one occasion an angry buzzing, almost terrifying in volume, resolved itself into a pair of these birds holding to each other's beaks and revolving like a horizontal pinwheel, *less than four feet from my eyes.* Around they went, a half-dozen times, then parted, the female perching and preening on a twig of the oak-scrub just beyond arm's reach, with the male two feet farther away and giving vent at three-second intervals to an explosive metallic *tzing*. This was, of course, made with the wings, but the bird was sufficiently screened so that I could not see it clearly.

On another occasion a female sat preening on a horizontal dead weed, when a male shot up the hill-side close to the ground, passed the female, mounted about twenty-five feet and darted down again in a long, narrow, vertical ellipse that flattened where it touched the hill-side. As he passed the female she fluttered and swung head downward on her perch. The male alighted above her, with vibrating wings, and coition took place in this position.

Nesting.—Major Bendire (1895) gives an interesting account of the nesting of the calliope hummingbird near Fort Klamath, Oreg., where he said that this species outnumbered the common rufous hummingbird about three to one. His first nest was found by the actions of the bird; he writes:

I had taken quite a long walk along the banks of Fort Creek on June 10, and, the day being a hot one, sat down with my back resting against the trunk of a bushy black pine whose lower limbs had been killed by fire; while resting thus one of these Hummers buzzed repeatedly about my head for a few seconds at a time, and then rose perpendicularly in the air, only to repeat the performance again. I had no idea then that this species nested in pines, but in order to give me an opportunity to watch its performance better I moved out from under the tree, and a few minutes later saw the bird settle on what I at first supposed to be an old clump of pine cones. On looking closer, however, I noticed its nest, which was ingeniously saddled on two small cones, and its outward appearance resembled a cone very closely. * * * Knowing now where to look for them, I had no further difficulty in finding their nests, and all of those observed by me were built in exactly similar situations. * * * They were usually placed on or against a dry cone on small dead limbs of *Pinus contorta*, from 8 to 15 feet from the ground, and on account of the brittle nature of these limbs they were rather hard to secure. The nests, while outwardly not as handsome as those of the majority of our Hummers, are nevertheless marvels of ingenuity, all those I have seen mimicking a small dead pine cone so perfectly as to almost defy detection unless one sees the bird fly on or off the nest. The majority found were saddled on one or two such cones, or on a small limb and resting against the sides of a cone. The outer walls are composed of bits of bark and small shreds of cone, and the inner cup is softly lined with willow down. An average nest measures about 1¼ inches in outer diameter by the same in depth; the inner cup being three-quarters of an inch in width by one-half inch in depth. The nests were generally so placed that the contents were protected by larger limbs or green boughs above.

He says of another nest: "This is composed interiorly of fine moss and willow down, and the outer walls are decorated with tiny shreds of bark, fine flakes of wood, and flakes of whitewash, fastened securely with cobwebs; it was placed on a knot in a rope hanging from the roof of a woodshed and within 5 feet of an occupied dwelling house. The materials out of which the nest is composed closely assimilate the rope and knot on which it is placed."

It seems to be the prevailing custom of this hummingbird to build its nest on a small branch or twig directly under a larger branch, or under a canopy of foliage, which serves to protect or conceal the nest from overhead; many observers have noticed this, and numerous photographs illustrate this type of location. This hummer has also developed to a high degree its skill in so placing its nest and so artfully camouflaging it that it fades into the picture as a natural part of its environment. James B. Dixon says in his notes that in the shaded portions of the aspen groves there are numerous dead, black or gray mistletoe knots, about the size of hummingbirds' nests, and the birds seem to realize the value of the protection thus offered; most of the nests that he found there were built either upon one of these knots or in such a position that the nest would look exactly like one of them; and he had difficulty in recognizing a nest until he could see a bird alight upon it.

Nine nests that Dr. Joseph Grinnell (1908) recorded in the San Bernardino Mountains of southern California "varied in height above the ground from twenty-two inches (measured) to seventy feet (estimated) ; I should judge the average height to have been about thirty-five feet, as the majority were above that height. The nests were all in cañons, though none were directly over or very near the water, as with some other species of hummingbirds. One was located in an alder, two in silver firs, and six in yellow and Jeffrey pines."

The first nest mentioned above, as 22 inches above the ground, is in the Thayer collection in Cambridge; it was near the end of a drooping bough of a young silver fir growing on a canyon side and only 15 inches from the face of a huge overhanging boulder; its general appearance is dark gray, being made of various gray and brown fibers, bark scales, and bits of inner bark; the bottom of the cavity only is lined with grayish-white down; it measures 1½ by 1¾ inches in outside diameter and 1⅛ inches by seven-eighths of an inch in inner diameter; it is only seven-eighths of an inch high outside and five-eighths of an inch deep inside.

Mr. Weydemeyer (1927) says of its nesting habits in northwestern Montana:

The nest of this Hummingbird is placed in a coniferous tree. Within this limit, the choice of an individual tree appears to depend more upon the location than upon the species. In the higher elevations of Lincoln County, nests are placed in alpine firs. Along the streams of the Transition zone, the trees most commonly used are the Engelmann spruce, western hemlock, and arborvitae. I have found one nest in a Douglas fir, but have seen none in pines. Near Libby I have observed nests in three species of trees within a few yards of each other along a stream. Evidently, to suit the requirements of the birds, the tree must be a conifer standing on the bank of a creek, or beside a road or other opening in the forest, with one of its lowermost branches swinging free from all other foliage and commanding a clear view in practically all directions.

The word "lowermost" is used with a purpose. All the nests of this species that I have seen have been placed on the lowermost living branch on its side of the tree. This habit determines the height of the nest above the ground or water. In the region considered here the distance generally ranges from four to ten feet. * * *

But little variation occurs in the general types of materials used in constructing the nests. In comparative bulk the average nest is composed approximately as follows: plant down, 60 per cent; tree lichens, 20 per cent;

ground and rock mosses, 10 per cent; tree mosses, 5 per cent; spider webs and fibers of insect cocoons, 1 per cent; miscellaneous material, 4 per cent.

The "shell" of the nest is formed principally of ground and rock mosses mixed with more or less plant down, strongly bound together with cocoon fibers, especially at the rim. Many species of moss are utilized, but generally only one kind is used in an individual nest. In many cases black fibrous tree moss also is used. This part of the nest contains the "miscellaneous material." In the fourteen nests examined this included conifer needles, grass, aspen bark, rotted wood, feathers (from the birds themselves), small leaves, and pieces of spider and insect skeletons (Diptera, Coleoptera, and Hymenoptera).

The exterior of this framework is thickly covered with gray or greenish lichens of the kind occurring on the tree in which the nest is placed. The pieces are bound to the moss by shreds of insect webs and cocoons, or by fibrous tree moss. The main body of the nest, within the sustaining framework, is composed of a thick, soft layer of various kinds of plant down, firmly compacted to form the interior cup. This down retains its shape without being bound with any other material.

Second year additions to a nest are composed mainly of down. Often the only added material is a thick layer of down in the bottom of the cup, and a thinner one on its sides. This method of addition decreases the depth of the cup about a quarter of an inch. In other cases, the rim of the nest is heightened also. If this is done, a new layer of lichen is added to the outside of the nest, making it impossible to determine, from the appearance of the exterior, how many years the nest has been used.

The foregoing paragraph indicates the methods employed by hummingbirds in repairing, or adding to, a last year's nest, a common practice among some species. But often, with this and other species, an entirely new nest is attached to or built upon the remains of a last year's nest; in this case the old nest can be easily recognized by its faded appearance. A series of two, three, or even four such nests, perhaps built during successive seasons, may occasionally be seen. Ridgway (1892, pl. 1) shows a cut of a 4-story nest of a calliope hummingbird.

Eggs.—The calliope hummingbird lays the usual set of two eggs. These are like other hummingbirds' eggs, pure white, without gloss, and varying in shape from oval to elliptical-oval. The measurements of 45 eggs average 12.1 by 8.3 millimeters; the eggs showing the four extremes measure **13.0** by **9.6** and **10.7** by **7.4** millimeters.

Plumages.—No information seems to be available about the development of the juvenal plumage, or about the early nest life of the young calliope hummingbird. In the full juvenal plumage, just after leaving the nest, the young male is practically indistinguishable from the adult female, as it still has the throat more or less streaked or spotted with bronzy brownish or dusky and with no sign of any purple in the gorget; I have seen birds in this plumage up to the first of July; some, but not all, young males have rather more rufous in the tail than the adult female has. Specimens taken in August begin to show more or fewer metallic-purple feathers in the gorget; slight advance toward maturity seems to continue during fall and winter, until the prenuptial molt, late in winter or early in spring, produces the fully adult plumage. The young female is like the adult female, but the upper parts are more bronzy and the feathers are indistinctly margined with dull brownish.

Food.—The calliope, like other hummingbirds, feeds on nectar from flowers and on the minute insects and small spiders that frequent the flowers. The sweet nectar in the flowers undoubtedly attracted the insects, but whether it was the nectar or the insects that first attracted the hummingbird is an open question; the insects may have been the original objects of their search, and the nectar developed a taste for sweets. Any brightly colored flowers are likely to attract these birds, but they seem to show a preference for red flowers, such as the scarlet paintbrush and the red columbine. The yellow flowers of *Mimulus implexus* also furnish a food supply for them. And Grinnell, Dixon, and Linsdale (1930) write: "In early May in the vicinity of Mineral this species appeared to have just one plant, a species of lousewort (*Pedicularis semibarbata*), which it frequented. The flowers grew on long spikes from leaf rosettes under snow-brush. The hummers had to fly down among close-set twiggage of the bushes to get at these flowers. Often they alighted almost on the ground to get at the horizontal tubes. By May 28 they were very active in a tract of blossoming manzanita at 6000 feet, even among snow banks. A female was seen at a snow-plant (*Sarcodes*) where these plants were first coming up, on June 26, beneath red firs."

The calliope hummingbird also hawks for insects on the wing, much after the manner of flycatchers; probably any small insect that becomes available is acceptable, but small species of Diptera, Hymenoptera, or Coleoptera seem to be most often taken. Milton P. Skinner tells me that he has seen one perched on a willow, turning its head and upper body from side to side with an almost clocklike motion, while watching for insects. Others have noticed its sallies into the air for passing insects, which its keen eyes have detected.

Behavior—Several observers have written of the territorial relations of this hummingbird and of its aggressiveness in defending its nesting territory and its foraging range. Grinnell, Dixon, and Linsdale (1930) write:

On a six-acre plot of ground where the activities of individual birds were observed closely through several nesting seasons four separate males kept distinct "stands" each for itself. As nearly as could be determined all the females that were seen on this plot were visitors whose nests were off in a belt of lodgepole pines on Battle Creek Meadows. Females came onto the plot to forage about flowers (*Castilleia*) that were plentiful there, and were then shown attention by the males.

The stand of one male was on a telephone wire directly above quantities of flowers to which a female frequently came. Another male divided his time among the growing tips of three closely adjacent young yellow pines slightly overtopping a sea of snow-brush. Another perched chiefly on one of the highest twigs of a service-berry thicket in an opening among firs. One male was established on the tallest, scrub black oak tip, driving away from the vicinity any approaching forager.

Grinnell and Storer (1924) write:

The males of all our hummingbirds are accustomed to harass birds many times their own size. A Calliope at Mono Meadow was seen to put a Wright Flycatcher to rout, the latter seeking seclusion in a ceanothus thicket. In Yosemite Valley another was seen driving at a Western Robin that was on the ground. The hummer would mount as much as 30 feet into the air and then dash down at the robin. Even Red-tailed Hawks are sometimes "attacked" by these pugnacious midgets. * * *

Like other hummingbirds the Calliope is often attracted by red objects. Whether this is a voluntary action based on esthetic appeal, or a reflex based on food-getting instinct, is problematic. At Chinquapin, on June 14, a female of this species darted into the front of our open tent and poised with seeming interest before a red-labeled baking powder can on the table. Then the bird went out into the sunshine, but it returned again twice before finally going away. Two of our three August records of this species were of individuals which were attracted in the same manner, the object being a red handkerchief in one case, and a sweater of the same color in the other.

Apparently the calliope is not always so aggressive or so pugnacious as are some other hummingbirds, for Henshaw (1886) says that it is "much less obtrusive, and in the contests of its larger neighbors it takes no part. When assailed, as it promptly is by the other kinds, it at once darts away to another spot where it can feed without molestation. It appears to be timid in every way, so much so that it is not an easy bird to collect."

Mr. Wyman (1920) says: "Ordinarily the Black-chins, of which a few haunted the same locality, would drive the Calliopes unmercifully. Once, however, a male Calliope shot close beside me up the hillside, just grazing the grass-tips, driving at a Black-chin that was quietly feeding. Within two feet of the latter he mounted vertically about thirty feet, then dropped like a plummet on the feeding bird, and both flashed down the hill-side with Calliope doing the chasing."

Aretas A. Saunders (1915) observed a bird of this species that "was very belligerent in protecting her home from all birds and other animals that approached too closely. A pine squirrel had ventured into the tree and the mother hummer chased it away immediately, following it a long way through the trees and darting at it first from one side and then from the other. The nest contained half-grown young when first found."

Field marks.—The small size of the calliope hummingbird will help to distinguish it from others, when the opportunity for comparison is favorable. The male is, of course, easy to recognize by the long, spreading, metallic-purple feathers against the snow-white background of its gorget. Aside from its small size, the female can be distinguished from the three species with which it is most likely to be associated by the amount of rufous in the tail; in the female calliope all but the central pair of rectrices have some rufous at the base; in the rufous female all the rectrices are more or less basally rufous; in the female broad-tailed only the three outer feathers are so marked; and in the female black-chinned there is no rufous in the tail.

Fall.—The males start on the southward migration rather early in the summer, or at least desert the females and move away from the breeding grounds. The females and young follow later. In the Yosemite region Grinnell and Storer (1924) saw no males after the end of June. Henshaw (1886), referring to New Mexico, says: "An utterly unaccountable fact noticed in connection with this species was the apparent rarity of females. Up to August 10 I had seen perhaps half a dozen, though constantly on the watch for them, while I had certainly seen not less than ten times that number of males. Subsequently to that date I saw a few more, but nothing like the number of males. By September the young were numerous in certain localities, notably in a large sunflower patch."

Of the migration in the Huachuca Mountains, Arizona, Harry S. Swarth (1904) writes: "After the summer rains the mountains present an exceedingly inviting appearance, particularly so in the higher parts, along the ridges and on various pine covered 'flats,' where, with the green grass, a multitude of brilliantly colored wild flowers springs up, often waist high, and in many places in solid banks of bright colors. In such places, in the late summer of 1902, I found the Calliope Hummingbird quite abundant, feeding close to the ground, and when alighting usually choosing a low bush. * * * The first one was shot August 14, and from then up to the time we left the mountains, September 5, they remained abundant in certain localities; none being seen below 9000 feet."

DISTRIBUTION

Range.—Western North America and Mexico.

Breeding range.—The breeding range of the calliope hummingbird extents **north** to southern British Columbia (150-mile House, Okanagan Landing, and Deer Park); and southwestern Alberta (Banff). **East** to southwestern Alberta (Banff); Montana (Fortine, Polson, rarely Sheep Creek, and Red Lodge); northwestern Wyoming (Yellowstone National Park); Utah (Escalante Mountains); and northern Baja California (Vallecitos). **South** to northern Baja California (Vallecitos); and southern California (Grant Creek, Mount Waterman and Mount Pinos). **West** to western California (Mount Pinos, Glenbrook, Battle Creek, and Steward Springs); Oregon (Gold Hill, Fort Klamath, and Weston); Washington (Yakima, Bumping Lake, and Lake Chelan); and British Columbia (probably Chilliwack and 150-mile House).

Winter range.—During the winter season the species appears to be concentrated in the southern Mexican States of Michoacan (Lake Patzcuaro); Mexico (Ajusco); and Guerrero (Taxco and Amula).

Spring migration.—Early dates of spring arrival are: California—Yosemite Valley, March 2; Azusa, March 6; Whittier, March 20; Grass Valley, April 23. Oregon—Weston, May 3; Anthony, May 6; Fort Klamath, May 16. Washington—Grays Harbor, April 22; Tacoma, May 10; Pullman, May 12. British Columbia—Okanagan Landing, April 25; Burrard Inlet, May 7. Arizona—Superstition Mountain, March 22; Santa Catalina Mountains, April 14. Idaho—Coeur d'Alene, May 20. Montana—Missoula, May 9; Fortine, May 11; Bozeman, May 25.

Fall migration.—Late dates of fall departure are: Montana—Corvallis, September 7; Fortine, September 14. Idaho—Priest River, August 24. New Mexico—Albuquerque, September 16. Arizona—Fort Verde, August 27; Apache, August 28; San Bernardino Ranch, September 11. British Columbia—Okanagan Landing, August 25. Washington—Ahtanum, August 12; Mount Adams, August 14. Nevada—East Humboldt Mountains, September 7. California—Yosemite Valley, September 4; Santa Barbara, September 11; San Bernardino Mountains, September 16.

Casual records.—A specimen was taken at El Paso, Tex., in 1851. Colorado has several records, as follows: One was collected at Breckenridge on June 30, 1882; one was found dead in Cheyenne Canyon, near Colorado Springs, on July 25, 1897; specimens also were reported from this general vicinity on July 18, 1915, and in August 1915; while several were seen on August 27, 1904, at Antonito. One was found dead near Shaunavon, Saskatchewan, on August 22, 1935. The species has been reported as occasional at Wrangell, Alaska, but the evidence is not considered satisfactory.

Egg dates.—California: 46 records, May 27 to July 30; 23 records, June 10 to 28, indicating the height of the season.

Utah: 7 records, July 3 to 23.

CALOTHORAX LUCIFER (Swainson)

LUCIFER HUMMINGBIRD

HABITS

This brilliant little hummer, with its deeply forked gorget of a vivid violet-purple, changing to reddish purple or blue in different lights, is only rarely found across our southwestern border in Arizona and western Texas. Its main range is on the tablelands of Mexico as far south as the City of Mexico, Puebla, and Chiapas. It was first added to our fauna by Henry W. Henshaw (1875), who took a female near Camp Bowie, Ariz., on August 8, 1874, and doubtfully recorded it as *Doricha enicura;* it was later determined to be a lucifer hummingbird. Some years later, in 1901, it was taken in the Chisos Mountains in western Texas by a Biological Survey party. It is apparently fairly common in these mountains, for Mrs. Bailey (1902) says that Mr. Bailey found it "with several other species common in June about the big agaves, which were then in full flower." Still later, Van Tyne and Sutton (1937) report the capture of two specimens in this region but say that the nest has not yet been found there. The lucifer hummingbird may be commoner along our southwestern border than is generally known, for it somewhat resembles Costa's hummingbird in size and color and might easily be overlooked.

Nesting.—Comparatively few nests of the lucifer hummingbird have been found. Wm. Bullock (1825), in his "Six Months in Mexico," gives us the first account of it: "They breed in Mexico in June and July; and the nest is a beautiful specimen of the architectural talen of these birds: it is neatly constructed with cotton, or the down of thistles, to which is fastened on the outside, by some glutinous substance, a white flat lichen resembling ours."

W. W. Brown collected four nests of this species in Tamaulipas, Mexico, between June 15 and July 4, 1924. Three of these are now in the Thayer collection in Cambridge, and one is in the Doe collection in Gainesville, Fla. All the nests were built in shrubs and only a few feet above ground; one was recorded as 4 and one 6 feet up. The nests were made of soft vegetable fibers and down, mixed with the scales of buds, blossoms or seeds, and bits of lichen, all completely covered and held in place with cobwebs or very fine fibers.

Eggs.—The lucifer hummingbird lays the usual hummingbird set of two eggs, which are indistinguishable from the eggs of other hummingbirds of similar size. The measurements of 6 eggs average 12.7 by 9.7 millimeters; the eggs showing the four extremes measure 13.8 by 10.0, 12.4 by 10.1, and 12.0 by 9.2 millimeters.

Plumages.—Not much seems to be known about the immature plumages of this species, but the sexes are apparently alike in juvenal plumages and resemble the adult female, though a little grayer on the under parts. One young male, collected September 15, has one violet-purple feather on its throat, indicating an approach to the adult plumage during the fall and winter. I have seen adults of both sexes molting from September to December, during which time the complete annual molt probably occurs.

Food.—We have no definite data on the food of this species, which probably does not differ materially from that of other hummingbirds. It is said to be devoted to the flower clusters of the tall, flowering agave, where it finds a bountiful supply of nectar, as well as numerous small insects and spiders.

Mr. Bullock (1825) gives the following interesting account of its spider hunting:

The house I resided in at Xalapa for several weeks was only one story high, enclosing, like most of the Spanish houses, a small garden in the centre, the roof projecting six or seven feet from the walls, covering a walk all round, and leaving a small space only between the tiles, and the trees which grew in the centre. From the edges of these tiles to the branches of the trees in the garden, the spiders had spread their innumerable webs so closely and compactly that they resembled a net. I have frequently watched with much amusement the cautious peregrination of the humming bird, who, advancing beneath the web, entered the various labyrinths and cells in search of entangled flies, but as the larger spiders did not tamely surrender their booty, the invader was often compelled to retreat; being within a few feet, I could observe all their evolutions with great precision. The active little bird generally passed once or twice round the court, as if to reconnoitre his ground, and commenced his attack by going carefully under the nets of the wily insect, and seizing by surprise the smallest entangled flies, or those that were most feeble. In ascending the angular traps of the spider great care and skill was required; sometimes he had scarcely room for his little wings to perform their office, and the least deviation would have entangled him in the complex machinery of the web, and involved him in ruin. It was only the works of the smaller spider that he durst attack, as the larger sort rose to the defence of their citadels, when the besieger would shoot off like a sunbeam, and could only be traced by the luminous glow of his refulgent colors. The bird generally spent about ten minutes in this predatory excursion, and then alighted on a branch of the Avocata to rest and refresh himself, placing his crimson star-like breast to the sun, which then presented all the glowing fire of the ruby and surpassing in lustre the diadem of monarchs.

Behavior.—The same observer writes:

When attending their young, they attack any bird indiscriminately that approaches the nest. Their motions, when under the influence of anger or fear, are very violent, and their flight rapid as an arrow; the eye cannot follow them, but the shrill, piercing shriek which they utter on the wing may be heard when the bird is invisible. They attack the eyes of the larger birds, and their sharp, needle-like bill is a truly formidable weapon in this kind of warfare. Nothing can exceed their fierceness when one of their own species invades their territory during the breeding season. Under the influence of jealousy they become perfect furies; their throats swell, their crests, tails, and wings expand; they fight in the air (uttering a shrill noise) till one falls exhausted to the ground. I witnessed a combat of this kind near Otumba, during a heavy fall of rain, every separate drop of which I supposed sufficient to have beaten the puny warriors to the earth.

Field marks.—The lucifer hummingbird might be mistaken, by the casual observer, for Costa's hummingbird, as the two are somewhat alike in size and in the shape and color of the gorget, but there are decided differences in shape and color pattern. In Costa's the entire top of the head is of the same brilliant violet-purple as the gorget, whereas in the lucifer hummer only the throat gorget, with its elongated lateral extension is of this brilliant color. Furthermore, the male lucifer has a deeply forked tail, with very narrow lateral feathers. The female lucifer has a rounded, or double rounded, tail and buffy under parts. But the best field mark for both sexes is the long, decidedly decurved bill; no other North American hummingbird has such a curved bill.

DISTRIBUTION

Range.—Southern Mexico; accidental in Arizona and Texas.

The normal range of the lucifer hummingbird is from Jalisco (Bolanos) south to Guerrero (Taxco and Chilpancingo) and east to Puebla (Chalchicomula).

Casual records.—A specimen was collected in the Chisos Mountains, Texas, on June 7, 1901; and an adult female was taken at Fort Bowie, Ariz., on August 8, 1874.

Egg dates.—Mexico: 6 records, June 15 to July 4.

AMAZILIA TZACATL TZACATL (de la Llave)

RIEFFER'S HUMMINGBIRD

PLATES 71, 72

HABITS

CONTRIBUTED BY ALEXANDER FRANK SKUTCH

This glittering green hummingbird, with a bright chestnut tail, abundant and familiar over a wide range in the warmer portions of both Americas, is merely a wandering straggler within the territory of the United States, where it has been recorded only twice, both times in the neighborhood of Brownsville, Tex., just north of the Mexican border. Its breeding range extends from the Mexican State of Tamaulipas to eastern Ecuador. In the Central American portion of this range it is, from Panama to Guatemala, the member of the family most numerous in the cultivated areas of the humid Caribbean lowlands. Thus Charles W. Richmond (quoted by Bendire, 1895) wrote that it "is extremely abundant in the lowlands of eastern Nicaragua. It outnumbers in individuals all the other (five) species of Hummingbirds found in the same region. On the Escondido River this species is confined to the banana plantations and the shrubbery around the houses, where it finds an abundance of food and good nesting sites. It is the plantation Hummer, only two other species occasionally wandering into the plantations from the forest, which is the home of the other species." Similarly George K. Cherrie (1892) affirms that in Costa Rica it is "the most abundant species about San José, and indeed the most abundant species found on either coast." This is certainly true, in my own experience, of the Caribbean coastlands of Costa Rica; but on the Pacific side of the country Rieffer's hummingbird is abundant only in the more humid regions from the Gulf of Nicoya southward. About the shores of the Gulf it mingles with the related cinnamomeous hummingbird (*Amazilia cinnamomea*), and along the Pacific side of Central America to the northward, where the dry season is long and severe, it is entirely replaced by the latter species, which here is almost as familiar and abundant on the plantations, in the flower gardens, and in the light, open woodlands as its green-breasted relative on the opposite coast.

A bird of the clearings, Rieffer's hummingbird is found in the forest only in the more open glades and seldom far from its edge. While most abundant in the lowlands, it extends upward into the highlands to an altitude (in Costa Rica) of about 5,000 feet and (on the authority of Mr. Cherrie) is found occasionally as high as 6,000 feet.

Courtship.—No hummingbirds, so far as we know, actually associate in pairs; and the male never joins a female in the duties of a nest. The purpose of the male's courtship, then, is to effect temporary union with the female, resulting in the fecundation of the eggs, not to attach unto himself a mate. Two strikingly different modes of courtship are found in this great family, and may be characterized as "dynamic" and "static." In the former, well exemplified by the broad-tailed hummingbird (*Selasphorus platycercus*), the male gives a thrilling aerial display, which centers around the female, rising high into the air and swooping down in front of her as she perches, swinging back and forth in a great, open U, the arms of which may be 50 or 60 feet high. In the "static" courtship the male establishes his headquarters in one particular spot, where he is to be found day after day during the breeding season. Usually he has a favorite perch, where he rests to deliver untiringly the calls, frequently weak and unmelodious, which draw the females' attention to himself. Among many species, the males group themselves into assemblies made up of two to many individuals, but frequently they are found "singing" alone. This "static" form of courtship is far more prevalent among the Central American hummingbirds than the set aerial display. So far as we know, the same species does not practice both types of courtship.

The courtship of Rieffer's hummingbird is neither persistent nor likely to draw the bird-watcher's attention. In a number of years past, in districts where the species is abundant, I have not once witnessed an aerial display of definite form comparable to that of the broad-tailed hummingbird. So far as it has any particular mode of courtship, this appears to be of the "static" type; but even in the less arduous occupation of sitting and calling, Rieffer's humming-bird is far less assiduous than many others of the Central American species. The scanty information I have on this subject is sum-marized in an entry made in my notebook on October 17, 1936, while I lived at Rivas de El General, in southwestern Costa Rica:

"These mornings, when I stand in the old cornfield at dawn to watch the golden-naped woodpeckers arise, I hear the quaint little songs of the Rieffer's hummingbirds. This morning I distinctly heard three of them, apparently situated at different points along the edge of the forest, at the head of the clearing. The one I watched was perching on a twig in the top of a fallen tree, 6 feet above ground, just outside the edge of the forest. The 'song' is quite distinct from that of any other hummingbird that I know, and easy to recognize once it has been heard; but as usual with hummingbirds' songs, I find it difficult to paraphrase in human words, or to describe it in such a fashion as to give anyone who has not heard it a notion of its quaint pleasantness. *Tse-we ts' we* is as near as I can come to it in alphabetical notation; but I am not well satisfied with what I have written. Sometimes the phrase is repeated several times con-tinuously; sometimes the bird sings *Tse-we ts' we tse-we*. These hum-mingbirds sing most actively in the dawn, and less and less as the day grows older.

"I first heard Rieffer's hummingbirds singing here last December, when I watched a bird that perched very near the position of the one I watched this morning. Probably he was the same individual. During the greater part of the dry season I failed to notice the odd little song; but now it has been a month or so since it was resumed. The males seem to have a singing assembly here at the edge of the forest, where they are to be found every morning; but they perform less constantly than many other kinds of hummingbirds."

Nesting.—In the Caribbean lowlands of Central America Rieffer's hummingbird has been found nesting at all seasons, and there are records of nests, from one part or the other of this region, for each of the 12 months. In the Province of Bocas del Toro in western Panama the majority of the nests were discovered during the drier weather from January until May. Although in the lowlands the nesting period, for the species as a whole, is unusually long, even for tropical birds, and is peculiar in including both the dry and rainy seasons, we do not know how many broods each female may raise in a year, or what period the breeding activities of a single individual may cover.

At Rivas, on the Pacific slope of southern Costa Rica, the hummingbirds of several species, including Rieffer's, behave in their choice of a breeding season essentially as the members of the family that dwell in the higher mountains, although here the altitude is only 3,000 feet and the avifauna in general is that of the humid lowlands, with a slight admixture of species representative of the subtropical zone. In this region there is, in most years, a pronounced dry season of four months, from December to March, inclusive, while the remaining eight months are very wet. The great majority of birds of all kinds breed between the vernal equinox and the June solstice; but there is a scattering of nests of birds belonging to the most diverse families at all periods of the year. The hummingbirds, however, breed chiefly during October, November, December, and January, the very months when nests belonging to birds of other families are fewest.

During a residence of a year and a half at Rivas, I recorded six nests of Rieffer's hummingbirds during November, December, and January but not a single one during the other nine months, when nests were just as assiduously sought by myself and the boys I had reporting them to me. Flowers, although many are to be found throughout the year, reach their maximum profusion *in the clearings* during December and January, and their minimum abundance at the end of the dry season in March.

The highest point at which I have seen a nest of Rieffer's hummingbird is the Hacienda Las Cóncavas, near Cartago, Costa Rica, where, at an altitude of 4,500 feet, I found a nest with two well-feathered nestlings on November 3, 1935. The bird was nesting in the wettest and least agreeable season of the year, at a time when scarcely any of the Central American birds of other families breed at so high an elevation.

The nests of *Amazilia* are placed in trees or bushes in the clearings where the birds reside, without any distinct preference for any particular type. Frequently a thorny lime or orange tree is chosen, or a bougainvillea vine; but as often a thornless kind is selected for the nesting site. Sometimes even a low herbaceous plant is favored. I have found their elevation to vary from 2 to 20 feet from the ground. The open cup is constructed in a variety of situations but almost invariably on some slender support. If some variety of citrus tree has been chosen, it may rest in the angle between an upright branch and one of its large thorns attached to both by cobwebs; or in another kind of plant it may be placed in the axil of a slender leaf stalk or in the angle between a thin horizontal branch and a vertical stem. Sometimes a leaf alone suffices for its foundation. One of the most attractively situated I ever found was attached near the drooping tip of a large frond of the thorny pejibaye palm (*Guilielma utilis*); another was fastened to the palmately compound leaf of the Brazilian rubber tree; a third straddled the slender rhachis of the pinnately compound leaf of an akee (*Blighia sapida*), supported on each side by the opposite leaflets. At times the bird selects a very inadequate foundation. I once found a nest attached to a frail and decaying twig, which in its descent from somewhere higher in the tree had caught on a horizontal branch and hung loosely beneath it, draped about with the fronds of a slender, creeping species of polypody fern, which covered the bough and dropped in festoons below it. The one requirement of a nesting site is a horizontal support sufficiently slender to be grasped by the bird's feet—for from such a perch the building operations are always begun—close to some vertical or oblique support to which the side of the nest may be anchored. Frequently the nest is situated above or close beside a path along which people are constantly passing.

The nest is an open cup, formed exteriorly of weathered strips of grass, leaves, bits of weed, fibers, and the like, and abundantly lined with soft, felted plant down, the whole bound together by cobwebs liberally supplied. The outer surface is tastefully decorated with gray lichens and green mosses, which sometimes are allowed to hang in long, waving festoons beneath it. Rarely, as in the nest I found on Barro Colorado Island, this ornamentation is very sparingly applied, so that the prevailing color of the exterior is grayish or tawny, from the fibers and down employed in its construction. Sometimes an otherwise beautiful nest is marred by a long piece of withered grass leaf, used in building the foundation, and carelessly allowed to hang beneath it. The dimensions of a typical nest are: External diameter 1¾ inches, height 1¼ inches; internal diameter 1¼ inches, depth ⅞ inch.

The moss- and lichen-covered nests blend so well with the green foliage among which they are usually placed that it would be extremely difficult to find them, especially when the white eggs are hidden by the emerald bird, if the female sat more closely. The locations of several nests, which otherwise I should probably never have found, were betrayed by the birds' darting off as I passed within a few yards of them. The instinct that leads the birds to build a nest to blend so well with its setting lacks fulfillment in a corresponding instinct to utilize this advantage by remaining motionless. Perhaps at the approach of really formidable enemies other than man the female does remain motionless on her nest; but when most small creatures, lizards or birds even many times her size, venture too near, she merely darts at them and usually puts them promptly to flight. Individual birds, however, differ greatly in the closeness with which they cover their eggs and young. One female, the closest sitter of all I found, whose nest was built in a young lime tree in a nursery where men were frequently at work, would allow me to approach within arm's length before deserting, to return within a few minutes and settle down on her eggs directly before me if I waited quietly at this distance.

I could scarcely have desired a nest located more conveniently for study than the first of this species I ever found. I was at the time engaged chiefly in work with the microscope in a little frame building that served as office and laboratory at the now abandoned experiment station of the United Fruit Co. beside the great Changüinola Lagoon, 20 miles from Almirante, Panama. On the afternoon of December 19, I raised my head from my work and noticed a hummingbird, of a kind still unknown to me, perched on the petiole of a ramie plant (*Boehmeria nivea*) just outside the window, scarcely 3 yards from where I sat and separated from me only by a screen. An oddness in her manner of perching attracted my attention, and, looking more intently, I perceived something light colored almost hidden beneath her. When she flew off, I went out to examine her perch and found there a little tuft of plant down, fastened in the angle between the hairy petiole and the stem with cobweb, a piece of white thread, and several hairs from cattle, which grazed all about the small enclosure. During the succeeding days, as I sat at my work table poring over bits of banana tissue, *Amazilia* labored steadily at her growing nest. The rite of adding a new bit of material followed an invariable routine. Returning with a tuft of down in her slender bill, she would alight softly on the incipient nest, push in the stuff where it was needed, and then proceed with the shaping of the structure. She bent down her head and, moving around and around, with her long bill shaped the substance to the contour of her body. As she pressed the yielding down more closely to her breast, she erected the bronze-green feathers of her crown, and her folded wings vibrated as if she thrilled in anticipation of the completed nest and the nestlings it was intended to cradle. Then she sat facing in a set direction; and from the way her body bounced up and down I concluded she must be kneading the material together with her toes, although, as they were hidden beneath her, I was unable to see them in action. Sometimes she would dart away and then, as if the kneading and shaping had not been done to her satisfaction, return with empty bill to continue the moulding operations. So, as the nest grew, it became just large enough to fit snugly about the central portion of her body, leaving neck and head and rump and tail protruding beyond its rim.

Hummingbirds of this species do not seem to have any prescribed order for the addition of the various elements of which the nest is composed. This particular bird began with a wad of down, then bound around it strips of fibrous vegetable material, such as grass blades softened by partial decay, and fastened them there with cobweb. Others begin with strips of grass and banana-leaf epidermis, adding the down later when they can get it. It seems to be merely a matter of convenience or luck in finding the proper materials. I once found a nest built entirely of fine grass and pieces of weeds but so devoid of lining that the eggs touched the branch on which it rested. This was doubtless because down for the lining was not available; and under favorable conditions the downy lining is added simultaneously with the fibrous materials, which impart rigidity to the structure. Although the lichens and mosses appear to be merely an ornament of the nest, and do not constitute an essential part of the structure, they are often added before the foundation portions of the walls are completed.

Because of torrential rains that interrupted her work, this hummingbird required 12 days for the completion of her nest; but others, building during more favorable weather, may finish their task in a week.

The attachment of Rieffer's hummingbird to a nest site once chosen is very strong. Soon after the eggs had hatched in the nest whose construction has been described, the nestlings were attacked and killed by ants. The deserted nest was then used as a quarry by another hummingbird, who removed most of the down to her own new structure on the opposite side of the building. Six weeks after the destruction of the nestlings, all that remained of their nest was its basal portion, a shallow cup of grass and fibers with hardly any lining, darkened and discolored by the elements. The original builder now reclaimed it, added fresh bits of grass to the walls, increasing their height, and attached new lichens to the exterior. With the nest in this condition, she laid her two eggs upon the hard, impacted bottom; but afterward, in the intervals of incubation, she continued to build up and line the old structure, until at length it was as comfortable, and appeared as solid, as when new. In Guatemala I once found a nest containing eggs, built upon an older nest of the same kind that had turned sideways.

Eggs.—As with the great majority of hummingbirds, Rieffer's lays two eggs. The interval between the laying of the first and second is two days (about 48 hours). The eggs are pure white and oblong or oblong-ovate, often with little difference between the two ends. The measurements of six eggs removed temporarily from their nests in Honduras average 14 by 8.7 millimeters; the eggs showing the four extremes measure 14.2 by 8.6, 14 by 9.1, and 13.5 by 8.6 millimeters.

Young.—As she builds, so the female hummingbird incubates quite alone; and no male of her kind takes an interest in her labors. During her recesses she continues to seek fresh downy material and cobweb to add to her nest, even when it is already well padded. The period of incubation is normally 16 days. I have never enjoyed a better opportunity to watch the care and development of the young than was offered by the nest in the ramie plant, just outside the window before my work table in Panama.

The newly emerged nestlings were like ugly grubs, blind, black-skinned, and naked except for two lines of short, tawny down extending the length of the back, one on each side of the middle line. The slender bill of the adult was represented by a mere bump, hardly longer than that of a newly hatched pauraque (*Nyctidromus albicollis*). At intervals one of the graceless creatures reared up spasmodically, opening wide its yellow-lined mouth in a voiceless call for nourishment, to sink again exhausted, with drooping head, into the nest. The mother's time for the first week was divided between brooding and feeding her offspring, which she did in the customary manner of the family, by regurgitation. Sitting upright on the rim of the nest, she thrust the rapierlike bill into the nearest gaping mouth, pushing it down until it seemed that it must pierce the entrails of the nestling. Then with a convulsive jerking of the body she regurgitated a portion of the contents of her crop into that of her infant. Both nestlings were as a rule fed at each return to the nest, and often each was given food twice, alternately. When the nestlings are older, sometimes each is fed four times at a single visit of their mother. After feeding, she usually returned to brooding, repeatedly thrusting out her long, white tongue as she sat on the nest. Although during the day she flew off, twittering her complaint, at my too near approach, at night she would permit me to advance and touch her on the nest, in the beam of a flashlight.

With these constant ministrations the youngsters grew amazingly, and at the age of six days, when the beady black eyes first began to peep out of the still-naked head, and the bill had lengthened considerably, they quite filled the bottom of their downy cup. The next day the eyes were fully open, and the tawny tips of the feathers began to protrude from their sheaths. But at this stage the nest was invaded by fire ants, and my observations temporarily interrupted. Six weeks later the mother returned, repaired the old nest, laid two more eggs, and hatched from them two nestlings, which lived to take wing. They passed through a most eventful infancy, attended by many mishaps and tribulations. First the renovated nest became loose on the supporting stem; and I was obliged to fasten it up with pins to save the occupants from spilling out. The leaves that had originally shaded it died and fell away with age, exposing the still unfeathered nestlings to the full glare of the afternoon sun. They sat with necks stretched upward, mouths widely gaping, and glassy, staring eyes. Once I saw the mother perch on the rim of the nest with wings partly spread, attempting to shield them from the sun's rays; but her position was not well chosen and her shadow fell to one side of them, and they continued to pant. Later she covered them on the nest; but one nestling, pushing its head out between her wing and body, continued to gasp. Fearing they might succumb, I attempted to arrange a sunshade; but I had not yet learned the toughness of young hummingbirds.

Their vitality was amazing. Exposure to the sun, a 4-foot fall when the old nest finally broke to pieces, and repeated handling by fingers many times larger than themselves had not killed them. Now a still more severe ordeal awaited them—24 hours of rain with hardly a let-up, and some beating tropical downpours in the interval. The mother had definitely ceased to cover them, and the scant foliage of the ramie, which remained above the nest I had improvised for them, afforded slight protection. After a night of this severe punishment, I watched them through much of the dreary day. When the heavy downpours came, and the big drops beat ceaselessly upon them, the 2-week-old birds sat in the improvised nest with eyes closed and bills pointing straight to heaven, shaking their heads from side to side when struck by a particularly large drop. Their budding plumage gave little comfort; and the cool rain soaked them to the skin. *Amazilia* attended them faithfully the whole day. At intervals between the heavy showers she came, her black bill dusted with the white pollen of the banana flowers in which she had been probing, perched on the rim of the paper cup, and fed her wet offspring. Often one or the other or sometimes both of the nestlings refused to accept nourishment, when she gently touched its bill once or twice with hers as if to coax it to take food; but often it was too wet and miserable to be tempted. At each visit she ran over the plumage of the nestlings, or a part of the nest, with her tongue, an act I never witnessed in dry weather; and from the way her throat worked, I concluded she was sucking up some of the excess water. And with these unfailing maternal ministrations, the unfledged birds pulled through the ordeal. Then I began to understand something of the secret of the wide distribution and great abundance of the species. Their nesting habits appear very imperfect, for the nest seems to sacrifice utility to beauty, and in a region where a large proportion of the birds build some sort of covered nest to protect its occupants from burning sun and beating rain, theirs is open to the sky, and moreover is too small to accommodate the two nestlings until they are ready to leave it. Their success as a species resides rather in the inherent toughness of fiber of the nestlings, coupled with the indefatigable attentions of the devoted mother.

Before leaving the nest, the fledglings acquired the plumage of the adults, although the colors were not so bright, and tufts of brown down still adhere to the tips of the green feathers, giving them a rather rough appearance. Two days before their departure from the nest, when I attempted to touch them they would ruffle up their feathers and attack a finger with their bills, which were still considerably shorter than the adult's. The first bird flew off as I was examining the nest, at an age of 21 days. The folded wings spread and began to whir, in a moment it rose into the air, and, uttering a low twitter as it went, flew away until it was lost from sight among the bananas. The maiden flight showed power and control. The second bird left two days later, aged 22 days. The mother continued to feed them by regurgitation for a number of days after their departure; but I am unable to state just how long.

The nestling period of these birds was perhaps a few days longer than normal because of the untoward circumstances attending it. In the case of another nest I watched in Panama, the nestlings took flight at the ages of 19 and 20 days, respectively. From a nest near Tela, Honduras, the nestlings departed at ages of 18 to 19 days, respectively, while from a second nest both departed at the age of 19 days.

Rieffer's hummingbird sits lightly on her nest, and a greater portion of her body protudes above it than is the case with most other birds. This is the outcome of the closeness with which she molds it to the central portion of her body and then often continues to add down to the interior after the eggs have been laid, further decreasing the size of the cavity. The nestling, at the time of its departure, is almost as large as the adult, and naturally the two are very much crowded in the small nest. Before they depart the wall is always more or less flared outward by the pressure of their bodies, while one or the other is forced to an uncomfortable position on the rim. Especially when the nest is softened by water during rainy periods, it is sometimes literally burst asunder by the pressure of the growing bodies it contains. In one case that came under my observation the nest split down the side, then turned almost inside out and dropped its two helpless occupants on the ground. I found them next morning, after a showery night, in the grass beneath the ruined structure, among wandering fire ants, which probably would eventually have devoured them had I not replaced them on the remains of their nest, where they sat a week more before they were able to fly away.

Plumages.—Dr. Frank M. Chapman (1925) states that "there is but little variation with sex, age, or season in this species. The male usually has the throat more solid green and the abdomen darker than the female, from which young males are not distinguishable."

Behavior.—About the habitations of men, where these humming-birds seem most at home, they spend their time probing for insects or nectar in the great red blossoms of *Hibiscus sinensis*, which is everywhere a favorite shrub for hedges, dooryards, and the town plaza, or else in the blue trumpets of the *Thunbergia*, which scrambles over fences and up the sides of houses; or they hover before the coral vine, the blue flowers of *Clitoria*, or the blossoms of some fruit tree. At other times they enter the banana groves and poise beside the long, pendent inflorescences, where they probe the white blossoms clustered beneath their heavy red bracts, swarming with the little, black, stingless bees, which gather their pollen and rich nectar. Early in the morning one may see them bathing on the dewy surface of the broad banana leaves, over which they glide with vibrant wings, gathering up the heavy dew drops in their plumage. They are no more sociable than other kinds of hummingbirds and dart fiercely at another of the same or a different species if he ventures too near; but the bird attacked almost invariably retreats at the first dashing onslaught, closely followed by the pursuer; and I have never witnessed two birds engage in an encounter face to face, or one inflict injury on another.

A surprising aspect of the behavior of the Rieffer's hummingbirds, as I watched them near Almirante, Panama, during the early part of 1929, was the frequency with which they pilfered material from one another's nests. About our house at the research station larceny of this kind was shockingly prevalent; and I believe that about half of the failures to rear a brood that came to my attention were to be attributed to this unsocial practice. The condition was probably local and possibly even seasonal; I have never noticed it elsewhere; but then never elsewhere have I seen so great a concentration of hummingbirds' nests. It was induced to a large extent, I think, by the inadequate supply of down for lining the nests, added to the close proximity in which they were placed, sometimes 100 feet or less from each other, which made robbery easier than a long expedition afield to gather soft materials. To this may be added the hummingbird's passion for bringing more down to a nest in which incubation is already in progress and which is already quite adequately lined. The presence of eggs did not render a nest sacred to other hummingbirds, which sometimes continued to tear away material until they fell to the ground.

One unfortunate Rieffer's hummingbird, which tried to establish a nest in a cashew tree growing in a corner of our yard, was so impeded in her efforts to build by the thievery of her neighbors that at the end of a month of fairly continuous effort she had nothing to show for her labor. With the usual attachment of her kind to one particular location, she tried to build only in the cashew tree and an avocado tree standing close beside it. A removal to a more distant site might have brought her better fortune. In these two trees she made at least 12 fresh beginnings of her nest, each of which was in a short time more or less completely obliterated. The behavior of this bird is recorded in detail in my article in The Auk (Skutch, 1931); and to this the reader must be referred.

DISTRIBUTION

Range.—Eastern Mexico, Central America, and northwestern South America; casual in southern Texas; nonmigratory.

Rieffer's hummingbird ranges **north** to northern Veracruz (Tampico); and British Honduras (Orange Walk and Corosal). **East** to British Honduras (Corosal and Belize); Honduras (Tela and La Ceiba); Nicaragua (Matagalpa, La Libertad, and Bluefields); Panama (Gatun and Barro Colorado Island); western Venezuela (Chama); central Colombia (Puerto Berrio, Bogota, and Fusugasugo); and western Ecuador (Perucho, Babohoyo, and Chimbo). **South** to Ecuador (Chimbo); Costa Rica (Boruca, Puntarenas, and Barranca); and southwestern Guatemala (Santa Lucia). **West** to Guatemala (Santa Lucia); western Tabasco (Teapa); eastern Oaxaca (Choapan, Playa Vincente, and Tuxtepec); and Veracruz (Orizaba, Cordoba, and Tampico).

The birds found in Ecuador have been described as a geographic race or subspecies.

The claim of this species to a place in the list of birds of the United States rests upon two specimens captured at Fort Brown, Tex., in June and July 1876.

Egg dates.—Central America, Caribbean lowlands from Panama to Guatemala: 24 records, January to December, covering every month.

Costa Rica, Pacific slope, 3,000 feet: 6 records, November 7 to January 9. Caribbean slope, 4,500 feet: 1 record (nestlings), November 3.

AMAZILIA YUCATANENSIS CHALCONOTA Oberholser

BUFF-BELLIED HUMMINGBIRD

HABITS

This is another Mexican species that extends its range northward into the valley of the lower Rio Grande in Texas. It is the northern form of a species inhabiting eastern Mexico and Yucatan, from the Rio Grande to extreme southeastern Mexico, which has been divided into three subspecies. This race is described by Ridgway (1911) as "similar to *A. y. cerviniventris*, but under parts of body much paler (light cinnamon buff to pale pinkish buff) and green of upper parts averaging more bronzy."

The buff-bellied hummingbird was added to our fauna by Dr. James C. Merrill (1878), who took the first specimen within our borders on the military reservation of Fort Brown, Tex., on August 17, 1876. He found it to be an "abundant summer visitor" and says that "it seems perfectly at home among the dense, tangled thickets, darting rapidly among the bushes and creeping vines, and is with difficulty obtained. A rather noisy bird, its shrill cries usually first attract one's attention to its presence."

While George F. Simmons and I were collecting with R. D. Camp, near Brownsville, Tex., in 1923, Captain Camp told us that this hummingbird had become very rare in that vicinity, but we saw two or three in the tangled thickets along a resaca near town; they tried unsuccessfully to shoot one, but I could plainly see the long, rufous tail and the buff underparts, which served to identify the species. As many nests have been taken in Cameron County, Tex., this hummingbird is probably still rather common in the open woodlands and chaparral thickets in that vicinity, coming out occasionally into the open gardens and about the plantations, though much of its original habitat has been destroyed to make room for citrus orchards and vegetable farms.

Nesting.—The first nest found within the United States is thus described by Dr. Merrill (1878): "A Hummer's nest, undoubtedly made by this species, was found in September, 1877, within the fort. It was placed on the fork of a dead, drooping twig of a small tree on the edge of a path through a thicket; it was about seven feet from the ground, and contained the shrivelled body of a young bird. The nest is made of the downy blossoms of the tree on which it is placed, bound on the outside with cobwebs, and rather sparingly covered with lichens."

Major Bendire (1895) writes:

I have eight of these nests before me, all taken in Cameron County, Texas, which are readily distinguishable from those of other species breeding in the United States whose nests are known. They are composed of shreds of vegetable fiber, thistle down, and an occasional specimen is lined with a vegetable substance resembling brown cattle hair; but the majority are lined with thistle down. The outside is covered with bits of dry flower blossoms, shreds of bark, and small pieces of light-colored lichens, securely fastened in place by spider webs. The nests are neatly built, and are usually saddled on a small, drooping limb, or placed on a fork of a horizontal twig, at distances of from 3 to 8 feet from the ground. Small trees or bushes of the Anachuita (*Cordia boissieri*) ebony and hackberry seem to furnish their favorite nesting sites, though occasionally a nest is found in a willow. An average-sized nest measures 1⅜ inches in outer diameter by 1¼ inches in height; the inner cup is seven-eighths of an inch in width by five-eights of an inch in depth. Open woods and the edges of chaparral thickets near roads or paths seem to be preferred for purposes of nidification. Probably two broods are raised in a season. The earliest nesting record I have is April 23; the latest June 16.

There are three nests of the buff-bellied hummingbird in the Thayer collection in Cambridge, one collected in Tamaulipas, Mexico, and two in Cameron County, Tex. The latter two compare very well with the nests described above, in location, in size, and in materials used in construction. But the Tamaulipas nest, collected on April 15, 1908, is quite different; it is a very tall structure, apparently a series of three nests built upon the top of one another, perhaps the work of three seasons or the home of three broods; it measures 2½ inches in overall height and 1½ inches in external diameter; the inner cavity is 1 inch in diameter and is hollowed to the depth of 1 inch, this hollow being nearly twice as deep as in the other nests. The nest is made of thistledown, some with the seeds attached, and other woolly substances, reinforced with very fine twigs, weed stems, small dry leaves, strips of inner bark and lichens, all bound together with spider webs; and it is lined with pale buff down.

Eggs.—So far as I know, the buff-bellied hummingbird always lays two eggs. These are oval or elliptical-oval and pure white. The measurements of 50 eggs average 13.24 by 8.65 millimeters; the eggs showing the four extremes measure **15.3** by 8.9, 14.0 by 9.4, and **11.8** by **7.7** millimeters.

Plumages.—The sexes are alike in all plumages, and young birds are much like their parents, although the green of the throat is more mixed with grayish buff.

DISTRIBUTION

Range.—Coastal regions of southern Texas and eastern Mexico.

The buff-bellied hummingbird breeds **north** to the lower Rio Grande Valley in Texas (Brownsville). From this point the range extends southward through eastern Tamaulipas (Matamoros and Altamira); eastern San Luis Potosi (Valles); Veracruz (Tampico, Cordoba, and Tlacotalapan); Yucatan (Merida); Quintana Roo (Palmul and Acomal); to Chiapas (Ocozucuantla).

The race of this species that is found in Texas and northeastern Mexico is known as *Amazilia y. chalconota*. Other races occur in southern Mexico and in Yucatan.

While apparently not regularly migratory, nevertheless it appears that those birds breeding in the Rio Grande Valley leave in October for winter quarters in southern Tamaulipas and Veracruz, returning in April.

Egg dates.—Texas: 30 records, March 24 to July 16; 15 records, May 9 to June 9, indicating the height of the season.

AMAZILIA SALVINI (Brewster)

SALVIN'S HUMMINGBIRD

HABITS

This seems to be a doubtful species, and evidently is only a hybrid. Only two specimens are known. The type, an adult male, was taken at Nacosari, Sonora, Mexico, by John C. Cahoon, on March 31, 1887, for William Brewster (1893); this specimen is now in the collection of the Museum of Comparative Zoology at Cambridge. The other specimen, now in the collection of Dr. Louis B. Bishop (1906), was taken for him by H. W. Marsden at Parmerlee, Cochise County. Ariz., on July 4, 1905; this is a young female.

The best authorities seem to agree that *salvini* is a hybrid between one of the races of *Amazilia violiceps* and one of the races of *Cynanthus latirostris*, but which race of each is involved seems open to discussion. Ludlow Griscom (1934) writes:

A careful study of the color and structural characters of the type convinces me that *Cyanomyia salvini* Brewster is a hybrid between *Amazilia violiceps conjuncta* and *Cynanthus latirostris* Swainson. These closely related genera differ in (1) *Amazilia* has the frontal feathering extending forward to and partially concealing the nasal operculum; (2) the tail is slightly forked in *Cynanthus*, truncate in the section of *Amazilia* with which we are here concerned. In these respects *salvini* is an *Amazilia* as to the frontal feathering, but the tail is slightly forked as in *Cynanthus*. In size *salvini* resembles the *Cynanthus*, a considerably smaller bird than *A. violiceps*. The color characters combine the two supposed parents perfectly. The glittering violet crown plaque of *violiceps* combined with the plain green of *Cynanthus* produces a glittering bluish green plaque. The green upper back fading to dusky green is a perfect combination of the dusky versus dark green upperparts of the supposed parents. The tail is dark green instead of steel blue versus dull dusky bronzy green, and the feathers have the gray tips of *Cynanthus*. The underparts are white medially as in the *Amazilia*, but the sides of the neck and chest are glittering bluish green, passing to green on the sides and flanks, just as in *Cynanthus*.

The nest of the hybrid form has, apparently, never been found, but Robert T. Moore has sent me the following note on a nest of *Amazilia violiceps ellioti*, which very likely is one of the parent forms:

"This was found by Chester Lamb on a 'thorny bush overhanging a creek' in a wooded arroyo at Copalito, northeastern Sinaloa, July 29, 1936. The *situ* was the crotch of a dead twig 3 feet up from the ground at the extremity of a branch of the bush. The bulk of the nest is composed of the whitish cotton from the pod of the palo-blanco tree. The body of the structure is completely and tightly bound together on the entire external portion with very fine webbing, which may have been obtained from a spiderweb but looks surprisingly like the fine threads of the cotton itself. If so, they have been very carefully pulled out and each one worked separately into the nest. Three small dead twigs are attached to the external part, but the chief decoration is a very beautiful 'pale glaucous-green' lichen. I have not seen this particular lichen used elsewhere, and I am sure it is not the oak lichen, commonly used by the white-eared hummingbird. The interior of the nest has no lining other than the cotton itself, but there are four lichens well inside of the margin of the nest. The characteristic feature of the structure, which differentiates it from the nest of most other species I have seen in northwestern Mexico, is the use of the fine tendrils of cotton or cobwebs to swathe the external part of it."

HYLOCHARIS XANTUSI (Lawrence)

XANTUS'S HUMMINGBIRD

HABITS

The type specimen of this hummingbird, a female now in the United States National Museum, was taken in 1859 near Cape San Lucas, Baja California, by John Xantus and was named in his honor. Its center of abundance is in the vicinity of the Cape, but it ranges northward to about the twenty-ninth parallel of latitude, where it becomes rare.

William Brewster (1902) says:

This Hummingbird is peculiar to Lower California, but it is not strictly confined to the Cape Region, for Mr. Frazar found it common at a point about one hundred and fifty miles north of La Paz among the mountains opposite Carmen Island in latitude 26°, and Mr. Bryant has traced its extension still farther northward to about latitude 29°. It seems to be most abundant, however, in the mountains south of La Paz, especially on the Sierra de la Laguna, where it ranges from the highest elevations down to the lower limits of the oaks among the foothills. It also occurs—at least sparingly and locally at certain seasons—in the low arid country near the coast, for Mr. Frazar took a male at La Paz on February 11, and saw upward of a dozen at San José del Cabo in September. At the latter place, Mr. Belding found it "common in orchards" about the last of April, 1882. Among the mountains it shows a marked preference for cañons, especially such as have pools or small streams of water. Mr. Belding says that "in winter" it is "found only in mountain cañons," but Mr. Frazar's experience was exactly the reverse of this, for during his winter visit to the Sierra de la Laguna (November 27–December 2), the "whole top of the cold, sleety mountain was alive with Xantus's Hummers, which seemed to be attracted there by an abundant shrub covered with *dry* yellow blossoms, whereas in May and June they were confined quite closely to the cañons." The truth of the matter probably is that their movements, like those of most other members of this family, are dependent largely on the presence or absence, at any given locality or season, of the flowers on which they feed.

Chester C. Lamb (1925) evidently agrees with Mr. Brewster as to the center of abundance of this hummingbird, which he says is "in Laguna Valley, in the heart of the Sierra de la Laguna, situated south of La Paz." He continues:

These mountains are difficult of access, and it takes two days on mule back, over tortuous trails, to reach Laguna Valley, a small, uninhabited valley at an elevation of about 5500 feet. The Xantus Hummingbirds radiate out from this valley in all directions, and are very common in all the mountain canyons, right down to the open deserts. One may get into some of the favorable hummingbird localities of California and believe he has seen a great concourse of hummingbirds, but half an hour's walk across Laguna Valley and around the lower rim will astound one at the numbers seen. One day I endeavored in the course of a short morning's walk to count the number of Xantus Hummingbirds, but, going up to two hundred before the first hour, I gave up the actual count and started to estimate. One cannot see this large number of hummingbirds at any hour of the day, however. The very early morning hours are when they appear in the greatest abundance. At this time they come out of the oak and pine forests around the rim of the valley and seek a place to bathe, and also to feed and play around a red flowering shrub that grows along the stream on the floor of the valley.

Nesting.—Mr. Lamb (1925) was at "Comondu from March 30 to April 11, 1924, and during that interval twelve nests were discovered." He says:

At this altitude, 800 feet, the birds must start nesting early in February, as all but three nests contained large young or eggs about to hatch. I would not be surprised if they raised two broods annually at Comondu, though I did not stay long enough to prove the fact or to learn the period of incubation.

In their courting, the male Xantus Hummingbird does not fly up in the air and make the parabolic dive that the Costa Hummingbird does, but there is considerable chasing by individuals of one another around through the trees. The nesting birds of Comondu, where there are no oaks, have an entirely different style of nest building from those of the oak regions of the Sierra de la Laguna. The Comondu birds are not particular as to what kind of a tree they select in which to build their nests. The nests are usually placed low above the ground, and they are always very close to running water. * * *

At Comondu I noted two exceptions to the usual method of suspending nests to twigs. In one case a nest was found saddled to the dry spike of a date palm tree, and another was saddled on a dead limb of a fig tree. Other trees in which nests were found at Comondu were avocado, olive, lemon, orange, water willow and cottonwood. * * *

In the Sierra de la Laguna (Laguna Valley), nests are always in live oak trees, not necessarily near water. I made diligent searches in the pines and white oak trees, which, especially the latter, are much more abundant than the live oaks, but discovered no nests. Nearly all the nests found were hung at the ends of small twigs, from four to six feet from the ground, in very small live oaks. Two exceptions were nests found twelve feet up in large oaks. * * *

The nesting material of the Comondu birds and the Laguna birds was about the same, the nests being composed of fine plant down, dried flower heads, plant fibers and small feathers, all bound together with spider webbing. A nest from Comondu is covered on the outside with strips of bark of the water willow. Without exception all the nests of the Sierra birds are beautifully decorated with lichens from the oaks. The Comondu birds do not decorate their nests with lichens, these not being available, but sometimes they do attempt a little decoration with bits of bark or leaves.

The nesting dates of the Laguna birds are also different from those at Comondu. We arrived in the Sierra de la Laguna on June 16 and remained until July 7, and in that time no nests were found, though I am not sure that the birds were not nesting. August 3 I re-visited the mountains and remained in Laguna Valley and vicinity until September 3, and in this month discovered twenty-five nests. On September 1 I found a nest just ready for eggs. Of those found, the greater number contained young or heavily incubated eggs, so it might be said that the nesting season in Laguna Valley started about the middle of July and continued to the middle of September.

Mr. Brewster (1902) gives the following detailed description of a nest, found by Mr. Frazar:

A nest found at San José del Rancho, on July 28, was placed at the extremity of a slender, drooping oak twig, about eight feet above the ground. One side is built against and around the main stem (here only .12 inches in diameter), and the bottom rests securely on a terminal fork, from the ends of which hang a number of dry, bleached oak leaves, apparently of the previous year's growth. The chief, if not only, material composing the walls of this nest consists of small, woolly leaves of a pale sage-green color, intermixed with reddish-brown, catkin-shaped objects, which appear to be made up of numerous minute seed vessels attached in double, triple, or quadruple rows or clusters to stems an inch or more in length. The entire outer surface of the nest is wrapped with a net-work of spider-web silk so fine as to be well-nigh invisible but sufficiently strong and taughtly drawn to give the walls a firm, smooth outline. The interior is not lined save at the bottom, which is furnished with a soft bed of whitish down, evidently that of some bird. This nest measures externally 1.60 inches in diameter by 1.65 in depth; internally, .73 inches in diameter by .50 in depth.

Eggs.—The two eggs laid by Xantus's hummingbird are practically indistinguishable from those of other hummingbirds of similar size. They are pure dull white and vary in shape from oval to elliptical-oval. The measurements of 26 eggs average 12.3 by 8.4 millimeters; the eggs showing the four extremes measure 13.5 by 9.9, 11.4 by 7.8, 1.9 by 7.5 millimeters.

Plumages.—I have no information on the early plumages of the nestling, but in the juvenal plumage, which is probably fully acquired before the young bird leaves the nest, the sexes are apparently alike and closely resemble the adult female. The adult female is like the adult male, but she has no black on the head, no green on the throat, and the postocular stripe is buffy instead of white. Mr. Ridgway (1911) says that the young male has the "throat spotted with metallic emerald green or yellowish green." And the young female, he says, is "similar to the young male but without green on the throat."

Mr. Brewster (1902), who had a large series of these birds, taken every month in the year except October and January, makes the following general remarks on the seasonal variations in plumages:

The summer and autumn birds are by far the brightest colored, having the green of the back quite pure; the black of the forehead, sides of head and chin, deep velvety often glossed with violet or blue; the metallic green of the throat, clear and brilliant; the cinnamon rufous of the under parts, rich and pure. The spring birds (March, April, and May) are uniformly much duller and paler, the green of the back being much tinged with ashy or rusty, and the black of the head with brown, while the green of the throat is muddy in tone and but slightly iridescent.

One bird (No. 17,031, Triunfo, April 11, 1887) has the black of the head confined to the auriculars, and the green of the throat to a few central spots, the rest of the under parts being dull cinnamon rufous, and the entire upper parts dull green with most of the feathers tipped with rusty cinnamon.

This specimen is evidently a young male that is beginning to assume the adult plumage at its annual complete molt. Judged from what is available in the literature and what can be learned from the study of specimens, it seems that the young of both sexes are, at first, like the adult female with no green on the throat; and that the young male soon begins to acquire some metallic green feathers on the throat, but does not assume the fully adult plumage until the next spring; I have seen young males acquiring the green throat in April and in July, and in full molt in July. I have seen adults molting in July.

Food.—Not much is definitely known about the food of Xantus's hummingbird, which probably does not differ essentially from that of other hummingbirds, with due allowance for the species of insects and feeding plants to be found in its habitat. Dr. Frederic A. Lucas (1893) lists: "*Cecidomyia, Phora,* three specimens of *Solenopsis geminatus,* elytra of beetle, *Psyllus,* parts of spiders."

Behavior.—Mr. Lamb (1925) has this to say about the habits of this hummer:

At one place the hummingbirds' bath was discovered, where a trickle of water flowed over a flat rock a short distance and then dropped in a tiny waterfall. At one time I counted nine birds at once taking a bath. They would sit in the water and give themselves a thorough shower with their wings; then, to finish off, they would fly against the falls, breast first, and then they would back up to the falling water. Besides the birds busily bathing, there were as many more sitting around on the bushes, drying themselves.

Towards dark, in the winter time, the adult males have a habit of perching on some dead twig, and there, remaining motionless for a considerable period, give themselves up to song, uttering at regular short intervals their quite pleasing little tune. During the heavy tropical rains of that region the hummingbirds would disappear, but the minute the rain ceased they would be out again. These birds love the pines and live oaks of the high mountain regions, and are to be seen at all hours of the day hunting around those trees for the minute insects that constitute their food.

They seem to be of gentle disposition, though they do not permit the too close proximity of another species while feeding or at their nests. They are tame, but not so much so that the brooding female will ever allow a person to touch her. At most any time, a little squeak will bring one or two birds buzzing around one's head. When I had my work table out under the oaks the hummingbirds seemed much interested in my work, buzzing around the table and inspecting my instrument box. I had a fluff of cotton hanging nearby, which they soon learned made excellent nest building material.

Enemies.—Mr. Lamb (1925) says that ravens are very common in the Cape region of Baja California and are very destructive; one was caught in the very act of destroying a hummingbird's nest that he had just examined.

Field marks.—The only hummingbird with which Xantus's is likely to be confused is the white-eared, as both have the white postocular stripe; but, fortunately, their ranges do not overlap. The adult male *xantusi* is easily recognized by its blue-black face, white postocular stripe, bright metallic-green throat, cinnamon-rufous under parts, largely chestnut tail, and reddish bill. The female is similar but with no black on the head, no green on the throat, and has a black bill and a buffy postocular stripe. The young are similar to the adult female, though the young male may have the throat flecked with green.

DISTRIBUTION

Range.—The southern half of the peninsula of Baja California; nonmigratory. This species is normally found from about the central part of this Mexico State (Purissima) south to the cape district (San Jose del Cabo). A specimen was collected at Todos Santos Island off the northern part of the west coast on November 14, 1923. There are no records for the United States.

Egg dates.—Lower California (lowlands): 12 records, April 5 to May 17.

Lower California (mountains): 14 records, July 19 to August 5.

Mr. Lamb (1925) says that at Comodu they must start nesting in February and that in the Laguna Valley they probably nest from July 15 to September 15.

HYLOCHARIS LEUCOTIS LEUCOTIS (Vieillot)

WHITE-EARED HUMMINGBIRD

PLATE 73

HABITS

CONTRIBUTED BY ALEXANDER F. SKUTCH

The white-eared hummingbird is a common and widespread species of northern Central America and Mexico, occurring in the United States only in southern Arizona, where it was first discovered in the Chiricahua Mountains by Dr. A. K. Fisher (1894). Near the southern extremity of its range, in Guatemala, it is a bird of the highlands found chiefly at elevations between 4,000 and 9,000 feet, although in favorable localities it may extend upward to 11,000 feet above sea level. Here its favorite haunts are the more open woods of oak, pine, and alder and the clearings and bushy mountainsides where there is a profusion of flowering shrubs. Over much of the Guatemalan highlands, at the altitudes it prefers, it is one of the most abundant and familiar hummingbirds of the cultivated areas and the flower gardens, but it is rarely seen in the darker and more humid forests and almost never in the heavy cypress forests of the mountaintops. In the southern part of its range it is resident at all seasons, or at most performs short altitudinal migrations occasioned by the local abundance of flowers. But in Arizona, according to Oberholser (1925), the species is migratory, arriving probably in April and remaining until August or possibly September, although definite dates of arrival and departure are lacking. It is said to winter as far north as the Valley of Mexico and the State of Colima.

In El Salvador and Nicaragua the species is represented by the race *pygmaea*, which in the former country, according to Dickey and van Rossem (1938), ranges between 3,500 and 8,000 feet above sea level, dwelling in the undergrowth of the oak forests and in various sorts of scrubby growth.

Courtship.—In the highlands of western Guatemala, the rainy season normally extends from the middle of May to the middle of October. In November and December, the first months of clear, sunny weather, there is a greater profusion of bright, conspicuous blossoms than at any other period of the year. Hummingbirds of all kinds nest during this flowery season, despite frequent cold, biting winds, and the frosts that from November to the end of March form almost nightly on open fields above 7,500 feet. By the end of January blossoms have become far fewer as a result of continued dryness and frosts increasingly severe, and the nesting season of the hummingbirds is drawing to a close. During the period between the vernal equinox and the June solstice, when the vast majority of birds of all kinds raise their young, nests of the hummingbirds are unknown at higher elevations. During the season when the hummingbirds breed, the only other bird whose nests I have found, at altitudes in excess of 7,000 feet, is *Diglossa baritula*, an aberrant honeycreeper, which, like them, sucks the nectar of flowers.

Just as many of the plants that blossom during the dry season anticipate the return of bright weather and open their earliest flowers during the gloomy days of the later part of the rainy season, so the male white-eared hummingbirds prepare for their courtship well in advance of the cessation of the rains. By the end of August 1933, some of the male white-ears, on the mountains above Tecpán in west-central Guatemala, had chosen the positions they would occupy during the following months, and from time to time sounded in a tentative fashion the clear little notes that advertise their presence to the females. As September advanced with increasing mist and rain they lapsed into silence, but with the advent of October they became vocal again, and some tinkled from the same bushes where I had first heard them a month earlier.

As I roamed the bushy mountainsides and the open oak woods, it soon became clear to me that the male white-ears were not distributed uniformly or at random over the territory suitable to them but had congregated into definite groups which I came to call "singing assemblies." The largest of these assemblies that I discovered was made up of seven birds, whose perches were in the pine and oak trees surrounding an irregular open pasture. This group was very much spread out, with the two most distant individuals about 600 feet apart and out of hearing of each other (unless the hummingbirds' ears are sharper than my own); but each member of the assembly could certainly hear the calls of two or more of his neighbors. Another assembly consisted of five birds, scattered among tall raijón bushes that had taken possession of an abandoned pasture, the birds so spaced that each was about 90 to 100 feet from his neighbors. Other assemblies contained three or only two white-ears. Sometimes the birds perched as close as 60 feet from each other. Between these groups of hummingbirds were considerable stretches of similar terrain where one listened in vain for their reiterated notes.

Scattered here and there, however, were lone males, which remained aloof from the assemblies. One of these made his headquarters in a raijón bush beside the road, and here I frequently met him, perched on a dead twig and tinkling persistently. Another, with a weak, plaintive little voice, called from a low perch on a bush in an overgrown pasture, beyond hearing of all others of his kind.

The male white-ears sometimes chose low perches in the midst of a thicket, only 2 or 3 feet above ground, sometimes high, exposed ones, such as the dead twig of a pine tree 40 feet in the air. One bird, which engaged much of my attention, regularly alternated between a perch less than a yard from the ground in a thicket of raijón bushes, and an exposed dead twig in the top of an alder tree growing beside the thicket, fully a dozen times as high. Sometimes a strong wind caused a white-ear whose favorite perch was lofty and exposed to descend to some lower, more protected position close at hand. Whatever the nature of the station he had chosen, the bird was to be found there day after day, week after week, throughout the months of October, November, and December. When I departed the region at the end of the year, a number still sounded their little calls from the very spots where I first encountered them early in September.

Perhaps the most typical note of the male white-eared hummingbird in the singing assembly is a low, clear *tink tink tink*, sounding like the chiming of a small, sweet-toned silver bell. At least this is the note that I first discovered, and the one that I like best to remember. Some individuals toll their little bells very rapidly, others more slowly and deliberately. But as I began to know more and more white-ears, scattered over miles of mountainside, I came to realize that there was a surprising degree of variation in their voices. Many individuals persistently sounded notes so different from the usual clear tinkle that I did not recognize them as the utterances of white-ears until I had laboriously stalked the birds and actually watched them as they called. These notes were dull and flat, with no trace of the clear timbre characteristic of the majority of the species, or else high and squeaky, or low and melancholy. One that I frequently visited uttered rapidly and monotonously a single clicking note, a kind of harsh metallic buzzing almost painful to hear.

These individual differences in voice were surprising enough in themselves, but even more remarkable was the fact that the same type of voice was likely to be common to all the members of a singing assembly. If one bird of a group uttered a clear, silvery tinkle, his neighbors would be found to sing in the same strain; if I happened to be attracted to an assembly by a chirping note, I usually found that this note was common to all the members of the group. There were, of course, exceptions to this rule, but these were not sufficiently numerous to make me doubt its validity. But what is the explanation of this phenomenon? Not impossibly it was the result of imitation, and all the members of an assembly merely copied the vocal peculiarities of one bird that happened to be the first to begin to sing, or in some manner dominated his neighbors by his personality. But I suspect that the real cause was deeper. The individual variations in voice were so great that they seemed to me to result from variations in the structure of the vocal organs. I never heard the white-ear that produced the metallic rattle utter the clear, silvery tinkle, or *vice versa*. More than this, I find it difficult to believe that the same individual was physically capable of producing sounds so distinct. It is not impossible, although the point would be difficult of actual proof, that these peculiarities of voice are inherited, and that the males of the same assembly are somehow related by ties of blood.

Whether a clear dawn revealed the pastures white with frost, or day broke sadly over a world drenched in gray, wind-blown cloud mist, dreary and penetratingly chill, the white-eared hummingbirds always began to sing in the dim light of early dawn. Once the season of song was at its height, neither wind nor rain or cold, driving cloud mist could utterly quench the spirits or extinguish the voices of these tiny hummers. They sang most vigorously early in the morning, and less and less as the day advanced. In the afternoon their song was rather inconstant, for they were far less persevering in their vocal exercises than the violet-ears (*Colibri thalassinus*), one of which made almost as much volume of sound as a whole assembly of white-ears, and continued his chant far more constantly through the day. As he sang the male white-ear tilted upward his coral-red, black-tipped bill and turned his head restlessly from side to side. Sometimes he would interrupt his tinkling to utter a rapid twittering, which ran off into a very low buzz of a most peculiar tone. Perhaps this twittering and buzzing represented his true song, but it was far less melodious than the tinkling of those individuals with the clearest voices and would not bear comparison with the inspired little song of Elliot's hummingbird (*Atthis heloisa*). At intervals he vibrated his wings in the midst of his tinkling, or paused and slowly stretched them. Finally, becoming hungry, he flew off to suck nectar from the flowers, the nearest of which were often at a considerable distance from the singing-perch.

The territorial rights of each white-ear were respected by the others, and as a rule each sounded his little tinkle without much interference from his neighbors. But occasionally one invaded the domain of another, and a vigorous but inconsequential pursuit resulted. Sometimes one settled down close to the perch of a second, and the two sang face to face or side by side for a few moments, until one dashed at the other and both winged rapidly out of sight. Or else the two rose, spiring about each other, high into the air, only to separate without having come to grips or inflicted injury on each other. Then, the momentary flareup over, each would return peaceably to his own post and continue his tireless calling.

The purpose of so much vocal activity on the part of the males is without much doubt to attract the opposite sex. Their season of song coincides roughly with the nesting period of the females. Yet, in spite of many hours of watching, I was not able to determine the behavior of the males when a female approached or to witness actual pairing. The white-ears are so small and withal so shy that they are difficult to keep in sight; on the wing their movements are so swift that it is impossible to distinguish male from female, or even to follow them long with the eye. I saw three or four of these hummingbirds flying together, pursuing and pursued, so frequently that I suspect that they do not honor the rights of their neighbors when a female approaches, as manakins, which form similar assemblies for courtship, almost invariably do.

In January, when the blossoms become less abundant with increasing drought, the white-ears disperse and cease to call. During most of the year they are silent; and one is not likely to notice them unless he watches before a stand of flowers, which they visit for the purpose of sipping the nectar.

Nesting.—In the middle of October 1933, six or seven weeks after the males had selected their posts and begun to sing in a tentative fashion, I found a female just beginning her nest. Later I found a dozen more, which, together with four I had discovered in November 1930, brought the total up to 17; but some were never completed, all were well removed from the singing assemblies of the males, some far away, others just sufficiently distant to be out of hearing of the nearest male—that is, of course, too far away for *me* to hear his voice. With a single exception, all these nests were placed among the slender twigs of the raijón (*Baccharis vaccinioides*), a composite shrub common everywhere on the mountains, at heights varying from 5 to 20 feet above ground. The one nest not in a raijón bush had been built in the crotch of an ascending branch of a bushy *Eupatorium*. The nests were situated in bushy clearings or light, open woodland.

The female white-ear built her nest alone, without the assistance or even the encouragement of one of the males that sang so tirelessly beyond sight and hearing. The raijón bush she chose as its site was never far distant from the oak trees upon which she depended for the downy materials she needed. The leaves of several species, belonging to both the white and black oak groups, are covered on the lower surface with a dense, woolly cloak composed of rather short, crinkled, tawny hairs. This hairy covering is firmly attached to the epidermis and difficult to remove, except in places where a leaf-mining larva has devoured the underlying tissues. By seeking out the spots where the larva has separated the epidermis from the body of the leaf, the hummingbirds materially diminish the labor of gathering the down. But an even greater proportion of the material used in the nests is derived from the woolly insect galls growing on the oak leaves. The color of these galls varies from rusty brown or reddish brown to light buff. Although the dark-colored galls on the upper sides of the leaves are more abundant, the hummingbirds prefer the pale ones, which are found only on the lower sides of the foliage, and neglect, or use very sparingly, those with brownish hairs.

Thus insects, either indirectly, by laying the eggs that stimulate the leaves to produce hairy galls, or directly, by freeing the normal woolly covering from the body of the leaf and making it easy to remove, supply the white-eared hummingbird with practically all the downy stuff for her nest. Spiders, in spinning their webs, furnish her the material necessary to bind the down together and to attach the nest to the supporting twigs. Green mosses and grayish lichens are attached to the exterior for decoration. Some nests are very well covered with these plants, which give the prevailing color to the exterior, while others are so sparingly decorated that much of the down shows through. In form, the nest is roughly a hollow sphere with the upper quarter cut away. The outside diameter of the open cup varies from 1¾ to 2 inches; the height from 1¼ to 2¾ inches. The interior of the cozy little nest is very nearly as broad as deep and measures about an inch in both diameter and depth. The rim is quite noticeably incurved, and this helps to hold the eggs inside when fierce November winds whip the slender branches of the raijón bushes and threaten to roll them out.

Robert T. Moore contributes the following notes on nests of the white-eared hummingbird, found by Chester C. Lamb and himself in Chihuahua and Sinaloa, Mexico: "In his journal Mr. Lamb states that the Laguna Juanota nest was found 'in a small oak, 6 inches in diameter and 25 feet tall, growing in a grove of the same on the north hillside of a rocky butte at the lake.' It was saddled on a twig among the leafy extremities of a branch 2 feet from the trunk. The nest is composed almost entirely of a buff-colored plant down, the only exceptions consisting of one small oak twig woven loosely to the bottom of the nest and greenish gray lichens ornamenting the exterior portion. Measuring 1 by 1⅛ inches on the inside, it has no other lining except the plant down. The outside measurements are 1⅞ by 1½ inches."

He tells of a second nest, twice as large as the above, which resembles it closely, "except that two oak catkins have been woven into the sides and the lichen decorations are more complete."

Then, of a third nest, he says: "Its total bulk is nearly five times that of the first nest and four times that of the second, and yet the internal dimensions are actually less than either, namely 1 by $\frac{11}{16}$ inch. The internal depth, however, is almost twice as great as that of nest No. 1. The external measurements are length 3⅛, width 2¼, and depth 2⅛ inches. Furthermore, the structure of the external part of the nest is almost totally different, being completely swathed with a fine green moss, and having pine needles, dried twigs, and four or five small leaves, as well as a few lichens, woven into the external construction. There is no evidence whatever that this is a double nest.

"It is quite probable that the environment of the nest site had a great deal to do with the type of construction. This moss-covered abode was placed on a small shrub, growing out of rocks 4 feet up from the base of a cliff in a very dark and deep arroyo. In such a place much moss is available, whereas lichens are difficult to find. Three nest sites so dissimilar could hardly have been chosen as these three structures—an oak tree on the very highest point of a wind-blown mountain range, a cliff jutting out on the shore of a wind-protected small lake, and the bottom of a deeply shaded gorge. Dissimilarity of nesting period is also indicated—March, May, and August."

Eggs.—The number of eggs laid by the white-eared hummingbird appears invariably to be two. They are pure white and narrowly oblong. The measurements of six eggs, removed temporarily from their nests in the highlands of Guatemala, average 12.5 by 8.0 millimeters. The eggs showing the four extremes measure 12.7 by 7.9, 12.3 by 8.3, and 11.9 by 7.9 millimeters.

Young.—Incubation is carried on by the female alone, without ever so much as a visit from one of the males, which continue to sing as if oblivious of all the cares and labor of the other sex. Both of the female white-ears I watched sat deeply in their nests. When perfectly at rest, the eyes were only a trifle above the rim, the sides were entirely protected, the back was invisible to a person slightly below the level of the nest, while the tail and the tips of the longest wing plumes projected beyond the rim at the rear. They were far better protected than the Rieffer's hummingbirds of the warm lowlands, for the nests of these are comparatively broad and shallow, and much of the body of the sitting bird remains on the outside.

The white-eared hummingbirds' mode of entering and leaving their nests demonstrated clearly their lightness and skill upon the wing. Upon returning to their eggs after a recess, heavier birds alight upon the rim of the nest, or even upon a branch at a little distance, and walk or hop into the cup. The white-ears never alighted on the rim but invariably flew directly into the nest and, as they settled neatly over the eggs, folded their wings about them and were at once at rest. Most birds of other families, when they wish to leave the nest, step on the rim before taking flight, but the hummingbirds showed their mastery of the air by making their departure in a more direct manner. Still sitting on the eggs, they spread and vibrated their wings and rose directly into the air, with as little apparent effort as if they were lighter than the atmosphere, and ascended because their hidden moorings had been severed. Frequently they flew upward and backward until they had cleared the nest, then quickly reversed and darted forward and away. When they wished to turn their eggs, they flew backward from the bowl onto the rim, alighted on that portion that had been beneath the tail as they sat, bent down the bill into the cup, and in an instant flew away. Of course, I could not see the eggs or what was done to them, for the nests were above the level of my eyes as I watched; but this is the only significance I can find in the oft-repeated act; and moreover, if the hummingbirds did not turn their eggs on these occasions, they never turned them at all. They never rose up while incubating to adjust their eggs beneath them, as other birds do, doubtless because the length of the bill, coupled with the narrowness of the bowl, would have made this an awkward and difficult performance.

During the morning hours the white-ears devoted much time to seeking down and cobweb and bringing these materials to the nest. The down was deposited inside the cup, the cobweb wiped from the bill to the outer surface; and in addition an occasional lichen was attached there. Since the nests had been completed before the eggs were laid, these additions to its bulk appeared to be made from force of habit rather than from necessity; and it was interesting to find that the new materials were brought chiefly at the time of day when the birds had built most actively. The daily application of fresh cobweb was useful in that it served to prevent the binding of the nest, and its attachment to the supporting twigs, losing their strength with age. During the hours when the gathering of material claimed their attention, the birds spent very brief periods on the eggs, often only a minute and sometimes less; but in the afternoon, when they brought nothing back with them on returning from their recesses, they sometimes sat continuously for 20 or 30 minutes, rarely slightly longer. During the course of an entire day the average period of incubation of one white-ear was 9.7 minutes; her average recess was five minutes. Her separate sessions on the eggs during the forenoon ranged from less than 1 minute to 15 minutes, with an average of 7.4 minutes; her recesses varied from 1 to 10 minutes, with an average of 3.7 minutes. During the afternoon, when she sat more constantly, her sessions varied from 7 to 24 minutes, with an average of 15 minutes, and her recesses were of 2 to 17 minutes' duration. From her first departure in the morning until her final return in the evening, she devoted 7 hours 47 minutes to warming her eggs, while 3 hours 59 minutes were spent away from the nest.

When at length they are hatched, the new-born hummingbirds appear more like black grubs than the nestlings of a feathered creature. Their eyes are completely hidden by the tightly closed lids; the bill is represented by a mere bump; and the line of sparse brown fuzz along the center of the back does little to cover their bareness. They seem very small and very naked to survive the cold blustery days that during November and December are frequent on the higher mountains where they are raised. During the nights they are well protected from exposure, for their downy nests are thick-walled and warm, and their mother fits into the space above them as snugly as a cork in the mouth of a bottle, maintaining the vital spark within her children by means of her own marvelous capacity for heat production. It is during the day that the endurance of the nestlings is put to the most severe test, because they must be left uncovered at intervals while the mother forages for food. If ever nestlings seem to need the ministrations of a father, to help feed them and to warm them while the mother takes her recesses and seeks her food, it is these little hummingbirds; yet no male ever appears to aid in their care, for this is not the custom among hummingbirds. On cruel days when a wind that is half a gale drives the chilling cloud mist through the treetops and whips the limber branches that support the nests, one marvels that such minute creatures, smaller even than a honey bee, can maintain the temperature of their bodies above the death point, even during the few minutes for which they are left exposed while the mother forages. Sometimes, indeed, a tiny hummer only a few days old is found dead in its nest, apparently having succumbed to the inclement weather, in spite of the devoted attention of the mother.

Before the nestlings are large and strong enough to raise up and eject their droppings beyond the rim of the nest, these are removed from the interior by the mother, who, standing on the rim, grasps the particles between the tips of her mandibles and throws them out by sideways jerks of her heard, or else swallows them, and by this means keeps the nest decently clean. When they are slightly older, the young hummers barely manage to deposit their excrement on the rim, and then the parent, less careful than most passerine birds in the sanitation of her nest, no longer takes the trouble to remove it. Finally, with increasing size and strength, the nestlings are able to eject their droppings beyond the rim of the nest and no longer soil it.

When the young hummingbirds are seven or eight days old their pinfeathers begin to sprout. At the age of nine or ten days the eyelids begin to part, and the brown tips of the feathers to peep from the ends of their sheaths. Four days later the green portions of the contour feathers become visible; but still the black skin of the little birds is not entirely covered. They are 16 days old before the wing plumes begin to push from the ends of their sheaths, and 18 days of age before the rectrices escape their horny covering. The nestlings are brooded nightly by their mother until 17 or 18 days old, when they are well clothed with feathers. If frightened, they may fly from the nest at the age of 23 days, but if unmolested they do not depart until their twenty-sixth day. At the time of their departure they fly with strength and ease and never again return to the shelter of the nest. The fledgling white-ears closely resemble their mothers, except that the white postocular line is slightly tinged with buff. It is perhaps significant that these hummingbirds raised during cool and frosty weather in the highlands remain in the nest several days longer than the Rieffer's hummingbirds of the warm lowlands, which quit the nest at the age of 18 to 23 days.

The white-eared hummingbirds may raise two broods in a season. One female, which succeeded in raising a single nestling in her first nest, built a second structure, 40 feet from the first, during the week after her fledgling took wing. She had a busy week, for she satisfied the hunger of the young hummingbird in the intervals of working on the new nest. As a result of her divided attention, the second nest was far less perfect than the first. It was shallower, thinner walled, and carelessly finished; in fact, it seemed scarcely completed when the first egg was laid in it, ten days after the fledgling departed his cradle.

From my tent I watched this hummingbird as she incubated her second set of eggs. Her fledgling, a young male, was now 40 days old and had been out of the nest just two weeks. In size he was scarcely to be distinguished from his mother. His bill seemed slightly shorter, and his back was not such a bright green, because many of the feathers still bore the downy-brown tips which characterize the nestling plumage. He flew very well, and spent much time sucking nectar from the red blossoms of the salvias, which I could watch through the right window of the tent. When not occupied with visiting the flowers, he rested among the low branches of a little bushy thicket about 30 feet from his mother's second nest. Here she came to feed him during her absences from the eggs, in spite of the fact that he could now forage very well for himself. Once, indeed, he visited the flowers while his mother gathered food for him, then came to supplement his meal by what she had to offer. Perching beside him upon a low twig, she delivered the food, as always, by regurgitation, which she began with very violent convulsive movements of the body. He was a well-behaved youngster and never came to pester his mother with demands for food while she warmed her eggs, but always waited patiently for her to come to him. As he waited in his little thicket, he called slowly *tink tink tink*, an utterance that somewhat resembled the calls of the adult males on their singing perches, but was much fainter and weaker.

While she incubated her first set of eggs, the mother found much time for bringing additional cobweb and down to the nest, which was so well finished that it did not appear to require further attention. The hastily built second nest was in far greater need of additional material; but now the hummingbird was too busy with other things to give time to this and brought nothing to the nest during the morning which I passed with her. She was now more attentive to her duties and incubated more steadily; she came to and left the nest only eight times in four hours, as compared with 23 times during the same period of a morning while she incubated her first set of eggs. Even during a seven minutes' recess from the nest, she found time to satisfy her own hunger and to gather food for her fledgling.

It seems to be the unhappy fate of hummingbirds that their nests come to disaster even more frequently than those of other kinds of birds, and the white-ears are no exception to this rule. The nine completed nests I found in Guatemala in 1933 contained two eggs each, making a total of 18. Three of these nests were destroyed in some unknown manner while they still contained eggs, and one was deserted. Only nine eggs hatched. Of the nine nestlings, one succumbed to the cold, two were probably taken by the Indians, and three met unknown ends. Only three lived to leave the nest.

Plumages.—Dr. Frank M. Chapman (1925) writes: "Young females have the crown and upper parts more rusty than the adult, the under-parts buffy white, the sides rusty rather than green. Young males resemble the adult female, but usually have a few metallic blue feathers on the throat or forehead."

Dickey and van Rossem (1938) write of the closely allied race *pygmaea* in El Salvador, where apparently the species breeds in November and December, just as in the neighboring Republic of Guatemala: "A young male taken February 21 has nearly completed the postjuvenal body molt, and the iridescent blue and green feathers are rapidly filling in the chin and throat."

Food.—Like other hummingbirds, the white-ears subsist largely upon the nectar of flowers, which they supplement by minute spiders plucked from their webs and small volitant insects deftly snatched from the air. They seem to have no particular preferences as to the source of their nectar but visit indifferently a great variety of blossoms. At the beginning of their nesting season in the Guatemalan highlands, a bur-marigold (*Bidens refracta*), common in the open oak woods, is one of their principal food plants. With great patience the hummingbird poises on vibrant wings before a yellow flowerhead and rapidly moves its bill from floret to floret, an instant in each, and usually probes many in each head, before flying on to the next. Each tiny floret yields at best a minute quantity of nectar, but there are so many in a flowerhead that in aggregate they must supply a considerable amount. Later in the season, various species of *Salvia*, in particular the red *Salvia cinnabarina*, yield an abundance of nectar, which is secreted as a single large drop at the base of the corolla tube, and so is far more conveniently sipped than the sweet secretions of the bur-marigold heads, divided among a multitude of separate florets. Though usually the white-ear reaches the nectar through the throat of the corolla, once I watched an eccentric individual puncture the side of the tube of the lovely blue flowers of *Salvia cacalioefolia*, easily pushing his sharp bill through the delicate tissue of the corolla.

Behavior.—In April 1938, in southeastern Sinaloa, Mr. Moore observed four species of hummingbirds "feeding from the flowers of one large shrub at an altitude of about 6,000 feet. Approaching the proportions of a tree, this remarkable shrub, 20 feet in height and of the same width, was completely covered with globelike clusters of grayish-lavender blooms. At no time from sunrise to sunset were there less than four hummingbirds in this tree. Often there were as many as 20 of four different species, white-eared, broad-tailed, calliope, and Margaret's hummingbirds. The white-ears, like irascible knights of the air, were always ready to thrust lance at an assumed affront. It made no difference whether it was the tiny Margaret's or the larger broad-tailed, some white-ear would dive viciously at any intruder that dared to approach too close. The broad-tailed hummingbird, heavier and more powerful, would dart into the tree with direct flight and pompous hum, but his assurance would be quickly dispelled. A male white-ear would immediately launch an assault and drive the larger bird up the mountainside in ignominious retreat.

"The same dominance was exhibited on several afternoons in May 1937, when I visited the mammoth paintbrush beds on the slopes of Mount Mohinora at the 10,000-foot level. Here the white-ears outnumbered all the broad-billed, blue-throated, and Rivoli's together. In one of these astounding fields of color, perhaps 100 yards long and 100 feet wide, a dozen white-ears were feeding at one time. If one of the other larger species dived into the flower masses, even if at a point far removed from the nearest white-ear, one of the latter would immediately whirl to the attack and drive the Rivoli's and blue-throated hummingbirds, twice their size, into headlong flight.

During the drowsy hours of midday the white-ears would cease feeding and rest quietly at various points among the oak trees, generally choosing some spot in the shade. Should a blue-throated or Rivoli's choose this propitious moment to glide quietly into the flowerbeds, the nearest white-ear would come to life ρ∧d volplane down in a surprise attack. Not once out of many hundred times did I observe any of these three other species attempt to resist. It might seek some other point in the large mass of flowers, but the white-ear invariably pursued until the other bird had left the food area.

"The wing action of the white-eared hummingbird I compared with that of the calliope and the other species at Rancho Batel in 1936. Its wings beat more slowly, so that when poising in front of a flower they are not an indistinguishable blur, as in the case of the calliope, but there is a slightly visible wing stroke. Possibly because of this slower wing stroke, as well as the heavier, longer body, the rear end of the bird gradully drops as it continues to poise in front of the flower. If it feeds continuously from one cluster of small blooms, a curious rhythmic, but irregular motion of the tail up and down is created. At first the tail is horizontal and in the same plane with the body. When the tail begins to drop, the bird, in order to compensate for the increasing lack of balance, forcibly lifts it into the air. Timing these vertical beats, I found they averaged three to the second. At first I thought this downward and alternate upward sweep of the tail was for the purpose of moving the bird from one flower to another, but this was not the case. I never observed the calliope or Margaret's hummingbird doing this."

He says that, in spite of its pugnacious behavior, the white-eared hummingbird is the shiest of the four species mentioned above; and refers to its voice as "exceedingly high-pitched and sharply staccato."

DISTRIBUTION

Range.—Central America; casual in southeastern Arizona; not regularly migratory.

The range of the white-eared hummingbird extends **north** to central Sonora (Oposura); northern Chihuahua (Carmen); and northern Tamaulipas (Bravo). **East** to Tamaulipas (Bravo and Golindo); Veracruz (Jalapa and Orizaba); Honduras (San Juancito); and Nicaragua (Jinotego). **South** to Nicaragua (Jinotego and Matagalpa); Oaxaca (Totontepec and Villa Alta); and Guerrero (Amula and Chilpancingo). **West** to Guerrero (Chilpancingo and Taxco); State of Mexico (Coatepec and Jalapa); Durango (Durango); western Chihuahua (Jesus Maria and Pinos Altos); and Sonora (Oposura).

This range is occupied chiefly by the typical race, *H. l. leucotis*, but according to some systematists those in the north (which include the individuals noted casually in Arizona) are a distinct race to which the name *H. l. borealis* has been given. The birds found in Nicaragua also have been recognized as a distinct subspecies.

Casual records.—The species has been recorded a number of times from southeastern Arizona as follows: The first United States specimen was collected on June 9, 1894, at Fly Park, in the Chiricahua Mountains; one was taken in the Santa Rita Mountains on June 24, 1903; in 1915 a specimen was taken in the Santa Catalina Mountains; during the period from June 10 to December 31, 1919, 12 specimens were obtained in the Huachuca Mountains; and on August 11, 1933, an adult male was captured in Miller Canyon, of the Huachucas.

Egg dates.—Chihuahua and Sinaloa: March 26, May 23 and August 12 (Moore).

Guatemala: Sierra de Tecpán, Department of Chimaltenango, west-central Guatemala, 8,000–9,000 feet: 12 records, November and December. In 1933, nest building began about the middle of October. The earliest date of laying for which there is a record (computed from date of hatching) is about October 23; the latest, December 22 (Skutch).

CYNANTHUS LATIROSTRIS Swainson

BROAD-BILLED HUMMINGBIRD

HABITS

Robert T. Moore has kindly lent me a portion of his unpublished manuscript on the life habits of the birds of Sinaloa, and, with his permission, I am quoting from it most of what follows in the account of this species. As to the subspecific status of our form of the broad-billed hummingbird, he writes: "The comparison of our large series of 31 males and 24 females from northwestern Mexico, with 9 males and 3 females in the Moore collection, as well as others, from east-central Mexico, has convinced me that the northwestern birds, originally given the name of *magica* by Mulsant and Verreaux, should be differentiated on the basis of darker-green posterior underparts, whiter under tail coverts, and definitely smaller size. The Arizona form resembles this northwestern Mexican bird, rather than the eastern."

As to his personal experience with it in the field, he says: "My first acquaintance with the broad-billed hummingbird was made at the base of the great Butte, at Peña Blanca Spring, southern Arizona. A large group of ocotillos fringed the eastern ledges below the cliff, their red pennants providing an irresistible attraction. The birds did not seem to be interested in any other flowers. My real knowledge of the habits of this hummingbird has been acquired in the States of Sonora, Sinaloa, and Chihuahua, of northwestern Mexico.

"Our four nests have been found at altitudes from 45 feet at Culiacan, Sinaloa, to 1,450 feet at Guirocoba, Sonora. Specimens have been collected at the highest elevations—Palo Verdes Mines, 4,900 feet; on the Urique River, Chihuahua, taken by myself, 5,000 feet; and even on Mount Mohinora at nearly 10,000 feet—but no nests have been secured at these altitudes. Although I observed both sexes repeatedly during May on Mohinora, feeding within a few feet of me among the flowers in extraordinary mammoth beds of paintbrush, they showed no indications of breeding."

Courtship.—Mrs. Bailey (1928) refers to this briefly, as follows: "The courtship 'pendulum swing back and forth in front of a female,' when given by the Broad-bill, Mr. Willard says is 'higher pitched than that of any of the other small hummers,' having 'the *zing* of a rifle bullet' (MS.). It is of peculiar interest to hear from Mr. O. W. Howard that while in Arizona he saw several of the male Broad-bills in the vicinity of their completed nests."

Nesting.—Mr. Moore's (MS.) remarks on nesting follow: "The finding of my first nest at the Guirocoba Ranch, Sonora, was a welcome goad to a brain completely fagged by the terrific heat. The tropical sun was desiccating a tiny arroyo with relentless power. A female propelled its tiny atom of a body straight to a nest on the branch of a small tree, overhanging the bank of the arroyo and not 5 feet from the ground. It was an unusual demonstration of courage and confidence in human beings, for the nest on May 2, 1934, contained no eggs, being only half finished. I have known many ruby-throated hummingbirds to desert an unfinished home, if one climbed the nest tree, and never in my experience with some dozen of them has a single male or female protected an eggless nest, as this tiny parent did repeatedly during the next few days.

"When it came to the more arduous operation of nest building, involving the carrying of material and weaving instead of resting, she preferred the cooler hours of the day from 3:30 until dark, and did a prodigious amount of work. A red letter day of accomplishment was May 2. At 5:30 p. m. the nest had attained one half its final height, but at 9 o'clock the next morning the complete altitude of the walls had been erected. As the nest, now before me, is approximately 1 inch high on the outside, the above statement means that the bird built half an inch of wall material during the late afternoon and early morning hours. In addition, she added the lining and attached a considerable number of white cobweb strands, completely swathing the bottom of the nest with them and supporting and connecting its outer rim to the leaves and tiny branchlets in the vicinity. However, free access to the nest was not obstructed.

"The most interesting nest-building technique was displayed a number of times when I was within a few feet of the nest. The bird molded the bottom of it with quivering, caressing motions of the body. Often in the process the wings revolved at almost full velocity, certainly until they were blurred to sight, and yet the body of the bird appeared to be sitting in the nest throughout the action. I saw it performed a number of times; sometimes it gave the impression of a swaying motion, from one side to the other, without the body leaving the nest, or the wings ceasing to revolve. When the wings did not revolve, the bill moved rapidly along the outside of the abode, tucking in protruding ends of grasses.

"The bulk of the nest is composed of exceedingly fine material, mostly tiny shreds of buff-colored or brownish bark, grasses, and bits of dried leaves. The only larger pieces are three strips of bark placed upright, parallel with the tiny twig on which the nest is placed. I imagine these came from the sabino, a cypress that grows to a great height along a small stream not far away. Part of the inside of the nest is lined with a white material, probably some kind of minute plant down, but possibly cotton of fine texture. All these materials could be obtained from the fields nearby, which are cultivated by the Indians of the Guirocoba Plantation.

"Three other nests were secured by our expedition in Sinaloa, two of them in March at Culiacan and one on January 16, 1936, at San Lorenzo, Sinaloa. Examination of the sex organs of our numerous specimens proves that the birds are apt to breed at any time from January to August.

"As these last three nests contain two eggs each, it can be presumed that they are finished creations, although some hummingbirds attach ornamental bits of lichen to the exterior, even during the period of incubation. Not the slightest indication of this appears in any of these four nests. The January nest was taken at San Lorenzo by Chester C. Lamb, which differs somewhat from the other three. Like the March 1 nest, it was attached to the stalk of a vine. Placed 4 feet up in an espino tree, the body of the nest is composed almost entirely of cotton, but lined with a glossy-white plant down. The base is supported by a dried pod of the vine itself. On the outside are attached pieces of dried leaves and, according to Mr. Lamb, some 'short fibers of the palo-blanco pods.' The entire exterior is bound together with spiderwebs. The March 1 and March 7 nests from Culiacan display a lining of white plant down, covered on the periphery with bits of bark and leaves, but the bodies of the nests seem to be made of grasses and exceedingly fine, threadlike stalks of dried plants. The March 1 nest was placed in a 'dry bush, covered with dry vines' and the March 7 in an espino tree.

"In spite of these minor differences, these abodes are so similar that I think I could recognize them at random among a large number of other hummingbird nests. They all have some grass stalks in the

body, are lined with white plant down, are all adorned with bits of
leaves and bark on the outside, and not one of them has a single
lichen on any part of the nest. In addition, they are all very small,
with an inside diameter of only about three-quarters of an inch, and
all were placed within 5 feet of the ground. They differ markedly
from our nests of other hummingbirds of Sinaloa, such as the white-
ear, azurecrown, and the violaceous, all these having lichen adorn-
ments. The eggs are white, two in number, and at least in the case of
the San Lorenzo nest, were laid two days apart."

Roy W. Quillin (1935) records the finding of a nest of the broad-
billed hummingbird in Texas, the only nest so far reported for that
State:

"A nest of this species containing two eggs was found on May 17,
1934, at Talley's (Johnson's) Ranch, on the Rio Grande, southwest
of Mariscal Mountain, Brewster County, Texas. The nest was on the
very bank of the Rio Grande, on a drooping twig in a triple fork of
a small willow tree some ten or twelve feet above the ground on a
steep bank of the river and almost overhung the water. The nest
was composed almost entirely of the down of the willows ornamented
on the outside with yellow blooms and tiny mesquite leaves and bound
with spider or insect webs. The materials of the nest lashed it firmly
to the twigs on which it rested in an upright fork."

My acquaintance with the broad-billed hummingbird was a brief
one in Sabino Canyon, at the southern end of the Santa Catalina
Mountains, Ariz. In the rough, rocky bed of the stream flowing
through this rugged canyon, Frank Willard and I made a long and
laborious search for the nests of this hummingbird. It has been
found nesting here in a species of shrub that grows profusely along
the rough banks of the stream and among the rocks in its bed. Two
or three of the birds dashed by us at different times, in such rapid
flight that it seemed as if a whistling bullet had whizzed past us;
but we did not succeed in finding a nest; it was in April, and we were
perhaps too early. Mr. Willard had previously found a nest here, 5
feet up in a small willow over the water; he told me that O. W.
Howard had also found it nesting here. There is a nest from this
locality in the P. B. Philipp collection, taken by H. H. Kimball on
April 20, 1923, that was placed "in a hackberry bush growing against
a small sycamore at the edge of a creek, 4 feet from the water."

There are three nests in the Thayer collection, taken by W. W.
Brown, Jr., near Opodepe, Sonora, Mexico, on May 3, 10, and 13,
1905; one of these was in an apricot tree and the other two in mesquites; the construction of these nests compares very closely with
the excellent description given above by Mr. Moore.

Eggs.—Two eggs seem to be the usual, if not the invariable, rule with the broad-billed hummingbird. These are pure white, without gloss, and otherwise indistinguishable from the eggs of other hummingbirds of similar size. The measurements of 27 eggs average 12.6 by 8.5 millimeters; the eggs showing the four extremes measure **13.5** by 9.7, 13.4 by **9.8**, and **11.5** by 7.5 millimeters.

Plumages.—Mr. Moore says (MS.) : "The Moore collection contains no young, actually taken from a nest, but a young male, obviously not long out of the nest, was secured at the Guirocoba Ranch in extreme southeastern Sonora on March 26, 1931. The bill is only half the length of the adult, the tail the same, and the wings two-thirds, the postnatal molt being about four-fifths complete on wings, tail, entire upper parts, under tail coverts, and portions of the neck. Possessing very loose margins, the remiges are recurved. Two nearly parallel feather tracts on the throat are sharply defined, because the new feathers are still in their sheaths, and areas on throat and breast are bare.

"As to coloration, it is significant that the tail plainly shows the male characteristics, being almost identically like the fully adult male tail in miniature, revealing no white tips to the lateral rectrices as in the female and having the median pair blue, tipped with gray, instead of entirely bronzy green. The longest upper tail coverts show full development and might easily be mistaken for the median pair of rectrices. Therefore, it is clear that the sexes can be differentiated in this species, even in the juvenal plumage, when a few weeks old. Cinnamon-buff covers a large part of crown and occiput and reveals much wider margins on the back than in the May, June, and September worn juvenal plumage. The lesser and middle wing coverts show irridescent green, instead of bronzy.

"On the under tail coverts, although the plumage is looser than in the first winter plumage, the general appearance is immaculate white, as in practically all adult *magicus*, contrasting them sharply with *Cynanthus latirostris.* So many spots on the underparts are not feathered that, except for the under tail coverts, they are blotched with black and light buff.

"The most interesting peculiarity consists in a prominent white postocular streak. This is represented by a narrow streak, half the length, in the adult female and juvenile male of first winter plumage, which is reduced to dot or is obsolete in the adult male. This streak consists of nonpennaceous feathers, very loose in texture, as in the juvenile male, and contrasts with the typical feathers of the adult female.

"Five representatives of juvenile males in their first winter plumage form part of the Moore collection. They resemble the female coloration, except that the feathers of the upper parts are margined with buffy, much more narrowly than in the juvenal plumage, and the rectrices are exactly like the adult males. A female, from Los Leones, Sinaloa, March 22, 1934, which has acquired the complete juvenal plumage, has feathers of upper parts margined just as broadly with cinnamon-buff, as the young male in partial juvenal plumage, but differs in having a fully developed tail, just like the adult females. Consequently, the differences of the sexes can be determined in every plumage."

Young males begin to acquire some of the bluish-green feathers in the throat patch early in their first year but, apparently, do not acquire the full bluish-green gorget and the metallic bronze-green of the breast and sides until the first annual molt the next summer, when old and young become indistinguishable.

Food.—The broad-billed hummingbird evidently lives on similar food to that of other members of the family, the nectar of flowers and the minute insects that the flowers attract. Mr. Moore (MS.) mentions the red flowers of the ocotillo as attracting it and seeing it feeding in the beds of the paint brush, but probably any brightly colored blossoms would serve equally well as feeding places. He says: "A small shrub, the 'tavachin,' flaunts an extraordinary flower, resembling the royal poinciana, and fairly startles one with its scarlet glory. Belonging to the genus *Caesalpinia* or *Poinciana*, it provides the favorite rendezvous for *Cynanthus*, as well as many species of butterflies. The tiny homesteader made many excursions to obtain food from this plant, whose vivid red and yellow flowers flamed in the sunlit spaces across the sandy arroyo. She apportioned part of her time to the yellow flowers of a huge opuntia, which hung out perilously over her side of the arroyo. During the hottest period of the day she drowsed on a branch of the nesting tree, within 10 feet of the nest, not usually making food rounds until 3:30 in the afternoon. Between each round she would spend several minutes resting in the nest tree. At the beginning of each circuit I timed the average of inception, which was approximately 15 minutes, and each time she visited apparently every flower over again. A few less conspicuous blooms were also probed."

Cottam and Knappen (1939) examined four stomachs collected in Arizona, which "show that the bird feeds primarily on small insects and spiders." In their summary they mention fragments of plant lice, leafhoppers, jumping plant lice, miscellaneous bugs, root gnats, flower flies, miscellaneous flies including dance flies, ants, parasitic wasps, miscellaneous Hymenoptera, some undertermined insects, spiders, daddy-longlegs, and pollen grains.

Behavior.—Referring to the behavior of the female in the defense of her eggless nest, an unusual occurrence among hummingbirds, Mr. Moore (MS.) writes: "It is true that her little majesty was never real rude about it, for when I set up my camera without camouflage this bit of animated lightning betrayed no resentment, flew straight to the nest, twirled about on it two or three times, and showed no irritation because of the huge eye of the graflex. Curiously enough, the only time she really attacked was when I photographed her with moving picture camera 20 yards from the nest, as she fed from the scarlet flowers of the 'tavachin.' A formal visit to her home seemed perfectly proper, but an intrusion at the dinner hour was the epitome of rudeness. Even then the attack was only half-hearted, and chronic good nature took possession immediately, as she whirled from one brilliant flower to another.

"A male broadbill was observed feeding from the 'tavachin' and, although he several times flew within 10 feet of the nest tree, he never landed on it, nor did the female appear to object to his feeding 20 feet away across the sandy wash. The broadbill is a common bird of the region and the male bird might not have been the 'mate'. Although the males of United States hummingbirds do not make a practice of assisting about the nest, southern species often do. In Ecuador I have observed the male as well as the female violet-ear take turns incubating the same nest. Both individuals were collected to prove this habit.

"Such evidences of anger as the female exhibited were directed not so much at me as at the large blue swallowtail that insisted on appropriating the sweets from her flower garden. Several times she, as well as the male, chased it away, but they did not attempt to pursue the smaller butterflies. The flight of this bird from flower to flower is so characteristic that it can be recognized at some distance. Instead of darting straight to its object, as many hummingbirds do, *Cynanthus* progresses with a somewhat jerky, irregular flight. At least its short flight has an exceedingly nervous kind of movement, the tail bobbing up and down, lacking the precision of the Rivoli's undeviating course."

Dr. Alexander Wetmore (1932) says: "The broad-bill seems quieter and less active than some of the species that have been described, and frequently, after aggressive flight in pursuit of some intruder, I have seen the two combatants perch four or five inches from one another for a few seconds, while with raised wings they gave a low, chattering call." He also refers to the ordinary flight as "accompanied by a subdued humming sound." The sound produced by this bird in flight, as I have heard it, is more like the shriek of a passing bullet, far from subdued.

Field marks.—The most conspicuous and diagnostic field mark of the broad-billed hummingbird is the broad, purplish-red or carmine bill; the bill of the adult male is wholly red, except for the dusky tip; that of the young male and the female is basally red. The color pattern of the adult male is distinctive, green upper parts and breast, bluish-green throat, white posterior under parts, and glossy blue-black tail. The female, adult or young, has a grayish breast and some green in the tail. The young male has a tail like his father, and the young female one like her mother.

DISTRIBUTION

Range.—Southern Arizona, south to central Mexico.

Breeding range.—The broad-billed hummingbird breeds **north** to southeastern Arizona (Santa Catalina Mountains and Sabino Canyon); probably rarely southwestern New Mexico (Cloverdale Range); and central Nuevo Leon (Monterey). **East** to western Nuevo Leon (Monterey); and the State of Mexico (Chimalcoyoc). **South** to the State of Mexico (Chimalcoyoc); Jalisco (Lake Chapala); and southern Sinaloa (Escuinapa). **West** to Sinaloa (Escuinapa); Sonora (Tesia, San Javier, Moctezuma, and Saric); and southeastern Arizona (Santa Rita Mountains, probably Fresnal Canyon, and Santa Catalina Mountains).

Winter range.—The species appears to be resident throughout the Mexican portion of the range, although at this season it has been recorded south to Taxco, State of Guerrero. It withdraws entirely from the United States but winters north to central Sonora (Guaymas and Oposura).

Migration.—Little information is available concerning the short migratory flights that are made but early dates of arrival in Arizona are: Rillito Creek, near Tucson, March 13, and Santa Catalina Mountains, April 5. It leaves this region during the last of August and early part of September.

Egg dates.—Mexico: 16 records, January 16 to May 21; 8 records, March 25 to May 11, indicating the height of the season.

Arizona: 5 records, April 14 to July 15.

LITERATURE CITED

Abbott, Clinton Gilbert.
  1914. City nighthawks. Bird-Lore, vol. 16, pp. 10–13.
Aiken, Charles Edward Howard, and Warren, Edward Royal.
  1914. The birds of El Paso County, Colorado. II. Colorado Coll. Publ.,
    sci. ser., vol. 12, pp. 497–603.
Aldrich, Elmer C.
  1935. Nesting of the dusky poor-will. Condor, vol. 37, pp. 49–55.
Allard, Harry Ardell.
  1934. Speed of the ruby-throated hummingbird's flight. Auk, vol. 51, p. 84.
Allen, Arthur Augustus.
  1930. Rubythroat. Bird-Lore, vol. 32, pp. 223–231.
  1933. The nighthawk's story. Bird-Lore, vol. 35, pp. 171–179.
Allen, Charles Andrew.
  1880. Habits of Vaux's swift. Bull. Nuttall Orn. Club, vol. 5, pp. 55–56.
Allen, Joel Asaph.
  1871. On the mammals and winter birds of east Florida, with an examina-
    tion of certain assumed specific characters in birds, and a sketch
    of the bird-faunae of eastern North America. Bull. Mus. Comp.
    Zool., vol. 2, pp. 161–426.
Allen, Mary Pierson.
  1908. Hummingbird eccentricities. Bird-Lore, vol. 10, pp. 198–200.
Allen, W. E.
  1932. Note on food of California roadrunner (*Geococcyx californianus*).
    Bird-Lore, vol. 34, pp. 264–265.
American Ornithologists' Union.
  1910. Check-list of North American birds. Ed. 3.
  1931. Check-list of North American birds. Ed. 4.
Anthony, Alfred Webster.
  1892. Birds of southwestern New Mexico. Auk, vol. 9, pp. 357–369.
  1896. The roadrunner as a rat-killer. Auk, vol. 13, pp. 257–258.
  1897. Habits of Anna's hummingbird. Nidologist, vol. 4, pp. 31–33.
  1923. Ants destructive to bird life. Condor, vol. 25, pp. 132–133.
"Arkansas Hoosier."
  1890. The Caprimulgidae in Arkansas. Oologist, vol. 7, pp. 155–156.
Arnold, Leroy W.
  1930. Observations upon hummingbirds. Condor, vol. 32, pp. 302–303.
Attwater, Henry Philemon.
  1892. List of birds observed in the vicinity of San Antonio, Bexar County,
    Texas. Auk, vol. 9, pp. 229–238.
Audubon, John James.
  1840. The birds of America, vol. 1.
  1842. The birds of America, vol. 4.

473

BAILEY, ALFRED MARSHALL.
  1927. Notes on the birds of southeastern Alaska. Auk, vol. 44, pp. 351–367.
BAILEY, FLORENCE AUGUSTA MERRIAM.
  1896. Notes on some of the birds of southern California. Auk, vol. 13, pp. 115–124.
  1902. Handbook of birds of the Western United States.
  1904. Additional notes on the birds of the Upper Pecos. Auk, vol. 21, pp. 349–363.
  1907. White-throated swifts at Capistrano. Condor, vol. 9, pp. 169–172.
  1922. Koo. Bird-Lore, vol. 24, pp. 260–265.
  1923. Birds recorded from the Santa Rita Mountains in southern Arizona. Pacific Coast Avifauna, No. 15.
  1928. Birds of New Mexico.
BAILEY, GUY ANDREW.
  1905. The chimney swift. Bird-Lore, vol. 7, pp. 130–132.
BAILEY, HAROLD HARRIS.
  1907. Mortality among kingfishers. Auk, vol. 24, p. 439.
  1913. The birds of Virginia.
BAILEY, HARRY BALCH.
  1883. Memoranda of a collection of eggs from Georgia. Bull. Nuttall Orn. Club, vol. 8, pp. 37–43.
BAILEY, WILLIAM LLOYD.
  1900. The kingfishers' home life. Bird-Lore, vol. 2, pp. 76–80.
BAIRD, SPENCER FULLERTON.
  1858. Reports of explorations and surveys to ascertain the most practicable and economical route for a railroad from the Mississippi River to the Pacific Ocean, part 2. Birds. Vol. 9.
BANCROFT, GRIFFING.
  1930. The breeding birds of central Lower California. Condor, vol. 32, pp. 20–49.
BANGS, OUTRAM.
  1913. An unnamed race of the Carolina paroquet. Proc. New England Zool. Club, vol. 4, pp. 93–94.
BANGS, OUTRAM, and PENARD, THOMAS EDWARD.
  1921. Notes on some American birds, chiefly neotropical. Bull. Mus. Comp. Zool., vol. 64, pp. 365–397.
BANGS, OUTRAM, and PETERS, JAMES LEE.
  1928. Birds collected by Dr. Joseph F. Rock in western Kansu and eastern Tibet. Bull. Mus. Comp. Zool., vol. 68, pp. 313–381.
BARBOUR, THOMAS.
  1923. The birds of Cuba.
BARROWS, WALTER BRADFORD.
  1912. Michigan bird life.
BARTRAM, BENJAMIN SMITH.
  1799. Fragments of the natural history of Pennsylvania.
BASSETT, FRANK NEWTON.
  1921. The nuptial flight of the Allen hummingbird. Condor, vol. 23, p. 37.
  1924. The Anna hummingbird takes a shower bath. Condor, vol. 26, p. 227.
BATCHELDER, CHARLES FOSTER.
  1882. Notes on the summer birds of the upper St. John. Bull. Nuttall Orn. Club, vol. 7, pp. 147–152.
BAYNES, ERNEST HAROLD.
  1915. Wild bird guests.

BEAL, FOSTER ELLENBOROUGH LASCELLES.

1897. Some common birds in their relation to agriculture. U. S. Dept. Agr. Farmers' Bull. 54.

1915. Some common birds useful to the farmer. U. S. Dept. Agr. Farmers' Bull. 630.

BEAL, FOSTER ELLENBOROUGH LASCELLES, and MCATEE, WALDO LEE.

1912. Food of some well-known birds of forest, farm, and garden. U. S. Dept. Agr. Farmers' Bull. 506.

BEAL, FOSTER ELLENBOROUGH LASCELLES; MCATEE, WALDO LEE; and KALMBACH, EDWIN RICHARD.

1916. Common birds of Southeastern United States in relation to agriculture. U. S. Dept. Agr. Farmers' Bull. 755.

BEAL, MARY.

1933. The black-chinned hummingbird. Bird-Lore, vol. 35, pp. 96–97.

BECK, ROLLO HOWARD.

1897. Watching a poor-will. Nidologist, vol. 4, p. 105.

BEEBE, CHARLES WILLIAM.

1905. Two bird-lovers in Mexico.

BELDING, LYMAN.

1883. Catalogue of a collection of birds made near the southern extremity of the peninsula of Lower California. Proc. U. S. Nat. Mus., vol. 5, pp. 532–550.

BENDIRE, CHARLES EMIL.

1895. Life histories of North American birds. U. S. Nat. Mus. Spec. Bull. 3.

BERGTOLD, WILLIAM HARRY.

1906. Concerning the thick-billed parrot. Auk. vol. 23, pp. 425–428.

BEYER, GEORGE EUGENE; ALLISON, ANDREW; and KOPMAN, HENRY HAZLITT.

1908. List of the birds of Louisiana, pt. 5. Auk. vol. 25, pp. 439–448.

BISHOP, LOUIS BENNETT.

1896. Description of a new horned lark and a new song sparrow, with remarks on Sennett's nighthawk. Auk, vol. 13, pp. 129–135.

1906. Uranomitra salvini in Arizona. Auk, vol. 23, pp. 337–338.

BLAKISTON, THOMAS WRIGHT, and PRYER, HENRY JAMES STOVIN.

1878. A catalogue of the birds of Japan. Ibis, 1878, pp. 209–250.

BOLLES, FRANK.

1894. From Blomidon to Smoky.

1912. Notes on whip-poor-wills and owls. Auk, vol. 29, pp. 150–159.

BOWLES, JOHN HOOPER.

1895. Further notes on Antrostomus vociferous whip-poor-will. The Museum, vol. 1, pp. 152–153.

1910. The Anna hummingbird. Condor, vol. 12, pp. 125–127.

1921. Nesting habits of nighthawks at Tacoma, Wash. Auk, vol. 38, pp. 203–217.

BRADBURY, WILLIAM CHASE.

1918. Notes on the nesting habits of the white-throated swift in Colorado. Condor, vol. 20, pp. 103–110.

BRALLIAR, FLOYD.

1922. Knowing birds through stories.

BREWER, THOMAS MAYO.

1874. A history of North American birds. Land birds. By Baird, Brewer, and Ridgway. Vol. 2.

BREWSTER, WILLIAM.

1879. On the habits and nesting of certain birds in Texas. Bull. Nuttall
Orn. Club, vol. 4, pp. 75–80.

1881. Notes on some birds from Arizona and New Mexico, with a description of a supposed new whip-poor-will. Bull. Nuttall Orn. Club,
vol. 6, pp. 65–73.

1882. On a collection of birds lately made by Mr. F. Stephens in Arizona.
Bull. Nuttall Orn. Club, vol. 7, pp. 193–212.

1889. Nesting habits of the parrakeet (*Conurus carolinensis*). Auk, vol. 6,
pp. 336–337.

1890. Food of young hummingbirds. Auk, vol. 7, pp. 206–207.

1893. Description of a new hummingbird from northern Mexico. Auk, vol.
10, pp. 214–215.

1895. The land-birds and game-birds of New England, by H. D. Minot.
Ed. 2.

1902. Birds of the Cape region of Lower California. Bull. Mus. Comp.
Zool., vol. 41, pp. 1–241.

1906. The birds of the Cambridge region of Massachusetts.

1937a. The birds of the Lake Umbagog region of Maine, part 3.

1937b. Concord River.

BRYANT, HAROLD CHILD.

1916. Habits and food of the roadrunner in California. Univ. California
Publ. Zool., vol. 17, pp. 21–58.

1925. Nesting of the Allen hummingbird in Golden Gate Park. Condor,
vol. 27, pp. 98–100.

BULLOCK, WILLIAM.

1825. Six months residence and travels in Mexico . . ., ed. 2. Vol. 2.

BURMEISTER, HERMAN.

1856. Thiere Brasiliens. Vol. 1.

BURNS, FRANKLIN LORENZO.

1915. Comparative periods of deposition and incubation of some North
American birds. Wilson Bull., vol. 27, pp. 275–286.

1921. Comparative periods of nestling life of some North American Nidi-
colae. Wilson Bull., vol. 33, pp. 4–15.

BURROUGHS, JULIAN.

1922. A chimney swift invasion. Bird-Lore, vol. 24, pp. 210–211.

BUTLER, AMOS WILLIAM.

1892. Notes on the range and habits of the Carolina parrakeet. Auk, vol.
9, pp. 49–56.

1898. The birds of Indiana.

CAMERON, EWEN SOMERLED.

1907. The birds of Custer and Dawson Counties, Montana. Auk, vol. 24,
pp. 289–406.

CAMPBELL, ARCHIBALD JAMES.

1901. Nests and eggs of Australian birds.

CAMPBELL, E. K. and D.

1926. Roosting swifts. Bird-Lore, vol. 28, pp. 395–396.

CANFIELD, JOSEPH BUCKINGHAM.

1902. A note on the night hawk. Amer. Orn., vol. 2, p. 217.

CAREY, HENRY REGINALD.

1909. Remarks on the habits of the kingfisher on the New Hampshire seacoast. Bird-Lore, vol. 11, pp. 161–164.

CARPENTER, FREDERIC HOWARD.
1886. Some ornithological explorations in the Dead River region of Maine. Ornithologist and Oologist, vol. 11, pp. 161–163.

CARTER, THOMAS DONALD.
1924. Nesting of chimney swifts. Bird-Lore, vol. 26, p. 330.

CASSIN, JOHN.
1862. Illustrations of the birds of California, Texas, Oregon, British and Russian America.

CHAMBERS, WILLIE LEE.
1901. Curious nest of Anna's hummingbird. Condor, vol. 3, p. 105.
1903. Early nesting of *Calypte anna* in the vicinity of Santa Monica, California. Condor, vol. 5, p. 133.

CHANCE, EDGAR.
1922. The cuckoo's secret.

CHANEY, RALPH WORKS.
1910. Summer and fall birds of the Hamlin Lake region, Mason County, Mich. Auk, vol. 27, pp. 271–279.

CHAPMAN, FRANK MICHLER.
1888. A list of birds observed at Gainesville, Florida. Auk, vol. 5, pp. 267–277.
1890. Notes on the Carolina paroquet (*Conurus carolinensis*) in Florida. Abstr. Proc. Linn. Soc. New York, year ending March 7, 1890, pp. 4–6.
1896. Notes on birds observed in Yucatan. Bull. Amer. Mus. Nat. Hist., vol. 8, pp. 271–290.
1912. Handbook of birds of eastern North America.
1915. The Carolina paroquet in Florida. Bird-Lore, vol. 17, p. 453.
1925. Notes on the plumages of North American birds. Bird-Lore, vol. 27, pp. 104, 327.
1931. The winter range of the chimney swift (*Chaetura pelagica*). Auk, vol. 48, pp. 119–121.

CHENEY, SIMEON PEASE.
1891. Some bird songs. Auk, vol. 8, pp. 32–37.

CHERRIE, GEORGE KRUCK.
1892. A preliminary list of the birds of San José, Costa Rica. Auk, vol. 9, pp. 322–329.
1896. An apparently new *Chordeiles* from Costa Rica. Auk, vol. 13, pp. 135–136.

CHILDS, JOHN LEWIS.
1905. Eggs of the Carolina paroquet. Warbler, vol. 1, pp. 97–98.
1906a. Nest and eggs of the blue-throated hummingbird. Warbler, vol. 2, p. 65.
1906b. Eggs of the Carolina paroquet. Warbler, vol. 2, p. 65.

CHRISTY, BAYARD HENDERSON.
1932. A hummingbird nest. Condor, vol. 34, pp. 241–242.

CLABAUGH, ERNEST DWIGHT.
1936. Nesting of the Allen hummingbird. Condor, vol. 38, pp. 176–177.

CLARK, FRANK CUTHBERT.
1902. Food of Anna hummingbird. Condor, vol. 5, p. 18.

CLARK, JOSIAH HUNTOON.
1900. Notes on the nesting of the blue-throated hummingbird. Auk, vol. 17, p. 294.

CLAY, MARCIA B.
    1929. The yellow-billed cuckoo. Bird-Lore, vol. 31, pp. 189–190.
COALE, HENRY KELSO.
    1920. Curious habits of the whip-poor-will. Auk, vol. 37, pp. 293–294.
COCHRANE, HENRY LANE.
    1914. A note on the breeding of the white-rumped swift (*Micropus pacificus*). Ibis, 1914, pp. 586–588.
COOKE, WELLS WOODBRIDGE.
    1884. Bird nomenclature of the Chippewa Indians. Auk, vol. 1, pp. 242–250.
CORDIER, ALBERT HAWES.
    1923. Birds, their photographs and home life.
COTTAM, CLARENCE.
    1932. Nocturnal habits of the chimney swift. Auk, vol. 49, pp. 479–481.
COTTAM, CLARENCE, and KNAPPEN, PHOEBE.
    1939. Food of some uncommon North American birds. Auk, vol. 56, pp. 138–169.
COUES, ELLIOTT.
    1874. Birds of the Northwest.
    1878. Habits of the kingfisher (*Ceryle alcyon*). Bull. Nuttall Orn. Club, vol. 3, p. 92.
    1888. New forms of North American *Chordiles*. Auk, vol. 5, p. 37.
    1897. How the chimney swift secures twigs for its nest. Auk, vol. 14, pp. 217–218.
    1900. The "churca" (*Geococcyx californianus*). Auk, vol. 17, p. 66.
    1903. Key to North American birds.
COUPER, WILLIAM.
    1876. Naturalist for April. Forest and Stream, vol. 6, p. 132.
DANFORTH, RALPH EMERSON.
    1921. An unusual accident. Bird-lore, vol. 23, p. 246.
DANIEL, JOHN WARWICK, Jr.
    1902. Summer birds of the Great Dismal Swamp. Auk, vol. 19, pp. 15–18.
DAVIS, WILLIAM B.
    1937. A Vaux swift and its young. Condor, vol. 39, vol. 222–223.
DAVISON, JOHN LESTER.
    1887. Birds laying their eggs in the nest of other birds. Auk, vol. 4, pp. 263–264.
DAWSON, WILLIAM LEON.
    1903. The birds of Ohio.
    1923. The birds of California. Vol. 2.
DAWSON, WILLIAM LEON, and BOWLES, JOHN HOOPER.
    1909. The birds of Washington. Vol. 1.
DAY, MARY F.
    1899. Home-life in a chimney. Bird-Lore, vol. 1, pp. 78–81.
DEKAY, JAMES ELLSWORTH.
    1844. Zoology of New York, or the New-York fauna, part 2. Birds.
DE LAUBENFELS, MAX WALKER.
    1925. Unusual notes of Texas nighthawk. Condor, vol. 27, p. 210.
DICKEY, DONALD RYDER.
    1915. The hummers in a foothill valley. Country Life in America, vol. 28, No. 2, pp. 35–39.
    1928. A new poor-will from the Colorado River Valley. Condor, vol. 30, pp. 152–153.

DICKEY, DONALD RYDER, and VAN ROSSEM, ADRIAAN JOSEPH.
1938. The birds of El Salvador. Field Mus. Nat. Hist. Publ., zool. ser.,
    vol. 23.
"DIDYMUS" [=HEADE, MARTIN JOHNSON].
1891. Florida hummingbirds. Forest and Stream, vol. 36, p. 455.
DIXON, JAMES BENJAMIN.
1912. The Costa hummingbird. Condor, vol. 14, pp. 75–77.
DIXON, JOSEPH SCATTERGOOD.
1935. Nesting of the black swift in Sequoia National Park. Condor, vol.
    37, pp. 265–267.
DREW, FRANK MAYO.
1882. Notes on the plumage of *Nephoecetes niger borealis*. Bull. Nuttall
    Orn. Club, vol. 7, pp. 182–183.
DRURY, CHARLES.
1887. Migration of night hawks. Journ. Cincinnati Soc. Nat. Hist., vol.
    10, pp. 148–149.
DuBOIS, ALEXANDER DAWES.
1911. A note on the nesting of the whip-poor-will. Auk, vol. 28, pp. 469–
    471.
1938. Observations at a rufous hummingbird's nest. Auk, vol. 55, pp. 629–
    641.
DUTCHER, WILLIAM.
1902. Results of special protection to gulls and terns obtained through the
    Thayer fund. Auk, vol. 19, pp. 34–64.
DYER, ERNEST I.
1939. More observations on the nesting of the Allen hummingbird. Con-
    dor, vol. 41, pp. 62–67.
EATON, ELON HOWARD.
1914. Birds of New York.
EATON, WARREN FRANCIS.
1936. Former occurrence of Carolina paroquet in New Jersey. Auk, vol.
    53, p. 82.
EIFRIG, CHARLES WILLIAM GUSTAVE.
1919. Notes on birds of the Chicago area and its immediate vicinity. Auk,
    vol. 36, pp. 513–524.
ELZEY, M. G.
1876. Game bag and gun. Forest and Stream, vol. 6, p. 122.
EVERETT, CONSTANCE and E. A.
1927. The fun of banding chimney swifts. Wilson Bull., vol. 39, pp. 111–
    112.
EVERMANN, BARTON WARREN.
1889. Birds of Carroll County, Indiana. Auk, vol. 6, pp. 22–30.
FINLEY, WILLIAM LOVELL.
1905. Hummingbird studies. Condor, vol. 7, pp. 59–62.
FINLEY, WILLIAM LOVELL and IRENE.
1915. With the Arizona road-runners. Bird-Lore, vol. 17, pp. 159–165.
1924. Changing habits of Vaux swift and western martin. Condor, vol. 26,
    pp. 6–9.
FISHER, ALBERT KENRICK.
1894. The capture of *Basilinna leucotis* in southern Arizona. Auk, vol. 11,
    pp. 325–326.
FISHER, WALTER KENRICK.
1904. Road-runners eat young mockingbirds. Condor, vol. 6, p. 80.

FLOYD, CHARLES BENTON.
    1937. Ruby-throated hummingbirds (*Archilochus colubris*) in cold weather.
        Bird-Banding, vol. 8, p. 79.
FORBUSH, EDWARD HOWE.
    1907. Useful birds and their protection.
    1927. Birds of Massachusetts and other New England States. Vol. 2.
FOREMAN, GRANT.
    1924. Cuckoos and jays. Bird-Lore, vol. 26, p. 182.
FOWLER, FREDERICK HALL.
    1903. Stray notes from southern Arizona. Condor, vol. 5, pp. 68–71, 106–107.
FRIEDMANN, HERBERT, and RILEY, JOSEPH HARVEY.
    1931. The genus *Cuculus* in North America. Auk, vol. 48, p. 269.
GANDER, FRANK FORREST.
    1927. The fly-catching habits of the Anna hummingbird. Condor, vol 29,
        p. 171.
GENTRY, THOMAS GEORGE.
    1877. Life-histories of the birds of eastern Pennsylvania. Vol. 1.
GILMAN, MARSHALL FRENCH.
    1915. A forty acre bird census at Sacaton, Arizona. Condor, vol. 17, pp.
        86–90.
GOFF, MILTON.
    1932. Roof drama. Bird-Lore, vol. 34, p. 202.
GOSS, NATHANIEL STICKNEY.
    1891. History of the birds of Kansas.
GOSSE, PHILIP HENRY.
    1847. The birds of Jamaica.
GRINNELL, JOSEPH.
    1898. Birds of the Pacific slope of Los Angeles County. Pasadena Acad.
        Sci. Publ. 11.
    1905a. The Pacific nighthawk. Condor, vol. 7, p. 170.
    1905b. Summer birds of Mount Pinos, California. Auk, vol. 22, pp. 378–391.
    1908. The biota of the San Bernardino Mountains. Univ. California Publ.
        Zool., vol. 5, pp. 1–170.
    1909. Birds and mammals of the 1907 Alexander expedition to southeastern
        Alaska. Univ. California Publ. Zool., vol. 5, pp. 171–264.
    1910. Birds of the 1908 Alexander Alaska expedition, with a note on the
        avifaunal relationships of the Prince William Sound district. Univ.
        California Publ. Zool., vol. 5, pp. 361–428.
    1914. An account of the mammals and birds of the lower Colorado Valley,
        with especial reference to the distributional problems presented.
        Univ. California Publ. Zool., vol. 12, pp. 51–294.
    1928. Notes on the systematics of west American birds, II. Condor, vol. 30,
        pp. 153–156.
GRINNELL, JOSEPH; DIXON, JOSEPH; and LINSDALE, JEAN MYRON.
    1930. Vertebrate natural history of a section of northern California through
        the Lassen Peak region. Univ. California Publ. Zool., vol. 35, pp.
        1–594.
GRINNELL, JOSEPH, and LINSDALE, JEAN MYRON.
    1936. Vertebrate animals of Point Lobos Reserve, 1934–35.
GRINNELL, JOSEPH, and STORER, TRACY IRWIN.
    1924. Animal life in the Yosemite.
GRISCOM, LUDLOW.
    1934. The ornithology of Guerrero, Mexico. Bull. Mus. Comp. Zool., vol.
        75, pp. 367–422.

HAMMERSLEY, GLADYS.

1928. Observations on the rufous hummingbird (*Selasphorus rufus*), 1927. Can. Field-Nat., vol. 42, pp. 149–150.

HANNA, WILSON CREAL.

1909. The white-throated swifts on Slover Mountain. Condor, vol. 11, pp. 77–81.

1917. Further notes on the white-throated swifts of Slover Mountain. Condor, vol. 19, pp. 3–8.

1937. California cuckoo in the San Bernardino Valley, California. Condor, vol. 39, pp. 57–59.

HARRIS, HARRY.

1919. Birds of the Kansas City region. Trans. Acad. Sci. St. Louis, vol. 23, pp. 213–371.

HARTERT, ERNST.

1912. Die Vögel der paläarktischen Fauna. Vol. 2.

HARTERT, ERNST, and HALL, ROBERT.

1904. On the birds collected by Mr. Robert Hall, of Melbourne, on the banks of the Lena River between Gigalowa and its mouth. Ibis, 1904, pp. 415–446.

HARTMAN, FRANK ALEXANDER.

1914. The cause of the peculiar sound made by nighthawks when volplaning. Science, new ser., vol. 39, pp. 326–327.

HASBROUCK, EDWIN MARBLE.

1891. The Carolina paroquet (*Conurus carolinensis*). Auk, vol. 8, pp. 369–379.

HENDERSON, JUNIUS.

1927. The practical value of birds.

HENSHAW, HENRY WETHERBEE.

1875. Report upon the ornithological collections made in portions of Nevada, Utah, California, Colorado, New Mexico, and Arizona, during the years 1871, 1872, 1873, and 1874. Wheeler's Rept. Expl. Surv. West 100th Merid., vol. 5, pp. 131–507.

1877. Description of a new species of humming-bird from California. Bull. Nuttall Orn. Club, vol. 2, pp. 53–58.

1886. List of birds observed in summer and fall on the upper Pecos River, New Mexico. Auk, vol. 3, pp. 73–80.

HERRICK, FRANCIS HOBART.

1901. The home life of wild birds.

1935. Wild birds at home.

HERSEY, FRANK SEYMOUR.

1923. Observations on the habits of the whip-poor-will (*Antrostomus v. vociferus*). Auk, vol. 40, pp. 534–536.

HESS, ISAAC ELNORE.

1910. One hundred breeding birds of an Illinois ten-mile radius. Auk, vol. 27, pp. 19–32.

HINE, JANE L.

1894. Observations on the ruby-throated hummingbird. Auk, vol. 11, pp. 253–254.

HOFFMANN, RALPH.

1927. Birds of the Pacific States.

HOLLISTER, NED.

1908. Birds of the region about Needles, California. Auk, vol. 25, pp. 455–462.

HOPKINS, H. C.
  1892. Oyster vs. kingfisher. Ornithologist and Oologist, vol. 17, p. 109.
HOWELL, ALFRED BRAZIER.
  1916. Some results of a winter's observations in Arizona. Condor, vol. 18, pp. 209–214.
  1927. Poor-wills attracted by arc light. Condor, vol. 29, p. 76.
HOWELL, ARTHUR HOLMES.
  1932. Florida bird life.
HOWES, PAUL GRISWOLD.
  1908. Notes on the black-billed cuckoo. Oologist, vol. 25, pp. 171–172.
HOXIE, WALTER [JOHN].
  1887. The capacity of eggs. Ornithologist and Oologist, vol. 12, p. 207.
HUEY, LAURENCE MARKHAM.
  1924. Nuptial flight of the black-chinned hummingbird. Condor, vol. 26, p. 229.
HUNT, RICHARD [MONTAGUE].
  1920. How fast can a roadrunner run? Condor, vol. 22, pp. 186–187.
HYDE, ARTHUR SIDNEY.
  1924. Chimney swift nesting in a cistern. Auk, vol. 41, pp. 157–158.
INGERSOLL, ERNEST.
  1920. The wit of the wild.
INGRAM, COLLINGWOOD.
  1908. Ornithological notes from Japan. Ibis, 1908, pp. 129–169.
JASPER, THEODORE.
  1878. The birds of North America.
JENCKS, FRED TINGLEY.
  1881. Kingbird and kingfisher. Ornithologist and Oologist, vol. 6, p. 64.
JENSEN, JENS KNUDSON.
  1923. Notes on the nesting birds of northern Santa Fe County, New Mexico. Auk, vol. 40, pp. 452–569.
JEWELL, H. W.
  1908. Nighthawks rear young in robin's nest. Journ. Maine Orn. Soc., vol. 10, p. 25.
JOHNSON, CHARLES EUGENE.
  1920. Summer bird records from Lake County, Minnesota. Auk, vol. 37, pp. 541–551.
JONES, A. E.
  1937. A cuckoo (*C. canorus* Linn.) incident. Journ. Bombay Nat. Hist. Soc., vol. 39, pp. 175–177.
JONES, LYNDS.
  1909. The birds of Cedar Point and vicinity. Wilson Bull., vol. 21, pp. 187–204.
JUDD, SYLVESTER DWIGHT.
  1902. Birds of a Maryland farm. Biol. Surv. Bull. 17.
KEMERY, V. MAX.
  1925. A nighthawk's unusual home ties. Bird-Lore, vol. 27, pp. 251–252.
KENNARD, FREDERIC HEDGE.
  1895. Two unique nesting-sites in and about camp buildings in Hamilton County, New York. Auk, vol. 12, p. 314.
KENNERLY, CALEB BURWELL ROWAN.
  1857. Description of a new species of *Cypselus* [*C. borealis*], collected on the North Western Boundary Survey, Archibald Campbell, Esq., Commissioner. Proc. Acad. Nat. Sci. Philadelphia, vol. 9, pp. 202–203.

KERSHAW, J. G.
1904. List of the birds of the Quangtung coast, China. Ibis, 1904, pp. 235–248.

KING, FRANKLIN HIRAM.
1883. Economic relations of Wisconsin birds. Geology of Wisconsin, vol. 1, pp. 441–610.

KNAPPEN, PHOEBE.
1934. Plecoptera as a bird food. Auk, vol. 51, pp. 103–104.

KNIGHT, ORA WILLIS.
1908. The birds of Maine.

KNOWLTON, FRANK HALL.
1896. Nighthawk catching insects by electric light. Osprey, vol. 1, p. 53.

KOBBÉ, WILLIAM HOFFMAN.
1900. The rufous hummingbirds of Cape Disappointment. Auk, vol. 17, pp. 8–15.

KOPMAN, HENRY HAZLITT.
1915. List of the birds of Louisiana, pt. 6. Auk, vol. 32, pp. 15–29.

KOZLOVA, E. V.
1932. The birds of south-west Transkaikalia, northern Mongolia, and central Gobi. Ibis, 1932, pp. 567–596.

LACEY, HOWARD [GEORGE].
1911. The birds of Kerrville, Texas, and vicinity. Auk, vol. 28, pp. 200–219.

LAMB, CHESTER CONVERSE.
1912. Birds of a Mohave Desert oasis. Condor, vol. 14, pp. 32–40.
1925. Observations on the Xantus hummingbird. Condor, vol. 27, pp. 89–92.

LATHAM, ROY.
1920. Unusual habits of chimney swift. Auk, vol. 37, pp. 132–133.

LA TOUCHE, JOHN DAVID DIQUES.
1914. The spring migration at Chiawangtao in north-east Chihli. Ibis, 1914, pp. 560–586.
1931. A handbook of the birds of eastern China. Vol. 2, pt. 1.

LAW, JOHN EUGENE.
1923. A guilty road-runner: Circumstantial evidence. Condor, vol. 25, pp. 133–134.

LAWRENCE, GEORGE NEWBOLD.
1874. Birds of western and northwestern Mexico, based upon collections made by Col. A. J. Grayson, Capt. J. Xantus and Ferd. Bischoff, now in the museum of the Smithsonian Institution, at Washington, D. C. Mem. Boston Soc. Nat. Hist., vol. 2, pp. 265–319.

LEMMON, ISABELLA McC.
1901. Two young hummingbirds. Bird-Lore, vol. 3, p. 108.

LEOPOLD, ALDO.
1922. Road-runner caught in the act. Condor, vol. 24, p. 183.

LEWIS, JOHN BARZILLAI.
1927. Chimney swifts nesting in a well. Bird-Lore, vol. 29, p. 265.
1929. Feeding habits of chimney swifts. Auk, vol. 46, pp. 546–547.

LINCOLN, FREDERICK CHARLES.
1917. Some notes on the birds of Rock Canyon, Arizona. Wilson Bull., vol. 29, pp. 65–73.
1924. A "territory" note on the belted kingfisher. Wilson Bull., vol. 36, pp. 113–115.

LINSDALE, JEAN MYRON.

 1938. Environmental responses of vertebrates in the Great Basin. Amer.
        Midl. Nat., vol. 19, pp. 1–206.

LINTON, EDWIN.

 1924. Chimney swifts at bedtime. Bird-Lore, vol. 26, pp. 252–253.

LIVESEY, T. R.

 1936. Cuckoo problems. Journ. Bombay Nat. Hist. Soc., vol. 38, pp. 735–758.

LOCKWOOD, MARY E.

 1922. Hummingbird and bass. Bird-Lore, vol. 24, p. 94.

LONG, WILBUR S.

 1935. Spring notes from Lawrence, Kansas. Auk, vol. 52, pp. 466–467.

LONGSTREET, RUBERT JAMES.

 1930. Bird study in Florida.

LORD, JOHN KEAST.

 1866. The naturalist in Vancouver Island and British Columbia. Vol. 2.

LOWERY, GEORGE HINES, Jr.

 1938. Hummingbird in a pigeon hawk's stomach. Auk, vol. 55, p. 280.

LUCAS, FREDERIC AUGUSTUS.

 1893. The food of hummingbirds. Auk, vol. 10, pp. 311–315.

LUSK, RICHARD DEWITT.

 1900. Parrots in the United States. Condor, vol. 2, p. 129.

MACFARLANE, RODERICK ROSS.

 1891. Notes on and list of birds and eggs collected in Arctic America,
        1861–1866. Proc. U. S. Nat. Mus., vol. 14, pp. 413–446.

MAILLIARD, JOSEPH.

 1913. Some curious nesting places of the Allen hummingbird on the Rancho
        San Geronimo. Condor, vol. 15, pp. 205–207.

MAILLIARD, JOSEPH, and HANNA, G. DALLAS.

 1921. New bird records for North America with notes on the Pribilof
        Island list. Condor, vol. 23, pp. 93–95.

MAYFIELD, GEORGE RADFORD.

 1921. Roof-nesting nighthawks. Wilson Bull., vol. 33, pp. 147–148.

MAYNARD, CHARLES JOHNSON.

 1896. The birds of eastern North America.

MCATEE, WALDO LEE.

 1908. The value of the nighthawk. Bird-Lore, vol. 10, pp. 150–151.

 1916. Common birds of Southeastern United States in relation to agricul-
        ture. U. S. Dept. Agr. Farmers' Bull. 755.

 1926. The relation of birds to woodlots in New York State. Roosevelt Wild
        Life Bull., vol. 4, pp. 1–152.

 1931. A little essay on vermin. Bird-Lore, vol. 33, pp. 381–384.

MCBRIDE, JOHN M.

 1933. Unusual roosting of the chuck-will's-widow. Auk, vol. 50, p. 107.

MCILWRAITH, THOMAS.

 1894. The birds of Ontario.

MEARNS, EDGAR ALEXANDER.

 1890. Observations on the avifauna of portions of Arizona. Auk, vol. 7,
        pp. 251–264.

MERRIAM, CLINTON HART.

 1890. Results of a biological survey of the San Francisco Mountain region
        and desert of the Little Colorado in Arizona. North Amer. Fauna,
        No. 3.

MERRILL, JAMES CUSHING.
1878. Notes on the ornithology of southern Texas, being a list of birds observed in the vicinity of Fort Brown, Texas, from February, 1876, to June, 1878. Proc. U. S. Nat. Mus., vol. 1, pp. 118–173.

MICHAEL, CHARLES WILSON.
1927. Black swifts nesting in Yosemite National Park. Condor, vol. 29, pp. 89–97.

MICHAEL, ENID.
1926. The habits of swifts in Yosemite Valley. Condor, vol. 28, pp. 109–114.
1933. A young black swift. Condor, vol. 35, p. 30.

MILLER, ALDEN HOLMES.
1925. The boom-flight of the Pacific nighthawk. Condor, vol. 27, pp. 141–143.
1932. Observations on some breeding birds of El Salvador, Central America. Condor, vol. 34, pp. 8–17.
1937. The nuptial flight of the Texas nighthawk. Condor, vol. 39, pp. 42–43.

MILLER, OLIVE THORNE.
1892. Little brothers of the air.

MINOT, HENRY DAVIS.
1877. The land-birds and game-birds of New England.

MOORE, WILLIAM HENRY.
1902a. Notes on some Canadian birds. Ottawa Nat., vol. 16, pp. 130–134.
1902b. Nesting habits of the chimney swift. Bird-Lore, vol. 4, p. 162.

MOUSLEY, WILLIAM HENRY.
1938. A study of the home life of the eastern belted kingfisher. Wilson Bull., vol. 50, pp. 3–12.

MUNRO, JAMES ALEXANDER.
1918. Notes on some British Columbia birds. Auk, vol. 35, pp. 234–235.
1919. Notes on some birds of the Okanagan Valley, British Columbia. Auk, vol. 36, pp. 64–74.

MUNSTERHJELM, L.
1922. Meddelanden f. Goteborgs Musei. Zoolog. Avdelning, 13.

MUSSELMAN, THOMAS EDGAR.
1926. Chimney swift banding. Wilson Bull., vol. 38, pp. 120–121.
1931. Disasters to swifts. Bird-Lore, vol. 33, p. 397.

NOWOTNY, DR.
1898. The breeding of the Carolina paroquet in captivity. Auk, vol. 15, pp. 28–32.

OBERHOLSER, HARRY CHURCH.
1896. A preliminary list of the birds of Wayne County, Ohio. Bull. Ohio Agr. Exper. Sta., techn. ser., vol. 1, pp. 243–354.
1914. A monograph of the genus *Chordeiles* Swainson, type of a new family of goatsuckers. U. S. Nat. Mus. Bull. 86.
1918. Description of a new subspecies of *Cyanolaemus clemenciae*. Condor, vol. 20, pp. 181–182.
1925. The migration of North American birds. Bird-Lore, vol. 27, pp. 103–104, 326.
1926. The migration of North American birds. Bird-Lore, vol. 28, pp. 255–261.

ORR, ROBERT THOMAS.
1939. Observations on the nesting of the Allen hummingbird. Condor, vol. 41, pp. 17–24.

PALMER, THEODORE SHERMAN.
    1918. Costa's hummingbird—its type locality, early history and name.
        Condor, vol. 20, pp. 114-116.
PALMER, WILLIAM.
    1894. An Asiatic cuckoo on the Pribylof Islands, Alaska. Auk, vol. 11,
        p. 325.
PATTON, F. A.
    1924. Birds of the foot hills. Nesting of the Sennett's night hawk. Oologist,
        vol. 41, p. 111.
PEARSON, THOMAS GILBERT.
    1911. The chimney swift. Bird-Lore, vol. 13, pp. 115-118.
PEMBERTON, JOHN ROY.
    1916. Variation of the broken-wing stunt by a roadrunner. Condor, vol. 18.
        p. 203.
PICKENS, ANDREW LEE.
    1927. Unique method of pollination by the ruby-throat. Auk, vol. 44, pp.
        24-27.
    1930. Favorite colors of hummingbirds. Auk, vol. 47, pp. 346-352.
PICKWELL, GAYLE BENJAMIN.
    1937. Winter habits of the white-throated swift. Condor, vol. 39, pp.
        187-188.
PICKWELL, GAYLE BENJAMIN, and SMITH, EMILY.
    1938. The Texas nighthawk in its summer home. Condor, vol. 40, pp.
        193-215.
POLING, OTHO CURTIS.
    1890. Notes on Eugenes fulgens. Auk, vol. 7, pp. 402-403.
QUILLIN, ROY WILLIAM.
    1935. New bird records from Texas. Auk, vol. 52, pp. 324-325.
RATHBUN, SAMUEL FREDERICK.
    1925. The black swift and its habits. Auk, vol. 42, pp. 497-516.
RAY, ROSE CAROLYN.
    1925. Discovery of a nest and eggs of the blue-throated hummingbird.
        Condor, vol. 27, pp. 49-51.
RESSEL, CYRUS B.
    1889. Birds of Chester County, Penn. Ornithologist and Oologist, vol. 14,
        pp. 97-101.
RICHMOND, CHARLES WALLACE.
    1893. Notes on a collection of birds from eastern Nicaragua and the Rio
        Frio, Costa Rica, with a description of a supposed new trogon.
        Proc. U. S. Nat. Mus., vol. 16, pp. 479-532.
RIDGWAY, ROBERT.
    1877. United States geological exploration of the fortieth parallel. Part 3:
        Ornithology.
    1892. The humming birds. Rep. U. S. Nat. Mus. for 1890, pp. 253-383.
    1898. Description of a new species of hummingbird from Arizona. Auk, vol.
        15, pp. 325-326.
    1911. The birds of North and Middle America, U. S. Nat. Mus. Bull. 50, pt. 5.
    1912. Color standards and color nomenclature.
    1914. The birds of North and Middle America. U. S. Nat. Mus. Bull. 50, pt. 6.
    1916. The birds of North and Middle America. U. S. Nat. Mus. Bull. 50, pt. 7.
ROBERTS, THOMAS SADLER.
    1932. The birds of Minnesota. Vol. 1.

ROBERTSON, JOHN McBRAIR.

1933. An unusual nesting of the black-chinned hummingbird. Condor, vol. 35, pp. 241–242.

ROCKWELL, ROBERT BLANCHARD.

1908. An annotated list of the birds of Mesa County, Colorado. Condor, vol. 10, pp. 152–180.

RUST, HENRY JUDSON.

1911. Western nighthawks. Oologist, vol. 28, pp. 186–190.

SAMUELS, EDWARD AUGUSTUS.

1872. Birds of New England and adjacent States.

1883. Our northern and eastern birds.

SAUNDERS, ARETAS ANDREWS.

1915. A summer at Flathead Lake, Montana. Condor, vol. 17, pp. 109–115.

1929. The summer birds of the northern Adirondack Mountains. Roosevelt Wild Life Bull., vol. 5, pp. 327–499.

1936. Ecology of the birds of Quaker Run Valley, Allegany State Park, New York. New York State Mus. Handbook, 16.

SAUNDERS, WILLIAM EDWIN.

1917. City nesting of nighthawks. Wilson Bull., vol. 29, p. 105.

SCHLAG, CARL W.

1930. Hummingbirds and their nests. Cardinal, vol. 2, pp. 195–200.

SCOTT, WILLIAM EARL DODGE.

1886. On the avifauna of Pinal County, with remarks on some birds of Pima and Gila Counties, Arizona. Auk, vol. 3, pp. 431–432.

1889. A summary of observations on the birds of the gulf coast of Florida. Auk, vol. 6, pp. 245–252.

1890. On the birds observed at the Dry Tortugas, Florida, during parts of March and April, 1890. Auk, vol. 7, pp. 301–314.

1892. Observations on the birds of Jamaica, West Indies. Auk, vol. 9, pp. 369–375.

SELLECK, G. H.

1916. A nighthawk family. Guide to Nature, vol. 9, pp. 4–6.

SENNETT, GEORGE BURRITT.

1878. Notes on the ornithology of the lower Rio Grande of Texas. Bull. U. S. Geol. and Geogr. Surv., vol. 4, pp. 1–66.

1879. Further notes on the ornithology of the lower Rio Grande of Texas. Bull. U. S. Geol. and Geogr. Surv., vol. 5, pp. 371–440.

1888. Descriptions of a new species and two new subspecies of birds from Texas. Auk, vol. 5, pp. 43–46.

SETON, ERNEST THOMPSON.

1890. The birds of Manitoba. Proc. U. S. Nat. Mus., vol. 13, pp. 457–643.

SHARP, CLARENCE SAUGER.

1907. The breeding birds of Escondido. Condor, vol. 9, pp. 84–91.

SHAW, TSEN-HWANG.

1936. The birds of Hopei Province.

SHELDON, HARRY HARGRAVE.

1922a. Top speed of the road-runner. Condor, vol. 24, p. 180.

1922b. Vaux swift in migration. Condor, vol. 24, pp. 184–185.

SHELLEY, LEWIS ORMAN.

1929. Twig gathering of the chimney swift. Auk, vol. 46, p. 116.

SHELTON, ALFRED COOPER.

1911. Nesting of the California cuckoo. Condor, vol. 13, pp. 19–22.

SHERMAN, ALTHEA ROSINA.
    1913. Experimenting in feeding hummingbirds during seven summers. Wilson Bull., vol. 25, pp. 153–166.
SHUFELDT, ROBERT WILSON.
    1885. On the feeding habits of *Phalaenoptilus nuttalli*. Auk, vol. 2, pp. 382–383.
SIMMONS, GEORGE FINLAY.
    1915. On the nesting of certain birds in Texas. Auk, vol. 32, pp. 317–331.
    1925. Birds of the Austin region.
SIMPSON, CHARLES TORREY.
    1920. In lower Florida wilds.
SKINNER, MILTON PHILO.
    1928. Kingfisher and sharp-shinned hawk. Auk, vol. 45, pp. 100–101.
SKUTCH, ALEXANDER FRANK.
    1931. The life history of Rieffer's hummingbird (*Amazilia tzacatl tzacatl*) in Panama and Honduras. Auk, vol. 48, pp. 481–500.
SLOANAKER, JOSEPH L.
    1913. Bird notes from the South-west. Wilson Bull., vol. 25, pp. 187–199.
SMITH, AUSTIN PAUL.
    1907. The thick-billed parrot in Arizona. Condor, vol. 9, p. 104.
    1915. Birds of the Boston Mountains, Arkansas. Condor, vol. 17, pp. 41–57.
SMITH, EMILY.
    1928. Black swifts nesting behind a waterfall. Condor, vol. 30, pp. 136–138.
SMITH, EVERETT.
    1883. The birds of Maine. Forest and Stream, vol. 19, pp. 504–505.
SMITH, HUGH MCCORMICK, and PALMER, WILLIAM.
    1888. Additions to the avifauna of Washington and vicinity. Auk, vol. 5, pp. 147–148.
SMITH, PHILO W.
    1900. Nesting of Stephens's whippoorwill. Osprey, vol. 4, p. 89.
SMITH, WILBUR F.
    1920. A hummingbird story. Bird-Lore, vol. 22, pp. 274–275.
SNYDER, LESTER LYNNE, and LOGIER, E. B. S.
    1931. A faunal investigation of Long Point, and vicinity, Norfolk County, Ontario. Contr. Roy. Ontario Mus. Zool., vol. 18, pp. 117–236.
SOULE, CAROLINE GRAY.
    1900. A hummingbird experiment. Bird-Lore, vol. 2, p. 158.
SPIKER, CHARLES JOLLEY.
    1935. A popular account of the bird life of the Finger Lakes section of New York, with main reference to the summer season. Roosevelt Wild Life Bull., vol. 6, No. 3.
SPROT, GEORGE DOVETON.
    1927. Notes on the courtship of the rufous hummingbird. Condor, vol. 29, pp. 71–72.
SPRUNT, ALEXANDER, Jr., and CHAMBERLAIN, EDWARD BURNHAM.
    1931. Second supplement to Arthur T. Wayne's birds of South Carolina. Charleston Mus. Contr. No. 6.
STEARNS, WINFRID ALDEN.
    1883. New England bird life, pt. 2. Edited by Elliott Coues.
STEPHENS, FRANK.
    1913. Nighthawk drinking. Condor, vol. 15, p. 184.

STERLING, E.
　1885. Night hawks nesting. Forest and Stream, vol. 25, p. 4.
STEVENS, HERBERT.
　1925. Notes on the birds of the Sikkim Himalayas. Journ. Bombay Nat.
　　　Hist. Soc., vol. 30, pp. 664–685.
STOCKARD, CHARLES RUPERT.
　1905. Nesting habits of birds in Mississippi. Auk, vol. 22, pp. 146–158.
STONE, WITMER.
　1894. Capture of *Ceryle torquata* (Linn.) at Laredo, Texas. A species new
　　　to the United States. Auk, vol. 11, p. 177.
STORER, TRACY IRWIN.
　1921. The northward range of the Allen hummingbird. Condor, vol. 23, pp.
　　　160–162.
STROTHER, W. A.
　1886. An albino nighthawk. American Field, vol. 26, p. 415.
SUTTON, GEORGE MIKSCH.
　1922. Notes on the road-runner at Fort Worth, Texas. Wilson Bull., vol. 34,
　　　pp. 3–20.
　1928. Notes on the flight of the chimney swift. Cardinal, vol. 2, pp. 85–92.
　1935. An expedition to the Big Bend country. Cardinal, vol. 4, pp. 1–7.
　1936. Birds in the wilderness.
SWARTH, HARRY SCHELWALD.
　1904. Birds of the Huachuca Mountains, Arizona. Pacific Coast Avifauna,
　　　No. 4.
　1912. Differences due to sex in the black swift. Auk, vol. 29, pp. 241–242.
　1920. Birds of the Papago Saguaro National Monument and the neighbor-
　　　ing region, Arizona.
　1922. Birds and mammals of the Stikine River region of northern British
　　　Columbia and southeastern Alaska. Univ. California Publ. Zool.,
　　　vol. 24, pp. 125–314.
　1929. The faunal areas of southern Arizona: A study in animal dis-
　　　tribution. Proc. California Acad. Sci., vol. 18, pp. 267–383.
SWENK, MYRON HARMON.
　1934. The interior paroquet as a Nebraska bird. Nebraska Bird Rev., vol.
　　　2, pp. 55–59.
SWINHOE, ROBERT.
　1860. Letter on birds of Lam-yit. Ibis, 1860, pp. 428–429.
　1870. On the ornithology of Hainan. Ibis, 1870, pp. 77–97.
　1874. Ornithological notes made at Chefoo. Ibis, 1874, p. 435.
TATE, RALPH C.
　1926. Some materials used in nest construction by certain birds of the
　　　Oklahoma Panhandle. Univ. Oklahoma Bull., vol. 5, pp. 103–104.
　1928. Rufous hummingbird in the Oklahoma Panhandle. Condor, vol. 30,
　　　pp. 252–253.
TAVERNER, PERCY ALGERNON, and SWALES, BRADSHAW HALL.
　1907. The birds of Point Pelee. Wilson Bull., vol. 19, pp. 133–153.
TAYLOR, WALTER PENN, and SHAW, WILLIAM THOMAS.
　1927. Mammals and birds of Mount Rainier National Park.
THAYER, GERALD HENDERSON.
　1899. The chuck-will's-widow on shipboard. Auk, vol. 16, pp. 273–276.
　1903. The mystery of the black-billed cuckoo. Bird-Lore, vol. 5, pp. 143–145.

THAYER, JOHN ELIOT.
1906. Eggs and nests of the thick-billed parrot (*Rhyncopsitta pachyrhyncha*). Auk, vol. 23, pp. 223–224.
THOMAS, EDWARD S.
1932. Chuck-will's-widow, a new bird for Ohio. Auk, vol. 49, p. 479.
THOMPSON, ALBERT ERVIN.
1937. A swift in a granite wall. Nature Mag., vol. 30, p. 141.
TODD, WALTER EDMOND CLYDE.
1916. The birds of the Isle of Pines. Ann. Carnegie Mus., vol. 10, pp. 146–296.
TORREY, BRADFORD.
1892. The foot-path way.
1903. The clerk of the woods.
TOWNSEND, CHARLES WENDELL.
1906. Notes on the birds of Cape Breton Island. Auk, vol. 23, pp. 172–179.
1912. Notes on the summer birds of the St. John valley, New Brunswick. Auk, vol. 29, pp. 16–23.
1918. Ipswich bird notes. Auk, vol. 35, pp. 182–185.
1920a. Supplement to the birds of Essex County, Massachusetts. Mem. Nuttall Orn. Club, No. 5.
1920b. Courtship in birds. Auk, vol. 37, pp. 380–393.
TULLSEN, H.
1911. My avian visitors: Notes from South Dakota. Condor, vol. 13, pp. 89–104.
TURNBULL, WILLIAM PATTERSON.
1869. The birds of eastern Pennsylvania and New Jersey.
TUTTLE, HENRY EMERSON.
1911. The nesting of the whip-poor-will. Bird-Lore, vol. 13, pp. 235–238.
TYLER, JOHN GRIPPER.
1913. Some birds of the Fresno district, California. Pacific Coast Avifauna, No. 9.
VAN ROSSEM, ADRIAAN JOSEPH.
1927. Eye shine in birds, with notes on the feeding habits of some goatsuckers. Condor, vol. 29, pp. 25–28.
1936. Notes on birds in relation to the faunal areas of south-central Arizona. Trans. San Diego Soc. Nat. Hist., vol. 8, pp. 121–148.
1938. See Dickey and van Rossem, 1938.
VAN ROSSEM, ADRIAAN JOSEPH, and BOWLES, JOHN HOOPER.
1920. Nesting of the dusky poor-will near Saugus, Los Angeles County, California. Condor, vol, 22, pp. 61–62.
VAN TYNE, JOSSELYN, and SUTTON, GEORGE MIKSCH.
1937. The birds of Brewster County, Texas. Univ. Michigan Mus. Zool., Misc. Publ. No. 37.
VAUGHAN, ROBERT E., and JONES, KENNETH HURLSTONE.
1913. The birds of Hong Kong, Macao, and the West River or Si Kiang in south-eastern China, with special reference to their nidification and seasonal movements. Ibis, 1913, pp. 163–201.
VISHER, STEPHEN SARGENT.
1910. Notes on the birds of Pima County, Arizona. Auk, vol 27, pp. 279–288.
VORHIES, CHARLES TAYLOR.
1934. Arizona records of the thick-billed parrot. Condor, vol. 36, pp. 180–181.

VROOMAN, ALBERT GEORGE.
1901. Discovery of the egg of the black swift (*Cypseloides niger borealis*). Auk, vol. 18, pp. 394–395.
WARREN, BENJAMIN HARRY.
1890. Report on the birds of Pennsylvania. Ed. 2.
WARREN, EDWARD ROYAL.
1916. Notes on the birds of the Elk Mountain region, Gunnison County, Colorado. Auk, vol. 33, pp. 292–317.
WATSON, SHEPPARD ARTHUR.
1933. The Vaux swift at Whittier, California. Condor, vol. 35, pp. 203–204.
WAYNE, ARTHUR TREZEVANT.
1910. Birds of South Carolina.
WELLS, JOHN GRANT.
1902. Birds of the island of Carriacou. Auk, vol. 19, pp. 343–349.
WELTER, WILFRED AUGUST.
1935. Nesting habits of ruby-throated hummingbird. Auk, vol. 52, pp. 88–89.
WESTOVER, MYRON F.
1932. The flight of swifts. Bird-Lore, vol. 34, pp. 253–254.
WETMORE, ALEXANDER.
1916. Birds of Porto Rico. U. S. Dept. Agr. Bull. 326.
1920. Observations on the habits of birds at Lake Burford, New Mexico. Auk, vol. 37, pp. 393–412.
1921. Further notes on birds observed near Williams, Arizona. Condor, vol. 23, pp. 60–64.
1927. The birds of Porto Rico and the Virgin Islands. New York Acad. Sci., vol. 9, pt. 4, pp. 409–571.
1932. Seeking the smallest feathered creatures. Nat. Geogr. Mag., vol. 62, pp. 65–89.
1935. The thick-billed parrot in southern Arizona. Condor, vol. 37, pp. 18–21.
WEYDEMEYER, WINTON.
1927. Notes on the location and construction of the nest of the calliope hummingbird. Condor, vol. 29, pp. 19–24.
WHEELER, HARRY EDGAR.
1922. Random notes from Arkansas. Wilson Bull., vol. 34, pp. 221–224.
WHEELOCK, IRENE GROSVENOR.
1904. Birds of California.
1905. Regurgitative feeding of nestlings. Auk, vol. 22, pp. 54–70.
WHITTLE, CHARLES LIVY.
1937. A study of hummingbird behavior during a nesting season. Bird-Banding, vol. 8, pp. 170–173.
WIDMANN, OTTO.
1907. A preliminary catalog of the birds of Missouri.
WILLARD, FRANCIS COTTLE.
1899. Notes on *Eugenes fulgens*. Osprey, vol. 3, pp. 65–66.
1911. The blue-throated hummingbird. Condor, vol. 13, pp. 46–49.
WILSON, ALEXANDER.
1828–1832. American ornithology. Vols. 1, 2.
WOODBURY, ANGUS M.
1938. Red-naped sapsucker and rufous hummingbird. Condor, vol. 40, p. 125.

WOODS, ROBERT S.
 1922. The development of young Costa hummingbirds. Condor, vol. 24,
       pp. 189–193.
 1924a. Some birds of the San Gabriel wash. Bird-Lore, vol. 26, pp. 1–9.
 1924b. Notes on the life history of the Texas nighthawk. Condor, vol. 26,
       pp. 3–6.
 1927a. Road-runner versus mockingbird. Condor, vol. 29, p. 273.
 1927b. The hummingbirds of California. Auk, vol. 44, pp. 297–318.
 1934. A hummingbird entangled in a spider's web. Condor, vol. 36, p.
       242.
WRIGHT, ALBERT HAZEN, and HARPER, FRANCIS.
 1913. A biological reconnaissance of Okefinokee Swamp: The birds. Auk,
       vol. 30, pp. 477–505.
WYMAN, LUTHER EVERET.
 1920. Notes on the calliope hummingbird. Condor, vol. 22, pp. 206–207.
ZAREGA, LOUIS AUGUSTUS DL.
 1882. The nighthawk in cities. Forest and Stream, vol. 18, p. 467.

INDEX

This index covers both Parts of this work. Part I contains pages 1 to 244 and Part II contains pages 244 through 506.

Harris, Harry, on Louisiana parakeet, 12.
Harris, W. G. F., viii.
Hartert, Ernst, on Khasia Hills cuckoo, 91.
on white-rumped swift, 308, 309.
Hartman, F. A., on eastern nighthawk, 228, 229.
Hasbrouck, E. M., on Carolina parakeet, 2
Haskin, L. L., on rufous hummingbird, 397, 398, 403.
Hedden, A. E., 2.
Heermann, A. L., 38.
Heggeness, H. G., on dusky poorwill, 197.
heloisa, Atthis, 455.
Atthis heloisa, 417.
heloisa ellioti, Atthis, 419.
heloisa heloisa, Atthis, 417.
heloisa margarethae, Atthis, 419, 420.
heloisa morcomi, Atthis, 418.
Heloise's hummingbird, 417.
Henderson, Junius, on Anna's hummingbird, 380.
Henry, T. C., 235.
henryi, Chordeiles minor, 232, 235, 240.
Henshaw, H. W., 411.
on Allen's hummingbird, 416.
on broad-tailed hummingbird, 388, 394.
on calliope hummingbird, 427, 428.
on lucifer hummingbird, 430.
on Nuttall's poorwill, 192.
on Rivoli's hummingbird, 320.
on roadrunner, 48.
on rufous hummingbird, 396, 405, 408.
Herbert, E. G., 104.
Herman, W. C., on Carolina parakeet, 6, 10.
Herrara, A. L., on groove-billed ani, 32.
Herrick, F. H., on black-billed cuckoo, 74, 76, 77.
on eastern belted knigfisher, 116.
on eastern nighthawk, 226.
Hersey, F. S., viii.
on eastern whippoorwill, 164, 174, 177.
hesperis, Chordeiles minor, 232, 235, 236, 240.
Hess, I. E., on eastern nighthawk, 210.
Himalayan cuckoo, 84.
Hine, Jane L., on ruby-throated hummingbird, 335.
Hirundo apus var. B. leucopyga, 305.
pacifica, 304.
Hoffmann, Ralph, on northern black swift, 267, 269.
on calliope hummingbird, 421.
on Costa's hummingbird, 362.
on Vaux's swift, 299, 301.
on white-throated swift, 317.
Hollister, Ned, on Texas nighthawk, 250.
Holt, W. L., on dusky poorwill, 195.

Hopkins, H. C., on eastern belted kingfisher, 120.
Hopwood and Mackenzie, 84, 104.
Horsfall, R. B., 227.
Howard, O. W., 468.
on broad-billed hummingbird, 466.
Howell, A. B., on coppery-tailed trogon, 106.
on Nuttall's poorwill, 190.
on roadrunner, 47.
Howell, A. H., 243.
on Carolina parakeet, 3.
on chuck-will's-widow, 148.
on eastern belted kingfisher, 114.
on Florida nighthawk, 237.
on Maynard's cuckoo, 51, 52.
howelli, Chordeiles minor, 232, 236, 242.
Chordeiles virginianus, 244.
Howes, P. G., on black-billed cuckoo, 72.
Howlsey, L. B., viii.
Hoxie, Walter, on eastern nighthawk, 213.
Hudson, W. H., 384.
Huey, L. M., 197.
on black-chinned hummingbird, 353.
hueyi, Phalaenoptilus nuttalli, 193, 197, 198.
Hummingbird, Allen's, 411.
Anna's, 371.
Arizona blue-throated, 325.
black-chinned, 352.
broad-billed, 465.
broad-tailed, 387.
buff-bellied, 444.
calliope, 420.
Costa's, 361.
Elliot's, 419.
Heloise's, 417.
lucifer, 430.
Margaret's, 419, 420.
Rieffer's, 432.
Rivoli's, 319.
ruby-throated, 332.
rufous, 396.
Salvin's, 446.
Texas blue-throated, 330.
white-eared, 452.
Xantus's, 447.
Hummingbirds, 319.
Hunt, Richard, on roadrunner, 38.
Hyde, A. S., on chimney swift, 274.
Hyer, E. S., 3.
Hylocharis leucotis borealis, 465.
leucotis leucotis, 452.
magica, 465.
xantusi, 447.

inferior, Chordeiles acutipennis, 252, 253.
Ingersoll, Ernest, on eastern whippoorwill, 172.
Ingram, Collingwood, on white-rumped swift, 306, 309.
Ishizawa, T., 308.

Plates

PLATE 37

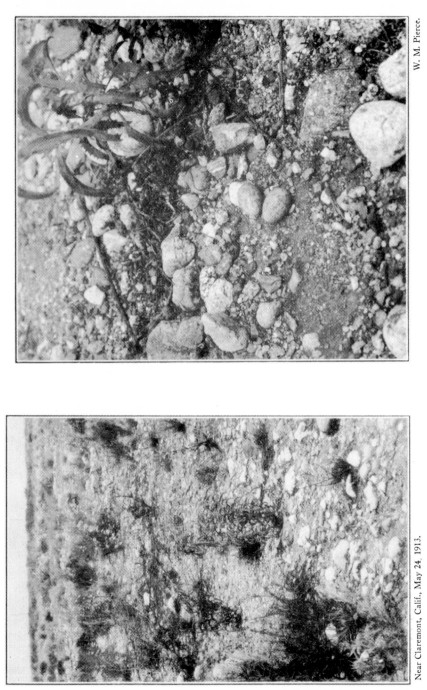

W. M. Pierce.

NESTING OF TEXAS NIGHTHAWK.

Near Claremont, Calif., May 24, 1913.

PLATE 38

May 16, 1923.

Downy young 2 or 3 days old.

Azusa, Calif., May 24, 1923.   R. S. Woods.

Young 10 days old.

TEXAS NIGHTHAWKS.

PLATE 39

May 30, 1923.

Young 16 or 17 days old.

Azusa, Calif., May 19, 1923.

R. S. Woods.

Female brooding young.

TEXAS NIGHTHAWKS

PLATE 40

W. L. Dawson.

Courtesy of National Association of Audobon Societies.

Santa Cruz, Calif., June 22, 1914.

HISTORIC NESTING SITE OF NORTHERN BLACK SWIFT (A. G. VROOMAN AT NEST).

PLATE 41

California State Redwood Park, 1926.   Emily Smith; F. R. Fulmer.

NESTING SITE OF NORTHERN BLACK SWIFT UNDER BERRY CREEK FALLS.

PLATE 42

Nesting site under shadow of a rock beside a cascade.

Fresno County, Calif.   A. E. Thompson.

Adult on nest.

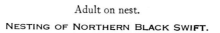

NESTING OF NORTHERN BLACK SWIFT.

PLATE 43

Sequoia National Park, Calif., August 7, 1933.

J. S. Dixon.
Courtesy of National Park Service.

Yosemite, Calif., August 22, 1926.

C. W. Michael.

Five weeks old.

YOUNG NORTHERN BLACK SWIFTS.

PLATE 44

Branchport, N. Y., June 17, 1900.   C. F .Stone.

Quincy, Ill.   T. E. Musselman.

NESTS OF CHIMNEY SWIFTS.

PLATE 45

Adult on nest in a silo.

Ithaca, N. Y.

Young.

A. A. Allen.

CHIMNEY SWIFTS.

PLATE 46

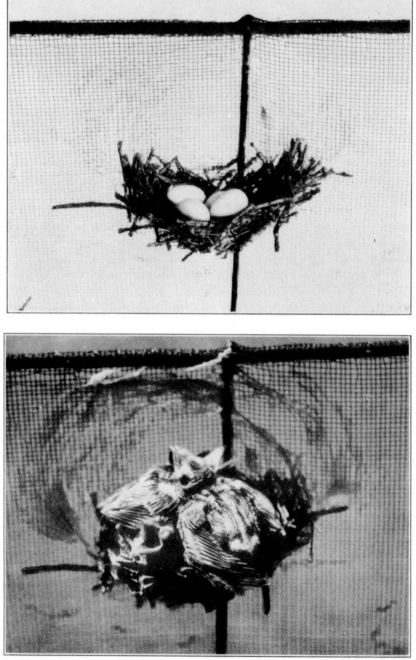

Arnprior, Ontario. C. Macnamara.

NESTING OF CHIMNEY SWIFTS ON A FIREGUARD ON A HEARTH.
(Note the circle of glue.)

PLATE 47

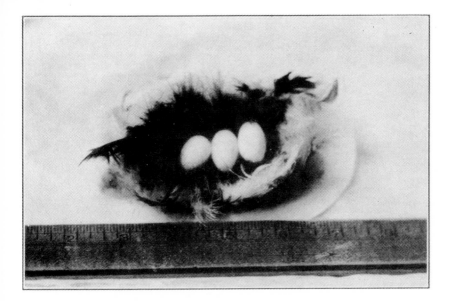

Colton, Calif., May 1916.   W. C. Hanna.

NESTS OF WHITE-THROATED SWIFTS.

PLATE 48

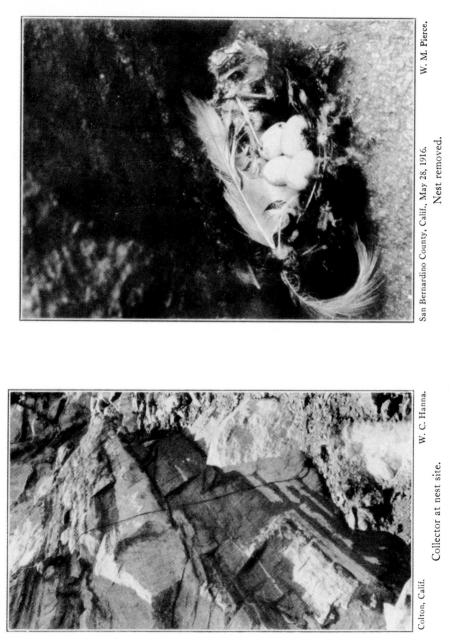

Colton, Calif.   W. C. Hanna.

Collector at nest site.

San Bernardino County, Calif., May 28, 1916.   W. M. Pierce.

Nest removed.

WHITE-THROATED SWIFT.

PLATE 49

NESTING SITES OF RIVOLI'S HUMMINGBIRD.

Huachuca Mountains, Ariz.

PLATE 50

Huachuca Mountains, Ariz.   F. C. Willard.

NESTS OF RIVOLI'S HUMMINGBIRD.

PLATE 51

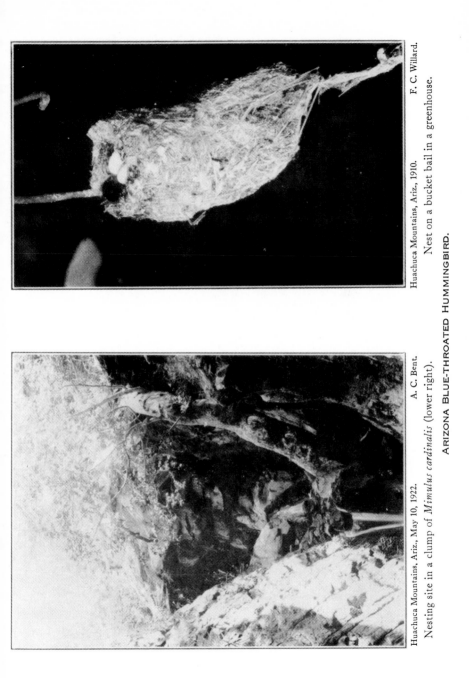

Huachuca Mountains, Ariz., 1910.   F. C. Willard.

Nest on a bucket bail in a greenhouse.

Huachuca Mountains, Ariz., May 10, 1922.   A. C. Bent.

Nesting site in a clump of *Mimulus cardinalis* (lower right).

ARIZONA BLUE-THROATED HUMMINGBIRD.

PLATE 52

Two young nearly grown.

Huachuca Mountains, Ariz.   F. C. Willard.

Nest under roof of a pavilion.

ARIZONA BLUE-THROATED HUMMINGBIRD

PLATE 53

Plymouth, Mass., June 8, 1902.   A. C. Bent.

Nest in a pitch pine.

Sangamon County, Ill., June 3, 1908.   A. D. DuBois.

Nest in an oak.

RUBY-THROATED HUMMINGBIRD.

PLATE 54

Oakland County, Mich., June 19, 1921.   W. E. Hastings.

Adult female.

Ithaca, N. Y.   A. A. Allen.

Female feeding full-grown young.

RUBY-THROATED HUMMINGBIRDS.

PLATE 55

Holderness, N. H.

H. F. Edgerton.

Mrs. Laurence J. Webster and her pets.

RUBY-THROATED HUMMINGBIRDS.

PLATE 56

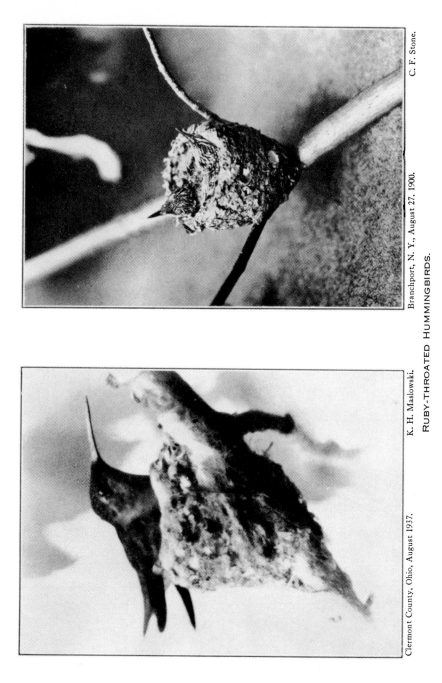

C. F. Stone.

Branchport, N. Y., August 27, 1900.

K. H. Maslowski.

Clermont County, Ohio, August 1937.

RUBY-THROATED HUMMINGBIRDS.

PLATE 57

Holderness, N. H.   H. E. Edgerton.

RUBY-THROATED HUMMINGBIRDS AT MRS. WEBSTER'S FEEDING STATION.

PLATE 58

Azusa, Calif., July 17, 1923.   R. S. Woods.

Adult male.

Azusa, Calif., June 13, 1938.   R. S. Woods.

A durable used nest.

BLACK-CHINNED HUMMINGBIRD.

PLATE 59

Azusa, Calif., April 19, 1923.   R. S. Woods.

Nest in a feijoa bush.

May 15, 1913.   W. M. Pierce·

Nest in a white-sage bush.

COSTA'S HUMMINGBIRD.

PLATE 60

Azusa, Calif., May 22, 1925.   R. S. Woods.

Young about 11 days old.

Azusa, Calif., June 2, 1933.   R. S. Woods.

COSTA'S HUMMINGBIRDS.

PLATE 61

Azusa, Calif., June 8, 1923. R. S. Woods.

Adult male.

Mojave Desert, Calif., May 7, 1916. W. M. Pierce.

Nest in *Opuntia ramosissima*.

COSTA'S HUMMINGBIRD.

PLATE 62

Azusa, Calif., February 22, 1931.   R. S. Woods.

Adult male feeding.

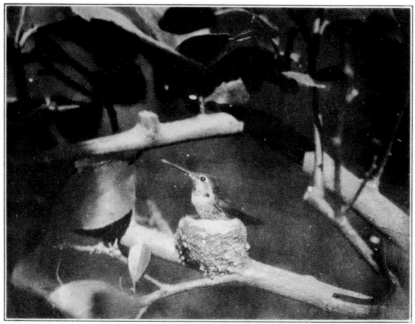

Claremont, Calif.   W. M. Pierce.

Nest in a lemon tree.

ANNA'S HUMMINGBIRD.

PLATE 63

Arizona.   F. C. Willard.

NEST OF BROAD-TAILED HUMMINGBIRD

PLATE 64

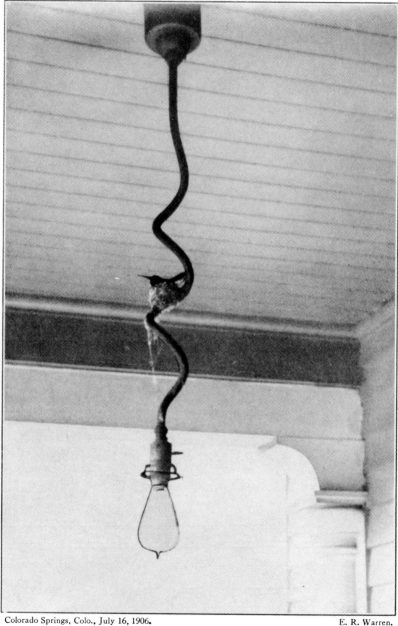

Colorado Springs, Colo., July 16, 1906. E. R. Warren.

BROAD-TAILED HUMMINGBIRD.

PLATE 65

J. E. Patterson.

NEST OF RUFOUS HUMMINGBIRD IN AN OAK TREE.

Bear Creek, Oreg., May 29, 1925.

PLATE 66

July 17, 1914.

Female shading eggs.

Flathead County, Mont., July 20, 1914.

A. D. DuBois.

Young 2 days old.

RUFOUS HUMMINGBIRDS.

PLATE 67

W. L. Finley and H. T. Bohlman.

Portland, Oreg.

NEST OF RUFOUS HUMMINGBIRD IN A VIRGINIA CREEPER.

PLATE 68

Ynes Mexia.

Berkeley, Calif.

Nest in a eucalyptus.

Nest in a Monterey pine.

ALLEN'S HUMMINGBIRD.

PLATE 69

Nest and small young in a Monterey cypress.

Berkeley, Calif.   Ynes Mexía.

Nest and two large young in a Monterey cypress.

ALLEN'S HUMMINGBIRD.

PLATE 70

Jackson County, Oreg., June 8, 1925.   J. E. Patterson.

Blue Mountains, Wash.   S. H. Lyman.

NESTS OF CALLIOPE HUMMINGBIRD.

PLATE 71

A. F. Skutch.

Tela, Honduras, September 7, 1930.

Nest in a lime tree.

A. F. Skutch.

Almirante, Panama, March 6, 1929.

Nest in a bougainvillea bush.

RIEFFER'S HUMMINGBIRD.

PLATE 72

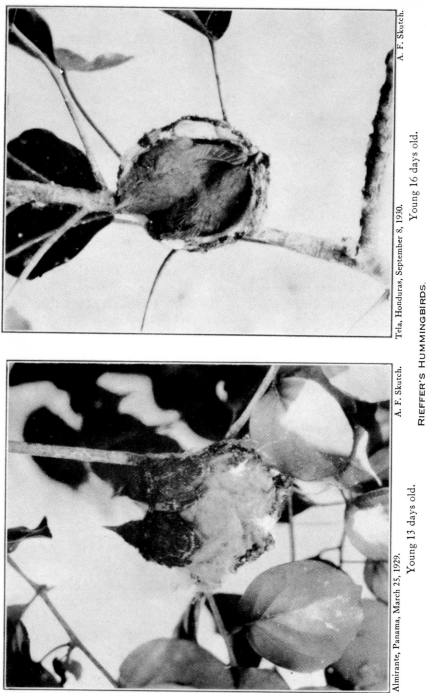

A. F. Skutch.

Tela, Honduras, September 8, 1930.

Young 16 days old.

RIEFFER'S HUMMINGBIRDS.

A. F. Skutch.

Young 13 days old.

Almirante, Panama, March 25, 1929.

PLATE 73

Near Tecpan, Guatemala, December 11, 1933.   A. F. Skutch.

NEST OF WHITE-EARED HUMMINGBIRD.